P9-AEZ-686

Packed Tower Design and Applications

RANDOM AND STRUCTURED PACKINGS

SECOND EDITION

Packed Tower Design and Applications

RANDOM AND STRUCTURED PACKINGS

SECOND EDITION

Ralph F. Strigle, Jr.

NORTON CHEMICAL PROCESS PRODUCTS CORPORATION

Gulf Publishing Company
Houston, London, Paris, Zurich, Tokyo

05827073

CHEMISTRY

Packed Tower Design and Applications
Random and Structured Packings
Second Edition

(Formerly Random Packings and Packed Towers: Design and Applications)

Copyright © 1994, 1987 by Gulf Publishing Company, Houston, Texas. All rights reserved. Printed in the United States of America. This book or parts thereof, may not be reproduced in any form without permission of the publishers.

Gulf Publishing Company
Book Division
P.O. Box 2608 ☐ Houston, TX 77252-2608

10 9 8 7 6 5 4 3 2 1

Library of Congress Cataloging-in-Publication Data

Strigle, Ralph F.
    Packed tower design and applications: random and structured packings/Ralph F. Strigle, Jr.—2nd ed.
        p.   cm.
    Rev. ed. of: Random packings and packed towers. c1987.
    Includes bibliographical references and index.
    ISBN 0-88415-179-4
    1. Packed towers. I. Strigle, Ralph F. Random packings and packed towers. II. Title.
TP159.P3S77   1994
660'.28423—dc20   93-5637
                                                       CIP

Printed on Acid-Free Paper (∞)

TP 159
P3 S77
1994
CHEM

CONTENTS

Influence of Packing Shape, Irrigated Packed Beds, High Liquid
Rate Performance, Liquid Holdup in Packed Beds, Pressure Drop
Calculation, Effects of Surface Tension and Foaming, Concurrent
Flow Operation, Cross-Flow Operation, Example Problem, Nota-
tion, References

Surface Wetting Characteristics, Pressure Drop, Geometric
Properties, Hydraulics of Operation, Liquid Holdup, Mass Transfer
Efficiency, Example Problem, Notation, References

Two-Film Theory, Gas-Film Mass Transfer Coefficient, Liquid-Film
Mass Transfer Coefficient, Overall Mass Transfer Coefficients,
Transfer Units and Theoretical Stages, Simplified Design

Procedures, General Design Concept, Choice of Solvent, Selection of Column Diameter, Physical Absorption, Solvent Absorption, Natural Gas Dehydration, Gas Drying, Sulfuric Acid Manufacture, Formaldehyde Absorption, Absorption with Chemical Reaction, Cracked Gas Scrubbing, Amine Systems, Hot Carbonate Systems, Multicomponent Absorption, Reboiled Absorbers, Example Problem, Notation, References

Design Theory, Simplified Design Procedures, Column Diameter Selection, Water Deaeration, Water Decarbonation, Ammonia Stripping, Amine Regeneration, Hot Carbonate Regeneration, Side Strippers, Example Problem, Notation, References

Gas Purification, Gas Scrubber Types, Particulate Removal, Gas Scrubbing, Scrubber Design Methods, Liquid-Film-Controlled Systems, Gas-Film-Controlled Systems, Scrubber Size Determination, Other Design Considerations, SO_2 Scrubbing, NOx Removal, Organic Vapor Control, Odor Control, Example Problem—Gas Scrubbing, Water Purification, Potable Water Stripping, Potable Water Stripper Design, Wastewater Stripping, Wastewater Stripper Design, Example Problem—VOC Stripping, Notation, References

Water Cooling Theory, Cooling Tower Design, Cooling Tower Fill, Gas Quench Towers, Quench Tower Design, Total Condenser Theory, Total Condenser Design, Partial Condenser Theory, Chlorine Gas Cooling, Vacuum Crude Stills, Atmospheric Crude Stills, Olefin Primary Fractionator, Olefin Water Quench Tower, Example Problem, Notation, References

Ideal Vapor/Liquid Equilibrium Systems, Nonideal Vapor/Liquid Equilibrium Systems, Vapor/Liquid Equilibrium Relationships,

Determination of Theoretical Stages, Condition of Feed, Maximum Operational Capacity, Minimum Operating Rate, Column Diameter Selection, Efficiency Considerations, HETP Prediction, Typical Design Efficiency, Efficiency in Multicomponent Systems, Effect of Lambda on Efficiency, High Purity Products, Feed Point Location, Azeotropic Distillation, Extractive Distillation, Example Problem, Notation, References

Maximum Capacity of Packing, Column Diameter Selection, Choice of Fractionating Device, Efficiency Considerations, Effect of Pressure on Azeotropic Distillation, Pasteurization, Styrene Purification, Caprolactam Manufacture, Dimethyl Terephthalate Purification, Glycol Separation, Refinery Vacuum Towers, High Vacuum Distillation, Tall Oil Fractionation, Heat Sensitive Materials, Example Problem, Notation, References

Characteristics of Packings and Trays, Maximum Column Capacity, Pressure Drop Considerations, Selection of Column Diameter, Typical Design Efficiency, Theoretical Stages and Reflux Ratio, Olefins Plant Cold Section, Demethanizers, Deethanizers, Ethylene/Ethane Fractionator, Depropanizers, Propylene/Propane Fractionator, Debutanizers, C-4 Separations, Other Olefin Fractionating Arrangements, Chemical Separations, Example Problem, Notation, References

Packing Support Plates, Vapor Distributors, Bed Limiters and Hold-Down Plates, Feed and Reflux Distributors, Liquid Redistributors, Wall Wipers, Liquid Collectors, References

General Considerations, Extractor Operation, Choice of Device, Depiction of Liquid Extraction, Mutual Solubilities, Effect of Temperature and Pressure, Interfacial Tension, Solvent Selection,

Alternate Depiction of Extraction, Equilibrium Considerations, Rates of Mass Transfer, Reactive Systems, Dispersed Phase, Packed Extractors, Column Capacity, Pressure Drop, Packing Size, Determination of Stages, Stage Efficiency, Extractor Internals, Coalescence of Dispersed Phase, Industrial Applications, Example Problem, Notation, References

ACKNOWLEDGMENTS

The author wishes to express his appreciation for the assistance of the many people who made this book possible.

Dr. K. E. Porter, Frank Rukovena, and Frank Moore performed technical reviews of the contents. Gail Hausch, Frank Petschauer, and Karl Nash provided engineering data and advice. Becky Costello, Louise Nikitin, Kathy Rowe, Vickie Roy, and Margie Goodell prepared and assembled the manuscript, tables, figures, and photographs as well as proofread the contents. Also, the author is grateful to the Norton Chemical Process Products Corporation for supplying much of the data on tower packings.

The contributions of all of these people are demonstrated throughout this volume.

FOREWORD

This revised edition of *Random Packings and Packed Towers: Design and Applications* reflects the ongoing development of packed tower technology as demonstrated by the change in the title to *Packed Tower Design and Applications: Random and Structured*. Mass transfer tower packings and packed tower applications have been evolving since the beginning of the twentieth century. Packed towers are now used by all of the major industries involved in mass transfer operations. These industries include petroleum refining, petrochemical, chemical, pharmaceutical, food processing, and environmental, to mention a few.

Tower packings were initially used in small diameter towers in such applications as absorbing, stripping, distillation, and extraction. Packings are now being used in a 39.5-ft diameter flue gas desulfurization absorber, a 29.5-ft diameter vacuum distillation tower separating ethylbenzene/styrene, and a 46-ft diameter crude oil vacuum tower. The use of packing has gone beyond vacuum and atmospheric services into high pressure distillation applications such as demethanizers and depropanizers. Ralph Strigle has made major contributions to expanding packed tower technology into these areas. In my years of association with Ralph, his insight and creativity have been a source of inspiration that more development is still possible.

Ralph's ability to combine his talent and experience with information from many sources and to present this information in a coherent manner is what makes this book unique and useful. The information presented provides good practical design methods based upon years of experience and will continue to be a useful guide to the practicing engineer and a sound introduction for students to the subject of packed tower mass transfer design.

Frank Rukovena, Jr.
Director, Mass Transfer Technology
Norton Chemical Process Products Corporation

PREFACE

As the chemical and hydrocarbon processing industries have become mature, emphasis has changed from a primary interest in capacity to concerns about energy efficiency and the environmental impact of processing operations. In order to maintain profitability, increased product recovery and reduced energy usage are needed to control rising manufacturing costs. Under pressure from the public and governmental agencies, processes are being modified in order to eliminate the production of byproducts and reduce the quantity of waste streams. The modification of existing mass transfer columns with modern tower packings can increase the number of mass transfer stages available. These additional stages permit greater product recovery through a reduction in losses of product in recycled or waste streams. Extra theoretical stages allow operation of distillation columns at a reduced reflux ratio, thereby lowering the energy required for the same product quality. Packed columns are increasingly being used to scrub vent gas streams in order to prevent air pollution. Such columns also are being installed to strip volatile components from wastewaters to permit the discharge to meet regulations.

During the last 25 years, significant changes have occurred in both the design of tower packings and the application of packed columns. Structured packings have become increasingly more widely accepted. Such packings contain multiple vapor and liquid flow paths that are geometrically identical in contrast to random packings in which the flow paths vary in shape and size. In spite of these differences, the design of columns using structured packings is done by the same methods as those which were developed for random packings.

Initially, structured packings were applied in vacuum distillation services because their very low pressure drop characteristics and low HETP values provided reduced pressure gradients per theoretical stage. Later, these packings were used to increase capacity in atmospheric distillations, since replacement of a random packing with a larger size in order to gain capacity would reduce the separation efficiency. As more information has become available, some high pressure distillations applications of structured packings currently are being installed.

The theoretical bases concerning mass transfer operations have been available in chemical engineering texts for many years and will not be developed further in this book. Rather, this book provides procedures for designing packed columns based on practical experiences acquired over 40 years that have produced satisfactory column performance. In many commercial situations, the application of rigorous theory is difficult because of the lack of sufficient data on physical or chemical properties. In addition, information on the desired operation may be available only from very small or laboratory-size columns with the resultant problems of scale-up. The empirical design methods presented in this book, in many cases, have been developed as a result of modifications to increase the capacity or efficiency of previously operating columns. These same methods also have been used to design new columns in similar services.

The applications of packed columns are many and varied. This book reviews many of the existing major applications of such columns so that the reader can evaluate their advantages compared to other mass transfer devices. New applications continue to be developed in processes that require separation operations. However, most engineers are not involved with many of these applications on a regular basis. Therefore, this book is an effort to provide the process engineer with a simple discussion of the mechanism of operation of a packed column as well as practical methods for the design of such a column. These procedures have been used for over a decade to design columns as large as 46 ft in diameter and for separations requiring as many as 128 theoretical stages. Particular characteristics of a system that need to be considered during the design to assure successful column operation are discussed. These design procedures are illustrated by an example problem at the end of each chapter.

No attempt has been made to optimize the design because each application has varying criteria. Operating cost, capital cost, column diameter, tower height, pressure drop, and energy consumption are some of the criteria. However, once the relative value is assigned to a design parameter, these methods can be used to provide the required column design. Also, these design methods have been used to evaluate the performance of an existing tower that is not operating satisfactorily. The chapter on column internals can be particularly helpful in evaluating the source of trouble. In many cases, simple modifications will enable the column to meet the desired performance.

1

RANDOM DUMPED PACKINGS

This chapter describes the various hydraulic phenomena that occur in a bed of random dumped tower packing shapes. First, those factors that influence only gas-phase flow are considered. Then, the more complex hydraulics that result when liquid is introduced onto the packed bed are examined. Finally, a method for predicting pressure drop in two-phase flow through the packed bed is developed.

A packed bed provides a mechanism for mass or heat transfer through which the gas and liquid phases usually flow countercurrently in the column. The presence of tower packing elements provides a resistance to the flow of these fluids that is greater than it would be in an empty column shell. Resistance to the liquid flowing downward normally is not of great importance because the liquid flows under the influence of gravity.

The gas that flows upward, however, must overcome the resistance offered by the tower packing elements. If only the gas phase is flowing through the packed bed, the bed might be treated as an extension of the theory of gas flow through beds of granular solids. For small particles and low gas flow rates the Reynolds number (Re) is low, and the gas phase is in laminar flow. Under these conditions the form drag loss accounts for almost all of the pressure drop, as the kinetic energy loss is low. This drag coefficient is inversely proportional to the Reynolds number.

Kozeny modeled a packed bed as a series of parallel, small diameter tubes of equal length and diameter [1]. Carman applied the work of Kozeny to experimentally determine pressure drops for the flow through packed beds [2]. This work produced the Carman-Kozeny equation for gas-phase pressure drop:

$$\Delta P = \psi \frac{Vu'}{\varepsilon^3} \left[\frac{1 - \varepsilon}{D_p} \right]^2 \tag{1-1}$$

However, in most applications the gas phase is in turbulent flow. Equation 1-1 does not apply where kinetic energy losses are high, as is the case for large values of the Reynolds number. Burke and Plummer used a model similar to that of Kozeny and derived an equation to express the pressure drop for packed beds with the gas phase in turbulent flow [3].

$$\Delta P = \psi \frac{V^2 \rho_G}{D_p} \left[\frac{1 - \varepsilon}{\varepsilon^3} \right] \qquad (1\text{-}2)$$

In this equation the pressure drop per unit of bed depth is a function of the second power of the gas flow rate as long as there is only single-phase flow. Pressure drop also is influenced by the void fraction of the packed bed. A smaller void fraction in a packed bed obviously results in a higher local gas velocity at a constant superficial gas mass flow rate. Packing size also influences pressure drop. Ergun combined the equation for form drag loss with the equation for kinetic energy loss to produce an equation for the pressure drop through a packed bed [4].

$$\Delta P = \psi_1 \frac{Vu'}{\varepsilon^3} \left[\frac{1 - \varepsilon}{D_p} \right]^2 + \psi_2 \frac{V^2 \rho_G}{D_p} \left[\frac{1 - \varepsilon}{\varepsilon^3} \right] \qquad (1\text{-}3)$$

This equation has been applied with some success to packed beds where the pressure drop is small compared to the column operating pressure.

Table 1-1

Characteristics of Ceramic Packings

Packing	Void Fraction	Bulk Weight lb/ft³	Single Phase Pressure Drop (in. H₂O/ft)	
			$G^\dagger = 900$	$G^\dagger = 1600$
1 in. Intalox® Saddles	0.721	43.9	0.30	0.96
1½ in. Intalox® Saddles	0.734	41.8	0.16	0.52
2 in. Intalox® Saddles	0.748	39.6	0.12	0.39
3 in. Intalox® Saddles	0.764	37.1	0.075	0.19
1 in. Raschig Rings	0.707	46.1	0.44	1.38
1½ in. Raschig Rings	0.720	44.0	0.27	0.87
2 in. Raschig Rings	0.737	41.4	0.22	0.73

†G is gas mass velocity in lb/ft²·h

Table 1-2

Characteristics of Metal Packings

Packing	Void Fraction	Bulk Weight lb/ft^3	Single Phase Pressure Drop (in. H$_2$O/ft)	
			G† = 1500	G† = 2700
#25 IMTP® Packing	0.962	18.8	0.38	1.24
#40 IMTP® Packing	0.971	14.5	0.24	0.79
#50 IMTP® Packing	0.977	11.3	0.15	0.50
#70 IMTP® Packing	0.982	9.0	0.079	0.24
1 in. Pall Rings	0.942	29.0	0.46	1.49
1½ in. Pall Rings	0.956	22.0	0.32	1.03
2 in. Pall Rings	0.965	17.5	0.22	0.72

†G is gas mass velocity in lb/ft^2·h

Table 1-3

Characteristics of Plastic Packings

Packing	Void Fraction	Bulk Weight lb/ft^3	Single Phase Pressure Drop (in. H$_2$O/ft)	
			G† = 1500	G† = 2700
#1 Super Intalox®	0.900	5.7	0.35	1.06
#2 Super Intalox®	0.928	4.1	0.24	0.75
#3 Super Intalox®	0.945	3.1	0.13	0.43
Intalox® Snowflake®	0.951	2.8	0.08	0.24
1 in. Pall Rings	0.902	5.6	0.44	1.26
1½ in. Pall Rings	0.914	4.9	0.34	1.02
2 in. Pall Rings	0.923	4.4	0.23	0.70
3½ in. Pall Rings	0.931	3.9	0.10	0.33
1 in. Tellerettes	0.873	7.2	0.30	0.91
2 in. Tellerettes	0.932	3.9	0.21	0.63
3 in. Tellerettes	0.919	4.6	0.14	0.42

†G is gas mass velocity in lb/ft^2·h

INFLUENCE OF PACKING SHAPE

Flow channels do not have a fixed shape or diameter in a bed of random dumped packings. The hydraulic radius (flow channel area divided by wetted perimeter) varies significantly with the channel shape. Further, these flow channels are not straight, nor are they of uniform length. Because the pressure drop per foot of bed depth is constant, the actual gas velocity varies with the hydraulic radius, as well as with the effective length of the flow channel. Even with single-phase flow through a packed bed, the effect of packing shape is not well defined. The development of packing shapes remains an empirical art in which the pressure drop produced in the actual packed bed must be experimentally determined.

Over the years many shapes have been proposed for tower packing elements, but only a few are widely used. Various packing shapes are shown in Figures 1-1 through 1-11. Probably the oldest random dumped tower packing shape in substantial commercial use is the Raschig ring (see Figures 1-1 and 1-2). This packing is a simple cylinder with a length equal to its outside diameter. It is manufactured from ceramics, metals, plastics, and carbon. Two modifications of this shape are the Lessing ring and the cross-partition ring. Both of these shapes use internal partitions. These packings have been installed in both a dumped and a stacked manner.

Figure 1-1. Raschig ring (ceramic).

Figure 1-2. Raschig ring (metal).

A further modification of the basic cylindrical shape involves installation of a helix inside the cylinder. The interior of this ring may contain a single, a double, or a triple helix. This spiral ring packing normally is made from ceramic and only should be installed by stacking.

The first of the modern dumped packings was the Berl saddle, developed in the late 1930s (see Figure 1-3). This shape has a significantly increased surface area per unit of packed volume compared to the Raschig ring. Another improved shape was the Intalox saddle (trademark Norton Chemical Process Products) developed in the early 1950s (see Figure 1-4). This design has two different radii of curvature that provide a greater degree of randomness in the packed bed.

In the early 1950s a significant improvement was made in the Raschig ring shape by B.A.S.F. Aktiengesellschaft. Their development, called the Pall ring, consists of a cylinder of equal length and diameter with ten fingers punched from the cylinder wall that extend into the packing element interior (see Figures 1-8 and 1-9). Although the Pall ring has the same geometric surface area as the Raschig ring, the interior surfaces of the Pall ring are much more accessible to gas and liquid flows due to the openings through the wall. Subsequent Pall ring modifications, such as Hy-Pak packing (trademark Norton Chemical Process Products), have further increased the percentage of internal surface area the packing element makes available for gas and liquid contact (see Figure 1-10).

Figure 1-3. Berl saddle (ceramic).

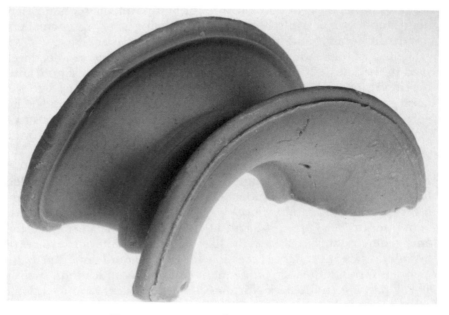

Figure 1-4. Intalox® saddle (ceramic).

A further modification of the Pall ring was developed by Mass Transfer Limited. Their Cascade (trademark Mass Transfer Ltd.) Mini-Ring also is a cylinder with fingers punched from the wall projecting into the interior of the ring; however, the height of the cylinder is only one-third the outside diameter. This shape is said to orient itself preferentially when dumped into a packed bed.

A newer packing element combines advantages of the shape of the Intalox saddle with that of a modern ring packing. This Intalox Metal Tower Packing, or IMTP packing (trademarks Norton Chemical Process Products), was developed by Norton Company in the late 1970s and is manufactured from metals only (see Figure 1-11).

A filamentous packing shape was developed by Dr. A. J. Teller in the 1950s. This Tellerette (trademark The Ceilcote Company) is manufactured only in plastic (see Figure 1-7). To satisfy the demand for a very low pressure drop packing for use in pollution control applications, Norton developed Intalox Snowflake packing (trademark Norton Chemical Process Products Corp.). This plastic packing has been available since 1987. This unique shape provides the maximum number of uniformly shaped, interstitial liquid drip-points. This feature causes continuous renewal of the liquid surface, which greatly enhances its mass transfer efficiency. This packing has found use in humidification, dehumidification, absorbers, scrubbers, and strippers.

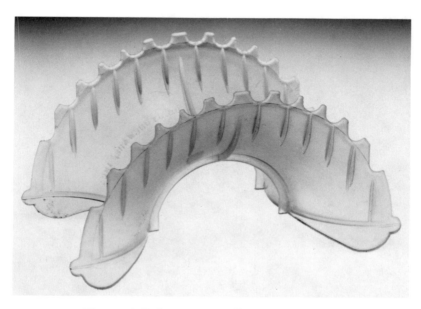

Figure 1-5. Super Intalox® saddle (plastic).

Figure 1-6. Intalox® Snowflake® tower packing (plastic). (Courtesy of Norton Chemical Process Products Corporation.)

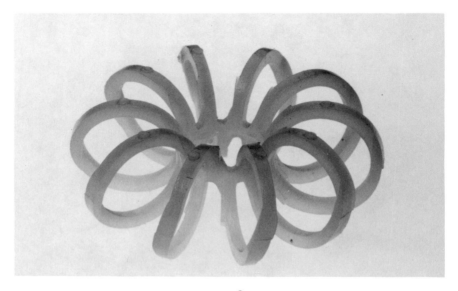

Figure 1-7. Tellerette® packing (plastic).

Figure 1-8. Pall ring (plastic).

Figure 1-9. Pall ring (metal).

Figure 1-10. Hy-Pak® packing (metal).

Figure 1-11. IMTP® packing (metal).

Packing element shape greatly influences resistance to flow (aerodynamic drag factor). However, the resistance to flow, even single-phase flow, produced by a packed bed cannot be predicted from first principles. Ceramic Intalox saddles and ceramic Raschig rings have similar void fractions but greatly different pressure drops (shape factors), as shown in Table 1-1. With more recently developed packings, a similar situation exists between Intalox Metal Tower packing and metal Pall rings, as shown in Table 1-2. The shapes of IMTP and ceramic Intalox saddle packings produce less pressure drop than metal Pall ring and ceramic Raschig ring packings, respectively, for the same gas mass flow.

In single-phase gas flow (where there is no liquid wetting the packing surface), the dry line relates the pressure drop to the gas rate:

$$\Delta P = \psi \frac{G*^2}{\rho_G} \qquad \text{or} \qquad \Delta P = \psi V^2 \rho_G \qquad (1\text{-}4)$$

The constant relating pressure drop to $V^2 \rho_G$ in Equation 1-4 for the dry line is actually the summation of the effects of packing shape factor, bed void fraction, and hydraulic radius of the packing as indicated in Equation 1-2. This constant can be determined from dry line pressure drop measurements for any particular type and size of packing, as long as the gas-phase flow is turbulent.

IRRIGATED PACKED BEDS

For packed beds used in gas and liquid contacting, the liquid can flow in the opposite direction to the gas (countercurrent operation), or it can flow in same direction as the gas (concurrent operation), or the gas flow can be transverse to the liquid flow (crossflow operation). The theory of pressure drop in irrigated packed beds is not as well developed as that for single-phase flow.

With countercurrent liquid and gas flow, as soon as a flowing liquid phase is introduced onto the packed bed, the pressure drop will be greater than that developed only with gas flow. Data collected over many years, representing 4,500 pressure-drop measurements, have been correlated for each packing in a plot of log ΔP vs. log G, as illustrated by Figure 1-12. The region of low gas flow rates gives an indication of how the liquid flow rate parameters on such a pressure-drop plot parallel the dry line up to high liquid rates. It has been demonstrated by several investigators that liquid holdup primarily is a function of liquid rate and almost independent of gas rate below the loading region [5, 6]. The highest gas rate at which pressure drop can be expressed by Equation 1-4, with ψ modified to account for the effect of liquid rate, sometimes has been called the lower loading point.

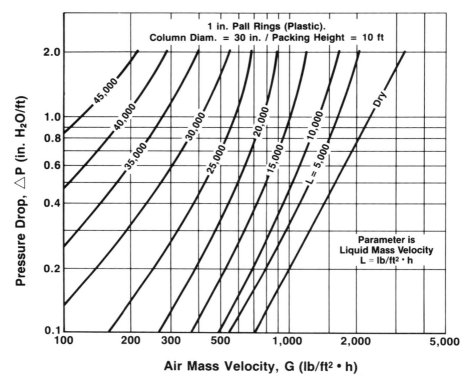

Figure 1-12. Pressure drop vs. gas rate (1-in. Pall rings—plastic).

At low liquid rates, the log ΔP vs. log G plot gives liquid rate parameters that appear to start parallel to the dry line, but gradually increase in slope as the gas flow rate increases. The rate of slope change of each of these curves is constant up to rather high gas flow rates. Of course, the rate of slope change of the dry line is zero. The rate of slope change of the other liquid rate parameters increases with increasing liquid flow rates. Thus, a plot of ψ in Equation 1-4 vs. G^{*4}/ρ_G^2 gives a straight line for any fixed liquid rate as shown in Figure 1-13.

As the pressure drop goes below a value of 0.10 in. H_2O/ft of packed depth, the modified Equation 1-4 may predict a pressure drop that is lower than the experimentally determined value. At a very low pressure drop, measurement tolerances, as well as static head due to the gas phase, may be significant. In addition, at low gas rates, the gas phase may not be in completely turbulent flow.

As the gas flow rate increases, the vapor begins to interact with the liquid affecting the liquid flow regime. At higher gas rates, the rate of change of pressure drop increases more rapidly than a constant value. This is

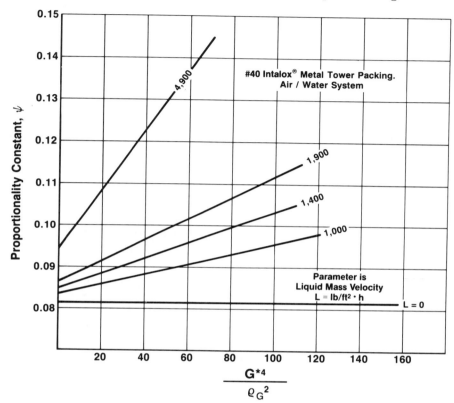

Figure 1-13. Rate of pressure drop change (#40 Intalox® Metal Tower Packing).

because liquid holdup increases with increasing gas rate. The gas rate at which this begins to occur has been called the upper loading point. Operation at higher gas rates is considered to be in the loading region of the packing [7, 8].

Above this gas rate, the column will approach the maximum hydraulic capacity, or flooding limit. The definition of flooding limit is not precise, but has varied with the observer. Some of the definitions of flooding limit which appear in the literature are as follows:

1. A distinct change in the slope of a plot of pressure drop versus gas rate.
2. A visual buildup of liquid on the upper surface of the packed bed.
3. A rapid increase in liquid holdup with increasing gas rate.
4. Formation of a continuous liquid phase above the packing support plate.

5. Onset of instability in column operation.
6. A considerable entrainment of liquid in the outlet vapor.
7. Filling of the voids in the packed bed with liquid.

Kister and Gill propose the following equation to predict the pressure drop at flood for random dumped packings [9].

$$\Delta P \text{ (flood)} = 0.115F^{0.7} \tag{1-5}$$

From this pressure drop, the gas rate at flood for any particular liquid rate can be calculated from a generalized pressure drop correlation. However, as these authors state, most of the data is based on an incipient flood point rather than a fully developed flooding condition.

Certainly, the hydraulic capacity limit of a packed bed has been reached when the rate of increase of pressure drop with gas flow rate approaches infinity. Likewise, the hydraulic capacity limit of a packed bed has been reached when the liquid holdup volume increases with gas flow rate to approach the void fraction of the bed. It has been demonstrated experimentally that both of the above phenomena occur at substantially the same gas rates in a bed of random dumped packing [10].

In distillation, maximum operational capacity (sometimes called "efficient capacity" because of the nature of the definition) is determined by the amount of liquid entrainment required to reduce separation efficiency (see Chapter 7). Data of Strigle and Rukovena for IMTP, metal Pall Ring, and ceramic Intalox saddle packings indicate that the pressure drop at maximum operational capacity is [11]:

$$\Delta P \text{ (at MOC)} = 0.119F^{0.7} \tag{1-6}$$

The use of maximum operational capacity produces a design that provides the desired efficiency, and the packed bed does not operate in an unstable region near its hydraulic capacity limit.

HIGH LIQUID RATE PERFORMANCE

The plot of log ΔP vs. log G also shows another hydraulic phenomenon that occurs at high liquid rates, as illustrated in Figures 1-12 and 1-14. The slopes of these liquid rate parameters at low gas rates are less than 2 at liquid rates above 40 gpm/ft^2 for 1-in. size packings or 55 gpm/ft^2 for 1½-in. size packings. Extrapolation of these curves leads to the conclusion that there still will be a pressure drop as the gas flow rate approaches zero. At a high liquid flow rate, depending on the size of the packing, the packed bed voids largely tend to be filled with liquid, and some of the gas phase actually is aspirated down the column in the liq-

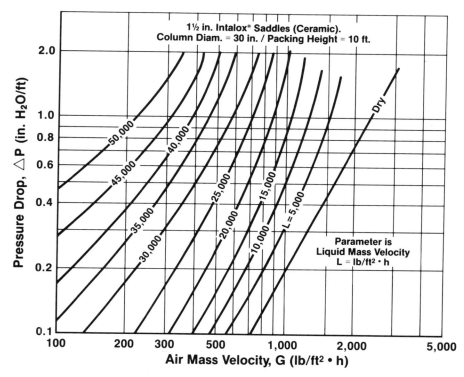

Figure 1-14. Pressure drop vs. gas rate (1½-in. Intalox saddles—ceramic).

uid phase. A sufficient liquid retention time in the base of the column will permit these aspirated gas bubbles to rise to the surface of the liquid pool and escape back into the gas phase. The packed bed, therefore, produces a pressure drop that is an indication of the internal gas flow passing upward through the bed. This internal gas flow is the sum of the externally introduced gas flow rate plus the recirculated gas released from the liquid at the bottom of the column [12].

Ordinarily, packed columns are not designed at liquid rates above those just enumerated because pressure drop cannot be predicted by the usual correlations. The prudent designer will use a large enough packing to avoid this area of operation. For example, 2-in. packings do not exhibit this phenomenon below a liquid rate of 70 gpm/ft², and 3½-in. packings have been operated at liquid rates as high as 125 gpm/ft².

The preceding flow rates apply for mobile liquids. High liquid viscosity tends to diminish the acceptable liquid flow rate. Smaller sizes of packings are more restricted than larger sizes by increasing liquid viscosity. The foregoing maximum design liquid rates are based on a liquid viscosity no higher than 1.0 cps for 1-in. size packings, 1.8 cps for 1½-in. size packings, and 3.2 cps for 2-in. size packings.

LIQUID HOLDUP IN PACKED BEDS

There are two different types of liquid holdup in a packed bed: static and operating. Static holdup represents that volume of liquid per volume of packing that remains in the bed after the gas and liquid flows stop and the bed has drained. The static holdup is dependent on the packing surface area, the roughness of the packing surface, and the contact angle between the packing surface and the liquid. The static holdup with no gas flow is a small value that can be assumed to be a constant independent of liquid flow rate, as suggested by Shulman *et al.* [5]. In addition, capillary forces will hold liquid at junctions between individual packing elements. Well designed tower packings normally do not trap stagnant pools of liquid within the packing element itself.

Operating holdup is that volume of liquid per volume of packing that drains out of the bed after the gas and liquid flows to the column stop. Total liquid holdup is the sum of the static holdup and the operating holdup. Operating holdup primarily is a function of the liquid flow rate. Shulman *et al.* propose that operating holdup is proportional to the 0.57 power of the liquid mass flow rate [13]. Below the loading region of the packing, the operating holdup is almost independent of the gas flow rate. However, the loading region is characterized by a rapid increase in liquid holdup with increasing gas rate [14]. A continuing increase in liquid holdup with pressure drop, which averages 0.014 ft^3 liquid per ft^3 packing for each 0.36 in. H_2O/ft increase in pressure drop, has been reported [10].

Liquid surface tension has practically no effect on operating holdup for high surface tension liquids, such as water. For ordinary organic liquids (σ about 27 dyne/cm) at low liquid rates, the operating holdup will be about 12% lower than for water. Holdup will be reduced up to 20%, for low surface tension systems (σ about 13 dyne/cm) at low liquid rates. At liquid rates above 7 gpm/ft^2 this effect of surface tension on liquid holdup diminishes. These measurements were determined at atmospheric pressure and should not be extrapolated to high-pressure distillations.

Liquid holdup increases with increasing liquid viscosity. Usual liquid holdup graphs show an air/water system and thus apply to a liquid viscosity of about 1 cps. If the liquid viscosity is increased to 2 cps the liquid holdup will increase by 10%. At 16 cps liquid viscosity, the holdup will be about 50% greater. If liquid viscosity is reduced to 0.45 cps, the holdup will be about 10% lower. At a liquid viscosity of only 0.15 cps, the holdup will be reduced by 20%. Viscous liquids tend to bridge the small void openings in beds of smaller size packings, resulting in a rapid loss of gas handling capacity as liquid rates are increased. It is recommended that only 1½-in. and larger size packings be used for handling liquids of 50 cps or higher viscosity.

The pressure drop through a packed bed represents not only the frictional loss and kinetic energy loss through the packing, but also the force exerted by the operating liquid holdup. Thus, at the same pressure drop, the packed bed has less volumetric liquid holdup in high liquid-density systems. Conversely, with low density liquids, the volumetric liquid holdup can be significantly greater than for water at the same pressure drop. In high pressure distillation, the volumetric liquid holdup will increase due to the buoyant effect of the high gas density, as well as aeration of the liquid phase (see Chapter 9).

At a constant mass of liquid holdup, the void fraction in the packed bed is reduced as the liquid density is lowered, due to the greater volume occupied by this holdup. Thus, the true gas velocity will be higher, which produces a greater pressure drop.

At atmospheric pressure, and in vacuum services, the static head produced by the gas is small and can be neglected. However, in high pressure fractionators requiring large numbers of theoretical stages, the static head of vapor can be appreciable from condenser to reboiler. This correction should be added to the calculated pressure drop to determine the bottom column pressure and reboiler temperature.

PRESSURE DROP CALCULATION

Calculating pressure drop is of considerable importance in atmospheric absorbers, heat transfer services, and vacuum distillations. Although pressure drop plots are available for most commercial types and sizes of random dumped tower packings, these data usually have been collected on air/water systems. While the air flow rate can be corrected for changes in gas density, no adequate method exists for handling the effect of liquid properties.

It is highly desirable for the designer to have a generalized correlation to predict pressure drop in a packed bed. Development of a single correlation to represent all the different applications of packings (absorption, distillation, etc.), as well as widely differing pressures of operation, is an ambitious undertaking. Reliable design of a packed column requires an understanding of the reasons some systems are less well predicted than other systems by a generalized pressure drop correlation.

Over the years, the Sherwood, *et al.* universal flooding correlation, proposed for random dumped tower packings operated in countercurrent flow, has been modified to provide a generalized pressure drop correlation [15]. Leva first modified this correlation to include parameters of constant pressure drop [16]. The abscissa of this correlation is known as the flow parameter:

$$X = \frac{L}{G}\left[\frac{\rho_G}{\rho_L}\right]^{0.5}$$ (1-7)

This flow parameter is the square root of the ratio of liquid kinetic energy to gas kinetic energy. The ordinate of this correlation includes the gas flow rate, the gas and liquid densities, the a/ε^3 ratio (which is characteristic of the particular tower packing shape and size), and a liquid viscosity term. Lobo *et al.* proposed the use of a packing factor to characterize a particular packing shape and size [17]. They determined that the a/ε^3 ratio did not adequately predict packing hydraulic performance. Eckert further modified this correlation and calculated the packing factors from experimentally determined pressure drops [18].

An extensive study was performed by Rollison, Petschauer, and Nash at Norton Company's Chamberlain Laboratories to determine the optimum location of these pressure-drop parameters. The data bank of 4,500 pressure-drop measurements was subjected to a statistical analysis. Pressure drops ranged from 0.05 in. H_2O/ft to 2.0 in. H_2O/ft and flow parameter values from 0.005 to 8. It was found that more than one-half (55%) of the packing types and sizes would produce a constant packing factor at all pressure drops. Packings smaller than 1-in. size often showed a small increase in the packing factor as the pressure drop was reduced. A few high-voidage, large-size packings showed a small decrease in the packing factor as the pressure drop was reduced. The locations of the pressure-drop parameters on the correlation, shown in Figure 1-15, essentially were the same whether a variable packing factor (to allow for these small deviations) or a constant packing factor was employed.

The resultant correlation predicts pressure drop within ±17% of measured values throughout its entire range. In the most widely used range of abscissa values (from 0.01 to 1.0), and for pressure drops from 0.25 to 1.0 in. H_2O/ft, the correlation predicts the pressure drop to an accuracy of ±11%. In its present form, this correlation probably represents the maximum accuracy possible, considering the many shapes and sizes of packings available. If greater accuracy is necessary, a separate correlation is required for each packing type and size.

The classical method for depicting the generalized pressure drop correlation (as illustrated in Figure 1-15) uses a logarithmic scale for both the abscissa and the ordinate. Using this graph requires a difficult interpolation between parameters of constant pressure drop. Figure 1-16 presents a rearranged correlation that uses a linear scale for the ordinate. Further, to facilitate use of the correlation in distillation calculations, the ordinate has been expressed in terms of the capacity factor (C_s). Also, the gravitational constant (32.2) has been included in the ordinate value.

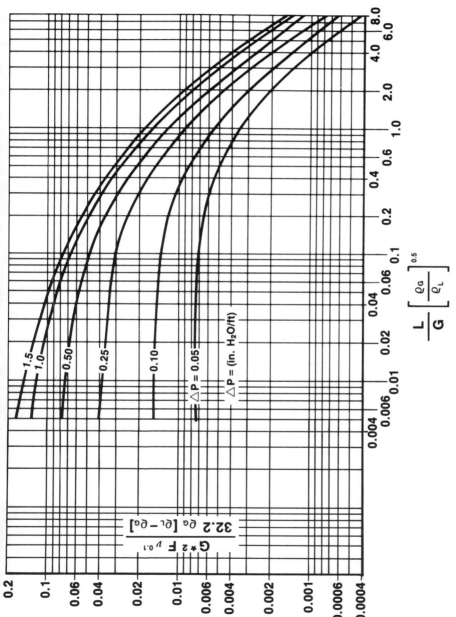

Figure 1-15. Generalized pressure drop correlation.

For abscissa values less than 0.02, which usually indicate the operation is under vacuum, special pressure drop equations can be developed from the packing dry line. In such operations, the liquid rate is low, and the liquid holdup is small. When holdup is only a few volume percent, the void fraction reduction of the packed bed is slight. Actual measurements indicate the pressure drop in operation can be lower than that predicted from Figure 1-15 using an abscissa value of 0.02. (See Chapter 8 for further discussion.)

Abscissa values greater than 1.0 are produced either by operations involving very high liquid-to-gas mass flow ratios or by high gas-to-liquid density ratios. The stripping of light hydrocarbons under high pressure is an example of the latter case. Experience in light hydrocarbon fractionators indicates that if the vapor density is 5% or more of the liquid density, the pressure drop can be significantly greater than that calculated from Figure 1-15. (Calculation of pressure drop in high pressure fractionators is discussed more fully in Chapter 9.)

Kister and Gill analyzed the generalized pressure drop correlation using another data bank of 3,000 pressure drop measurements [9]. They concluded that the correlation shown as Figure 1-16 gave a good-to-excellent fit for 80% of their data, and a reasonable fit for another 15% of the data.

As previously stated, at high liquid rates, pressure drop may be greater than that predicted from the generalized correlation, especially when smaller packing sizes are used. For operations carried out at liquid rates greater than those recommended for the packing size used (see Table 3-2 in Chapter 3), pressure drop should be calculated from a chart for the particular packing, rather than from the generalized correlation.

The packing factors given in Table 1-4 are for use with these generalized pressure drop correlations (Figures 1-15 and 1-16). These packing factors have been determined from experimental pressure-drop data; therefore, they are empirical rather than theoretical in nature. The use of pressure drop to determine column size is discussed in detail in Chapter 3.

EFFECTS OF SURFACE TENSION AND FOAMING

There is no general agreement on the effect of liquid surface tension on the capacity of a packed bed. Tests in an air/water system using surface active agents to reduce liquid surface tension showed a marked reduction of column capacity as surface tension was reduced [19]. These experimenters concluded factors other than surface tension are involved and that foaminess is a factor in the flooding of packed columns. Eckert's series of tests using aqueous methanol solutions showed that reducing surface tension had no effect on the capacity of a packed bed, as long as that was the only different factor [18]. Further experiments with surfactants incorporated in aqueous systems showed a marked increase in pressure

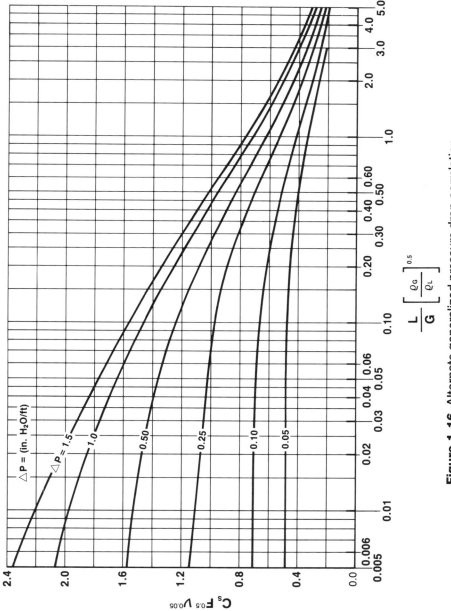

Figure 1-16. Alternate generalized pressure drop correlation.

22   Packed Tower Design and Applications

Table 1-4

Packing Factors (F)—Random Dumped Packings

	Nominal Packing Size (in.)							
	½	⅝	¾	1	1¼	1½	2	3 or 3½
IMTP® Packing (Metal)		51		41		24	18	12
Hy-Pak® Packing (Metal)				45		32	26	16
Super Intalox® Saddles (Ceramic)				60			30	
Super Intalox® Saddles (Plastic)				40			28	18
Intalox Snowflake® (Plastic)							13	
Pall Rings (Plastic)		95		55		40	26	17
Pall Rings (Metal)		81		56		40	27	18
Intalox® Saddles (Ceramic)	200		145	92		52	40	22
Raschig Rings (Ceramic)	580	380	255	179	125	93	65	37
Raschig Rings (1/32″ Metal)	300	170	155	115				
Raschig Rings (1/16″ Metal)	410	300	220	144	110	83	57	32
Berl Saddles (Ceramic)	240		170	110		65	45	
Tellerettes (Plastic)				35			24	17

drop. However, when antifoams were added to the liquid the pressure drop was lowered almost back to the level produced by a methanol solution with the same surface tension. Eckert deduced that foaming had caused the increase in pressure drop and that surface tension of a nonfoaming liquid had no effect on capacity. Later tests conducted by an independent research organization confirmed this conclusion.

Subsequent experience indicates that these experiments produced accurate conclusions with respect to absorption operations because the tests were performed in this manner. In distillation operations, however, low surface tension liquids most commonly are encountered in the fractionation of light hydrocarbons under high pressure. The effects of surface tension in such applications are discussed in Chapter 9.

The presence of foam in a packed bed causes a marked increase in pressure drop [20]. The foam represents a very low-density liquid phase that can significantly reduce the void fraction within the packed bed. It has been suggested that a packed bed could be used to measure the foaming tendency of a system. This could be accomplished by running various gas flow rates through a packed bed countercurrent to a nonfoaming, pure, inert liquid and measuring the resulting pressure drops. The liquid under evaluation then could be introduced into the column and pressure drops measured again—at the same gas flow rates. Any pressure drop increase would give a measure of the degree of liquid foaming. Further, such a test would indicate whether foaming would be induced by gas flow rates above a certain critical value.

In many systems there appears to be an operating froth present on the liquid surface, especially when mass transfer occurs between the gas and liquid phases. A knowledgeable designer will take into account the increase in pressure drop this froth produces above that for a nonfoaming system.

In some systems foam is induced because of the work done by the gas phase on the liquid phase. In such systems the pressure drop will increase at a faster rate with an increasing gas flow rate than it will with a nonfoaming system. The experienced designer operates the packed bed in these systems at a lower-than-normal gas flow rate, thus avoiding excessively high pressure drops.

A few systems produce stable foams in which the rate of foam generation equals or exceeds the rate of foam collapse at desired operating flows. Under these conditions, use of suitable antifoams is necessary for satisfactory packed bed operation. It may not be necessary to eliminate the foam completely, but merely to reduce it to a level that can be tolerated by the packed bed. Stable foams usually result from surface active agents and are controlled by the addition of antifoams. However, excessive quantities of antifoams, themselves, may produce a foaming system.

Pure liquids, or totally miscible solutions, normally are nonfoaming. Some low surface tension, halogenated organic liquids tend to foam slightly. Hydrocarbons with a molecular weight of 100 or more, organic liquids with a viscosity of 0.5 cps or greater, and partially immiscible liquids may foam moderately.

Heavy foaming can be expected in systems involving heavy oils, amines, or insoluble fine solids. Corrosion products or chemical breakdown end products often collect on the liquid surface and cause foaming. Filtration or adsorption operations commonly are employed to remove such contaminants from the system.

CONCURRENT FLOW OPERATION

Packed columns that operate with concurrent gas and liquid flows are not widely used. Countercurrent operation provides the greatest efficiency because mass transfer driving forces are at a maximum. However, in those operations where only a single mass transfer stage is required, concurrent operation may offer advantages.

A packed bed in concurrent flow has no conventional flooding limitation because liquid holdup tends to decrease with an increasing gas rate, as shown in Figure 1-17 [21]. The curve at zero gas flow shows the usual effect of liquid flow rate on operating holdup. As gas flows downward through the bed it accelerates the liquid velocity, thus reducing the volumetric holdup.

When liquid is added to a packed bed in concurrent flow, the pressure drop increases as shown in Figures 1-18 and 1-19, which apply to 1½-in. ceramic Intalox saddle and 2-in. plastic Pall ring packings, respectively.

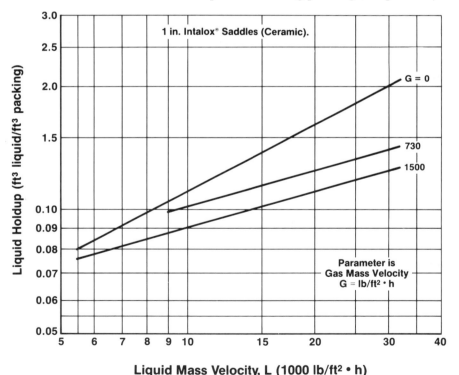

Figure 1-17. Concurrent flow liquid holdup (1-in. Intalox® saddles—ceramic). (From Dodds [21]. Reproduced by permission of the American Institute of Chemical Engineers.)

The parameters of constant liquid rate in Figure 1-18 are not curved, as is the case for Figure 1-14, where the same packing was operated in countercurrent flow. The dry line indicates that pressure drop is a function of the second power of the gas flow rate. At a liquid rate of 40 gpm/ft^2, the pressure drop in Figures 1-18 and 1-19 increases as the gas rate to the 1.7 power. As the liquid rate increases to 80 gpm/ft^2, the pressure drop increases as the gas rate to only the 1.1 power. At a very high liquid rate of 120 gpm/ft^2, the pressure drop increases as the gas rate to the 0.9 power, less than directly.

The pressure drop represents a loss of energy by the gas phase. As liquid flow is increased, more energy is required to accelerate the liquid velocity. This absorption of energy by the liquid phase represents an increasing percentage of the pressure drop as the liquid flow becomes greater.

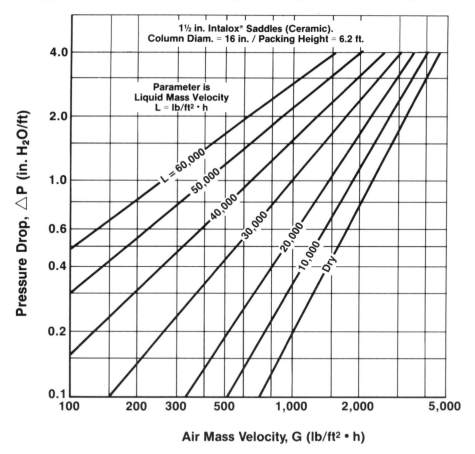

Figure 1-18. Pressure drop vs. gas rate—concurrent flow (1 ½-in. Intalox® saddles—ceramic).

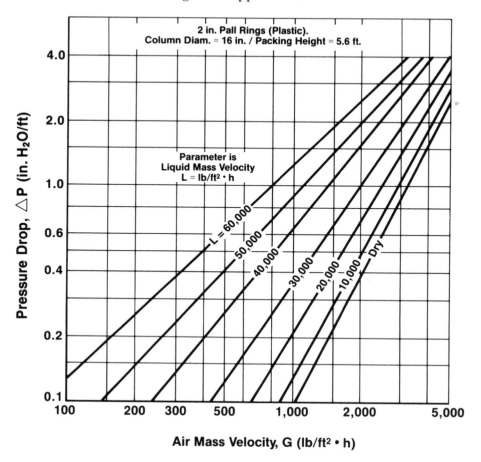

Figure 1-19. Pressure drop vs. gas rate—concurrent flow (2-in. Pall rings—plastic).

As can be seen from Figures 1-18 and 1-19 the pressure drop in concurrent flow can be 1.0, 2.0, or even 4.0 in. H_2O/ft of packed depth. Because of the higher allowable pressure drop, the capacity of a given diameter column is much greater in concurrent than in countercurrent flow operation. Gas and liquid contact intensity is greatly increased at higher flow rates; thus, mass transfer rates can be elevated in concurrent flow.

In those systems where there is practically no vapor pressure of solute above the liquid phase, concurrent flow operation should be considered. Such applications include:

1. Absorption of low concentrations of ammonia by dilute acids.
2. Removal of traces of H_2S or CO_2 by absorption into caustic soda solutions.
3. Drying of chlorine gas with recirculated concentrated sulfuric acid.

This highly turbulent contact produced in concurrent flow is especially useful in removing fine solids from a gas stream. Removal efficiency improves as power input increases. This application is discussed more completely in Chapter 5.

CROSS-FLOW OPERATION

A column in cross-flow operation is unique because the gas flow is transverse to the vertically downward flow of liquid, so that the area for gas flow can be different than the area for liquid flow. If A_R is the ratio of the area for gas flow compared to the area for liquid flow, then when A_R is 1 the pressure drop through a cross-flow bed is the same as through a countercurrent bed. As the value of A_R increases, the pressure drop through a bed in cross-flow operation becomes progressively less than for a bed having the same liquid flow area operated in countercurrent flow [22]. Thus, cross-flow operation will permit higher gas rates and the use of higher gas to liquid flow ratios than a countercurrently operated column.

However, operation in a cross-flow manner inherently produces a reduction in packing efficiency caused by reduction of liquid distribution quality due to deflection of the liquid by the gas stream. In addition, mass transfer driving forces are reduced as compared to a countercurrently operated column. In general, the efficiency of cross-flow towers is intermediate between concurrent and countercurrent columns.

EXAMPLE PROBLEM

An existing CO_2 absorber is 84-in. ID and operates at a pressure of 400 psia. The inlet gas analysis is as follows:

Component	Mol%
CH_4	2.7
CO_2	7.3
C_2H_6	75.0
C_3H_8	15.0

The inlet gas is bone dry and at a temperature of 85°F. The feed liquid is a 30 wt% aqueous diethanolamine solution containing 0.10 mol CO_2/mol DEA. The exit gas is to contain 0.5 mol % CO_2 and will be at 100°F, which is the same temperature as the inlet liquid.

What is the maximum capacity of this absorber if the effluent liquid contains 0.45 mol CO_2/mol DEA? The tower will be packed with #2 Hy-Pak packing, and because of the foaming tendency of this system, the pressure drop is not to exceed 0.25 in. H_2O/ft at the point of maximum loading.

The inlet gas has a molecular weight of 32.8 and a density of 2.78 lb/ft^3 at operating conditions. The absorbent liquid has a density of 62.8 lb/ft^3 and a viscosity of 2.5 cps. The 30 wt% DEA solution contains 2.853 lb-mol of DEA per 1,000 lb of liquid feed. Absorbing 0.35 mol CO_2/mol DEA indicates that 0.999 lb-mol of CO_2 will be absorbed in each 1,000 lb of DEA solution feed. The inlet gas stream contains 7.875 lb-mol of CO_2 per 100 lb-mol of inert gas. The specifications require only 0.503 lb-mol of CO_2 be present per 100 lb-mol of dry inert exit gas. Therefore, 7.372 lb-mol of CO_2 must be absorbed for each 100 lb-mol of inert gas feed to the column.

By material balance on the CO_2 absorbed, the inlet inert gas flow is 13.55 lb-mol per 1,000 lbs of liquid feed. The total inlet gas flow is 14.61 lb-mol (or 479.2 lb of gas) per 1,000 lb of liquid feed. The effluent liquid stream contains 43.9 lb of absorbed CO_2 per 1,000 lb of liquid feed. The dry exit gas is humidified to an equilibrium water content above the feed DEA solution. Thus, the exit gas stream contains 0.30 mol % water vapor. The effluent liquid flow will be 1,043.2 lb for each 1,000 lb of liquid feed.

With this information, the flow parameter at the bottom of the column, which is the point of maximum loading for an absorber, can be calculated:

$$X = \frac{1043.2}{479.2} \left[\frac{2.78}{62.8} \right]^{0.5} = 0.458 \tag{1-A}$$

From Figure 1-16, at this abscissa value and a pressure drop of 0.25 in. H_2O/ft, the ordinate value is 0.72. Therefore, because the #2 Hy-Pak packing has a packing factor of 26 from Table 1-4,

$$0.72 = C_s (26)^{0.5} (2.5)^{0.05} \tag{1-B}$$

or

$$C_s = 0.135 \text{ ft/s} \tag{1-C}$$

Thus, the allowable gas mass velocity at this pressure drop is 6,278 lb/ft^2·h at the bottom of the bed. The maximum inlet gas rate for this 84-in. ID column is 241,600 lb/h at a pressure drop of 0.25 in. H_2O/ft of packed depth. The inlet flow of a 30 wt% DEA solution is 504,200 lb/h. This is an irrigation rate of 26.0 gpm/ft^2, which is suitable for this size packing.

Although the maximum loading normally occurs at the absorber bottom, the top conditions should be checked. The exit gas flow is 219,800 lb/h with a density of 2.59 lb/ft^3. The flow parameter at the top of the bed has a value of 0.466. The C_s at the top of the column is 0.127 ft/s, which gives an ordinate value of 0.678 on Figure 1-16. The pressure drop at the top of the packed bed is 0.22 in. H_2O/ft, which is lower than at the bottom of the bed, as expected.

NOTATION

A_R	Flow area ratio (gas/liquid)
a_p	Surface area of packing (ft^2/ft^3)
C_s	Capacity factor (ft/s)
D_p	Packing diameter (ft)
F	Packing factor
G	Gas mass velocity (lb/ft^2·h)
G*	Gas mass velocity (lb/ft^2·s)
L	Liquid mass velocity (lb/ft^2·h)
Re	Reynolds number
u′	Viscosity (lb/ft·h)
V	Superficial gas velocity (ft/s)
X	Flow parameter
ΔP	Pressure drop (in. H_2O/ft)
ε	Void fraction
ν	Kinematic liquid viscosity (cst)
ψ	Proportionally constant
$ρ_G$	Gas density (lb/ft^3)
$ρ_L$	Liquid density (lb/ft^3)
σ	Surface tension (dyne/cm)

REFERENCES

1. Kozeny, G. J. Sitzber, *Akad. Wiss. Wein, Math-naturw,* K1. Abt., IIa, Vol. 136, 1927, p. 271.
2. Carman, P. C., *Journal of Society of Chemical Industry,* Vol. 57, 1938, p. 225 T.
3. Burke, S. P. and Plummer, W. B., *Industrial and Engineering Chemistry,* Vol. 20, 1928, p. 1996.
4. Ergun, S., *Chemical Engineering Progress,* Vol. 48, No. 2, 1952, p. 89.
5. Shulman, H. L. *et al. A.I.Ch.E. Journal,* Vol. 1, No. 2, 1955, p. 247.
6. Billet, R. and Schultes, M., *Institute of Chemical Engineers Symposium Series 104,* 1987, p. A159.
7. Leva, M., *Tower Packings and Packed Tower Design,* 2nd ed., United States Stoneware, 1953, p. 35.
8. Zenz, F. A., *Chemical Engineering,* Vol. 49, No. 8, 1953, p. 176.

9. Kister, H. Z. and Gill, D. R., *Chemical Engineering Progress,* Vol. 87, No. 2, 1991, p. 32.
10. Strigle, R. F., *Canadian Process Equipment and Control News,* April 1989, p. 66.
11. Strigle, R. F. and Rukovena, F., *Chemical Engineering Progress,* Vol. 75, No. 3, 1979, p. 86.
12. Woodburn, E. T., *A.I.Ch.E. Journal,* Vol. 20, No. 5, 1974, p. 1003.
13. Shulman, H. L., *et al., A.I.Ch.E. Journal,* Vol. 1, No. 2, 1955, p. 259.
14. Elgin, J. C. and Weiss, F. B., *Industrial & Engineering Chemistry,* Vol. 31, 1939, p. 435.
15. Sherwood, T. K. *et al., Industrial and Engineering Chemistry,* Vol. 30, 1938, p. 765.
16. Leva, M., *Chemical Engineering Progress,* Vol. 50, No. 10, 1954, p. 51.
17. Lobo, W. E. *et al., Transactions of American Institute of Chemical Engineers,* Vol. 41, 1945, p. 693.
18. Eckert, J. S., *Chemical Engineering Progress,* Vol. 57, No. 9, 1961, p. 54.
19. Meese, W. *et al., Petroleum Refiner,* Vol. 31, No. 10, 1952, p. 141.
20. Larkins, R. P. and White, R. R., *A.I.Ch.E. Journal,* Vol. 7, No. 2, 1961, p. 231.
21. Dodds, W. S. *et al., A.I.Ch.E. Journal,* Vol. 6, No. 3, 1960, p. 390.
22. Thibodeaux, L. J., "Fluid Dynamic Observations on a Packed, Cross-flow Cascade at High Loadings," American Institute of Chemical Engineers, Atlanta National Meeting, February 1978.

2

STRUCTURED PACKINGS

The previous chapter described the hydraulic phenomena occurring in beds of random dumped packings. This chapter is devoted to a discussion of the hydraulic operation of tower packings that are installed in an ordered manner. Many years ago it might have been interpreted that ordered packings simply were stacked beds of conventional random packing shapes plus some larger rings, such as cross-partition rings and spiral rings. Due to the high labor cost of stacking such packings, their use has declined rapidly since the late 1950s. This chapter will be concerned with the performance of packings manufactured in modular form to permit stacking in an ordered array in a column.

One of the earliest versions of modern structured packings was Panapak packing (tradename Pan American Refining Corporation) described by Scofield in 1950 [1]. This packing was formed from multiple layers of metal lath that were corrugated and assembled in such a manner as to produce a honeycomb-like structure. In a refinery vacuum column, Panapak packing produced only 12% of the pressure drop of the bubble-cap trays, which had been used for more than 25 years at that time.

Although knitted wire-mesh and wire-screen packings had been used for many years in distillation services where low HETP values were needed, these applications primarily were limited to small diameter columns [2]. A woven wire-mesh packing, which was arranged in rows of vertically corrugated elements, was developed in the 1960s in Switzerland [3]. Billet *et al.* published performance data on this Sulzer BX packing (trademark of Sulzer Brothers, Ltd.) in 1969 [4]. These investigators found that the HETP value of the packing increased with increasing vapor loading. Typically, the packing gave a pressure drop of only 0.07 in. H_2O per theoretical stage when operated at 50% of its maximum capacity. In 1985 Bravo *et al.* described the mass transfer characteristics of this packing [5].

Subsequently, other wire-mesh structured packings, such as Intalox Wire Gauze packing (trademark Norton Chemical Process Products) have been developed. Figure 2-1 shows HETP values for Intalox Wire Gauze packing in two vacuum distillations: ortho/para xylene at 50mm

31

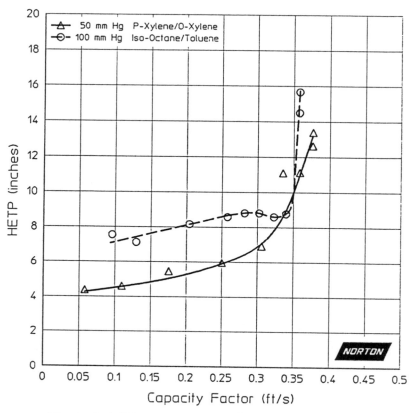

Figure 2-1. Efficiency of Intalox® wire-gauze packing.

Hg and iso-octane/toluene at 100mm Hg absolute. However, the high cost of such packings has limited their general use to demanding separations that involve high-vacuum service or a large number of required theoretical stages.

In the 1970s, a sheet metal structured packing was developed to reduce the expense of the wire gauze packing. This packing was manufactured from thin metal sheets that were crimped at a 45° angle to the horizontal and assembled alternately reversed into modules to form a honeycomb of triangularly shaped passages with one open side. Because the sheet-metal surfaces of this packing no longer wetted with liquid by capillary action, as was the case with wire-gauze structured packings, various methods were devised to improve its ability to wet uniformly by modifying the surface of the metal sheet.

Meier *et al.* in 1977 indicated that the Mellapak 250Y packing (trademark Sulzer Brothers, Ltd.), with about 0.50 in. depth of corrugation, would provide a surface area of 76 ft^2/ft^3 [6]. If the corrugation depth were only 0.25 in., the surface area would be doubled. On the other hand, if the corrugation depth were increased to 1.0 in., the surface area would be reduced by 50%. Later, Meier *et al.* published additional results on Mellapak 250Y packing that showed that this packing provided a low pressure drop per unit height similar to the Sulzer BX wire-gauze packing, but produced only 50 to 60% of the number of theoretical stages with the same packed height [7]. However, both the HETP value and the pressure drop per ft were lower than 2-in. metal Pall ring packing. Thus, the use of sheet metal structured packing will reduce the pressure drop per theoretical stage by a factor of 2 or more, compared to random packing. Pressure drop per theoretical stage for Intalox Structured packings is only 40% to 65% of that for IMTP packings of similar capacity.

These features make structured packing especially suited for use in vacuum distillation services where column size is controlled to a large degree by the pressure drop per theoretical stage. Since that time, such structured packings have found increasing application in vacuum services at pressures as low as 5mm Hg absolute. However, structured packings also are used in atmospheric and high-pressure distillation services when their capacity/efficiency characteristics are superior to random packings.

SURFACE WETTING CHARACTERISTICS

Wire-gauze structured packings are wetted by capillary action, which allows a small amount of liquid to spread out into a thin uniform film [8]. Thus, such packings are assumed to have 100% of their geometric surface area available for mass transfer.

Numerous surface variations have been developed for sheet-metal structured packings in an attempt to improve the wetting of the metal surface. Laboratory tests run using pure oxygen and carbon dioxide gases absorbed into water and ethanol, respectively, measured the rates of mass transfer and the interfacial areas of stainless steel packings from various manufacturers [9]. Figures 2-2 and 2-3 show the liquid-film mass transfer coefficients obtained for the following surface characteristics:

DE is deep embossed (Intalox Structured packing)

LP is lanced and perforated

LU is lanced but unperforated

SE is shallow embossed

GU is unperforated woven wire

Such surfaces will exhibit better mass transfer characteristics than an unperforated woven-wire packing (GU). These experiments indicate that

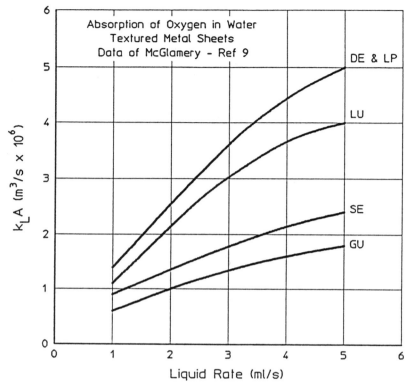

Figure 2-2. Absorption of oxygen in water-textured metal sheets (Data of McGlamery [9]).

mass transfer is enhanced through increasing the turbulence in the liquid film.

The wetted areas were calculated from the data shown in Figure 2-2. Figure 2-4 illustrates that interfacial area can be increased significantly by promoting spreading of the liquid through design of the surface texture impressed upon the metal sheet.

PRESSURE DROP

Figure 2-5 illustrates a typical section of Intalox packing 2T for use in a small diameter column. As with random dumped packings, pressure drop is determined for structured packings using an air/water system at atmospheric pressure and ambient temperature. Figure 2-6 is a plot of the pressure drop for Intalox Structured packing 2T. These curves have

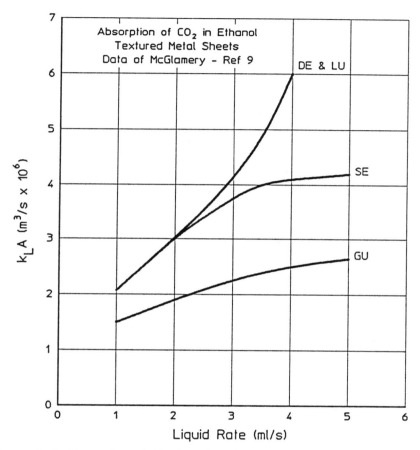

Figure 2-3. Absorption of CO_2 in ethanol-textured metal sheets (Data of McGlamery [9]).

similar shapes to Figures 1-12 and 1-14 (see Chapter 1), which depict the pressure drops for two random dumped packings.

A generalized method has been derived by Bravo *et al.* to predict the pressure drop for structured packings [10]. Their predictive equation is:

$$\Delta P = \frac{0.193 f \, \rho_G ve^2}{D_p g_c} \left[\frac{1}{1 - h_T} \right]^5 \tag{2-1}$$

where f is the friction factor. This factor for the four sizes of Flexipac (trademark Koch Engineering Company, Incorporated) and four sizes of Gempak (trademark Glitsch, Incorporated) structured packings obtained from dry bed pressure drop data was found to be:

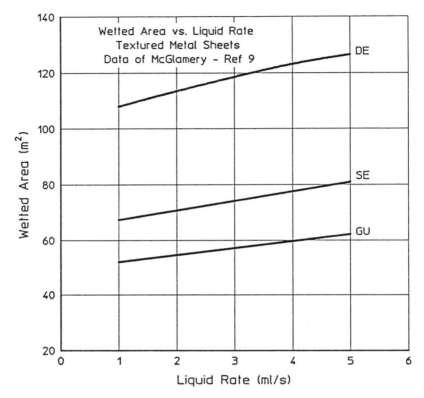

Figure 2-4. Wetted area vs. liquid rate-textured metal sheets (Data of McGlamery [9]).

$$f = 0.171 + \frac{92.7}{Re} \tag{2-2}$$

Due to the difference in surface characteristics, the friction factor for Intalox Structured packings was determined by Petschauer to be:

$$f = 0.219 + \frac{73.3}{Re} \tag{2-3}$$

The Reynolds number (Re) for the gas phase used in Equation 2-2 or 2-3 is:

$$Re = \frac{D_p Ve\rho_G}{\mu_G} \tag{2-4}$$

Figure 2-5. Intalox® structured packing (metal). (Courtesy of Norton Chemical Process Products Corporation.)

The effective gas velocity for structured packings that are corrugated at a 45° angle to the horizontal is:

$$Ve = \frac{V}{\varepsilon \sin 45°}$$

(2-5)

The value of h_T was correlated as a function of the Froude number (Fr) for several gas and liquid rates up to the loading point of the packing.

$$h_T = C_3 Fr^{0.5}$$

(2-6)

The Froude number for the liquid phase is given by Equation 2-7.

$$Fr = \left[\frac{L*}{\rho_L}\right]^2 \left[\frac{1}{D_p g_c}\right]$$

(2-7)

In this model, the equivalent diameter of the packing is taken to be four times the hydraulic radius where the triangular flow channel is considered to have two metal sides and one open side. Thus, if the included angle between the two sides of the flow channel is 90° in a plane perpendicular to the longitudinal axis of the flow channel, the hydraulic radius is 0.25 times the length of one side of the flow channel [11].

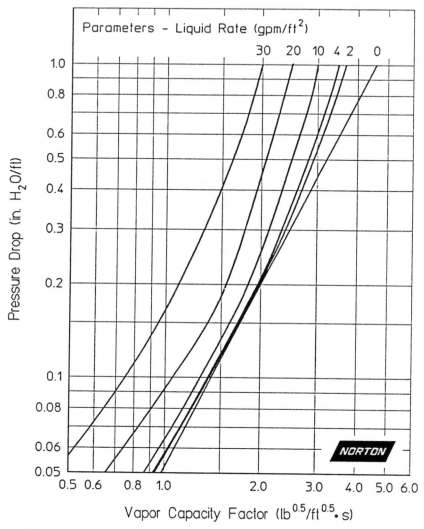

Figure 2-6. Pressure drop of Intalox® structured packing 2T.

Table 2-1 gives the values of the packing equivalent diameter and the constant C_3 for the various packings tested. Data for sheet metal type packings was obtained with an air/water system. This model is accurate for operations below the loading region of the packing in which liquid holdup is not a function of gas flow rate. However, this model is not suggested for use in high liquid rates or high liquid viscosity operations. Because D_p

Table 2-1

Parameter for Pressure Drop of Structured Packings

Packing	Equivalent Diameter (ft)	Constant C_3
Flexipac 1	0.0294	3.38
Flexipac 2	0.0589	3.08
Flexipac 3	0.1178	4.50
Flexipac 4	0.2357	7.26
Gempak 4A	0.0294	3.38
Gempak 3A	0.0442	3.87
Gempak 2A	0.0589	3.08
Gempak 1A	0.1178	4.50

Source: Bravo, *et al.* [10]
Flexipac is a trademark of Koch Engineering Co., Inc.
Gempak is a trademark of Glitsch, Inc.

appears in Equations 2-1, 2-4, and 2-7, its value has significant influence on the calculated pressure drop. The length of one side of the corrugation is not the packing equivalent diameter when the metal sheets are folded to other than about a 90° included angle between the two sides. With other included angles, the hydraulic radius of the flow channels no longer equals 0.25 times the length of a side of the corrugation.

Structured packings have identical gas flow channels throughout the bed, which usually are inclined 45° from horizontal. Thus, much of the form drag associated with random dumped packings is no longer experienced. The liquid flows in a film along the surface of the triangular flow channels in a manner similar to a wetted-wall column. Fair and Bravo state that the interfacial area for a structured packing increases rapidly with loading until it stabilizes at 80 to 100% of the geometric surface area of the packing [12]. This maximum area is reached at pressure drops between 0.30 in. and 0.45 in. H_2O/ft.

Because of the similarity of shape of the pressure drop curves for random and structured packings, the generalized pressure drop correlation (Figure 1-15) provides a quick method for estimating the pressure drop for structured packings, especially for operations outside the method of Bravo. However, the packing factor for use in that correlation is not constant. The packing factors for vacuum service and low liquid rates are lower than those applicable to systems that operate at higher liquid rates and pressures of atmospheric or above. Table 2-2 gives packing factors applicable to most systems for five different sizes of Intalox Structured packing. For operations at pressures below 500mm Hg absolute, or at liquid rates of 4 gpm/ft^2 or lower, the smaller packing factor should be used.

In 1988, Stichlmair *et al.* developed an improved correlation for predicting the pressure drop of structured packings [13]. This correlation makes a correction for the reduction of bed voidage due to the increase in liquid holdup with vapor rate. Thus, this method is able to predict the pressure drop for operations carried out in the loading region of the packing.

A review of the methods for prediction of pressure drop through structured packings was published by Fair and Bravo in 1990 [11]. These authors recommend the use of the Bravo method below the loading point and the Stichlmair method for operations in the loading region.

Table 2-2

Packing Factors for Intalox® Structured Packing

Packing Size	Packing Factor	
	Below 10 psia	Above 10 psia
Wire Gauze	17	22
1T	23.5	28
2T	15.5	20
3T	12.5	15
4T	11	13.5
5T	10	12.5

GEOMETRIC PROPERTIES

Commercial sheet metal structured packings are available from a number of manufacturers. Typically, such packings are produced in sizes that provide surface areas from 160 ft²/ft³ for the smallest size to 25 ft²/ft³ for the largest size. Obviously the small sizes have greater efficiencies (lower HETP values), but higher pressure drops than the large sizes. Although Sulzer BX wire-gauze structured packing was corrugated at a 60° angle to the horizontal, almost all sheet metal structured packings in wide commercial use are corrugated at a 45° angle to the horizontal. Greater corrugation angles have been supplied, but with limited commercial success.

Table 2-3 lists the geometric properties of one size sheet metal structured packings with surface areas of 61 to 76 ft²/ft³, as provided by several manufacturers [11]. The crimp width is measured from one undulation to a similar point on the adjacent undulation in a plane perpendicular to the longitudinal axis of the flow channel. The crimp depth is measured perpendicular to the crimp width and the longitudinal axis. Because alternate sheets are reversed in producing a module, the actual flow channel depth in a transverse plane varies from zero to twice the crimp depth.

Table 2-3

Geometric Properties of Sheet Metal Structured Packings

Packing	Surface Area (ft^2/ft^3)	Crimp Depth (inch)	Crimp Width (inch)	Void Fraction
Gempak 2A	68	0.480	1.055	0.95
Flexipac 2	68	0.492	0.984	0.93
Intalox® 2T	66	0.409	1.535	0.97
Mellapak 250Y	76	0.469	0.949	0.95
Montz B1-200	61	0.587	1.571	0.94

Source: Fair & Bravo [11]
Gempak is a trademark of Glitsch, Inc.
Flexipac is a trademark of Koch Engineering Co., Inc.
Intalox is a trademark of Norton Chemical Process Products Corporation
Mellapak is a trademark of Sulzer Brothers, Ltd.
Montz is a trademark of Julius Montz Co.

Because of the corrugations, the liquid and vapor flows through one layer spread in a series of parallel planes. During installation, vertically adjacent layers are rotated with respect to each other. The purpose of this manner of installation is to promote a uniform spread of vapor and liquid flows in all radial planes throughout the packed bed. Even though there may be perforations through the individual metal sheets, the flow of either liquid or gas through these perforations is a very small percentage of the total flow. In addition, each layer of structured packing normally is equipped with a wall-wiper that returns the liquid that has reached the column wall back into the packed bed.

HYDRAULICS OF OPERATION

The hydraulic operation of structured packings with countercurrent gas and liquid flows is somewhat different than that of random dumped packings. The wire-gauze type is wetted by capillary action, so that the entire geometric surface area becomes available for mass transfer at low liquid flow rates. Thus, Sulzer BX packing was found to have 2.4 times the static liquid holdup of Flexipac 2 or Gempak 2A sheet metal types of structured packings [14]. However, once the surface is completely wetted, capillary action has only a small effect as the liquid rate increases.

With sheet metal structured packings, the ratio of interfacial area to geometric area at low liquid flow rates will vary from 60% to 80% depending on the surface texture, as illustrated in Figure 2-4. This area ratio increases with increasing liquid flow.

The gas velocity has a lower effect on the interfacial area for structured packings than for random dumped packings. However, Fair and Bravo report that for a methanol/water distillation at atmospheric pressure, the liquid film was torn off the sheet metal structured packing at a pressure drop of about 0.6 in. H_2O/ft [12]. The separation efficiency of the packing was not impaired by this phenomenon, which these investigators believed was due to the increase in mass transfer coefficient with column loading. In industrial applications of such packings operated at high rates the entrainment of liquid into the vapor must be considered. If entrainment will cause difficulties then an entrainment eliminator with a high liquid-handling capacity should be installed.

Due to this entrainment of liquid, the maximum hydraulic capacity (flooding point) is difficult to determine. Fair and Bravo correlated flooding data for Mellapak 250Y packing [15]. Their correlation, shown in Figure 2-7, uses a flooding region that is characterized by a rapid increase in pressure drop with simultaneous loss of separation efficiency. This correlation is based upon data by Meier *et al.* on methanol/water and chlorobenzene/ethylbenzene distillations, as well as air/water results [7]. Spiegel and Meier stated that there is no interaction between vapor and liquid that affects the pressure drop of Mellapak below 60% of the capacity limit [16]. They suggest a normal design maximum capacity of 70% to 85% of the packing capacity equivalent to a pressure drop of 1.2 in. H_2O/ft.

For random dumped packings, Strigle and Rukovena showed that the pressure drop at the maximum capacity of the packing decreased as

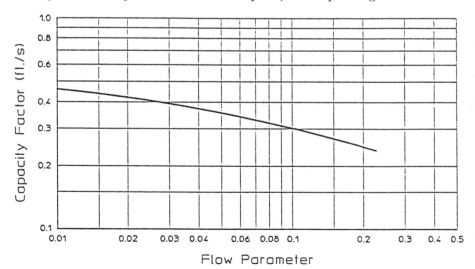

Figure 2-7. Flooding capacity of Mellapak® 250Y packing. (Source: Fair & Bravo [15].)

the packing size increased [17]. Data taken on Intalox structured packings indicate that this effect also occurs with sheet metal structured packings. Thus, designs should not be based on a fixed pressure drop value, regardless of packing size. These authors further proposed that the maximum operational capacity of a random packing be based on the maximum vapor rate obtainable before loss of normal separation efficiency. Due to the tendency of structured packings to entrain liquid in the vapor stream at high rates, this definition of capacity is appropriate for structured packings because they are used most commonly in distillation services.

Extensive tests on Intalox structured packing 2T have been carried out by the University of Texas at Austin with a system of cyclohexane/n-heptane at four different pressures using the same equipment as the previous tests on four other structured packings [18]. This data showed that the maximum capacity (C_s value) of the packing increased as the operating pressure was lowered.

There is a relatively large amount of data at operating pressures up to 1.6 atmospheres absolute; however, only a very few facilities are available that can be operated at high pressures. A series of proprietary tests were carried out by a research organization on Intalox structured packing 2T using a system of iso-butane/n-butane at pressures from 100 to 400 psia. Figure 2-8 gives the maximum operational capacity of this packing [19]. It is based on these two sets of test data, plus other distillation tests by the packing manufacturer.

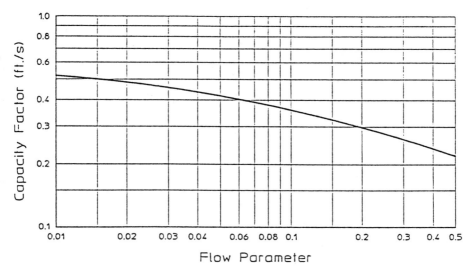

Figure 2-8. Maximum capacity of Intalox® structured packing 2T.

LIQUID HOLDUP

Chen and Chuang present a theoretical model for calculation of liquid holdup in structured packing [20]. They state that the liquid holdup is a function of the one-third power of the ratio of the Froude number to the Reynolds number. However, the proportionality constant is dependent on the loading and the packing characteristics. Rocha and Bravo investigated a way to better predict liquid holdup [14]. They measured static holdup and total liquid holdup for eight sizes of structured packings and compared the results to two holdup models. The static holdup for the same surface area packing varied by a factor of 2.8, depending on the surface texture of the sheet metal.

Manufacturer's tests on Intalox structured packing 2T indicate that the total liquid holdup of this structured packing is 2.4 times that of 2-in. metal Pall ring packing at low liquid rates (below 12 gpm/ft^2). However, as the liquid flow is increased to 20 gpm/ft^2, this holdup ratio is reduced to 1.9; while at very high liquid rates (up to 80 gpm/ft^2), the holdup ratio is only 1.4. These results are to be expected because this structured packing has 2.1 times the geometric surface area of the Pall ring packing. Further, the structured packing uses a surface texture to promote wetting, so that the static liquid holdup of the structured packing is greater. In addition, the operating liquid holdup for this sheet metal type structured packing was found to increase at the 0.50 power of the liquid flow rate. This is a somewhat lower effect than for random dumped packings, where the operating liquid holdup increases as the 0.57 power of the liquid rate (see Chapter 1).

MASS TRANSFER EFFICIENCY

Most of the experimental work on the efficiency of structured packings has been performed in a distillation mode. The HETP values for these packings are discussed in detail in Chapters 7, 8, and 9. Meier *et al.* reported on the absorption of 1,600 ppm SO_2 from air into water at atmospheric pressure using Mellapak 250Y packing [6]. They found HTU values for this structured packing were 33 to 44% lower than for 2-in. metal Pall rings at liquid rates of 16 to 25 gpm/ft^2.

A standard system for absorption of 1% CO_2 from air at atmospheric pressure into 4 wt% sodium hydroxide solution was employed to measure the mass transfer coefficient of Intalox structured packing 2T. At a gas rate of 3.5-ft/s and a liquid rate of 10 gpm/ft^2, the K_Ga value was determined to be 3.80 lb-mol/h·ft^3·atm at 75°F and 25% conversion to sodium carbonate. This K_Ga value is over 20% greater than for 1-in. metal Pall ring packing, as given in Table 3-3 (see Chapter 3). The results of these tests suggest that the structured packing better utilizes the surface available. At this liquid rate, the packing surfaces should be completely wetted and the geometric surface areas of these two packings differ by less than 5%.

For this test system the K_Ga value was found to increase at slightly less than the 0.10 power of the liquid flow rate. This variation of mass transfer co-efficient with liquid rate is much less than for random dumped packings where K_Ga varies as the 0.22 to 0.34 power of liquid rate for this liquid-film controlled system (see Chapter 3). This variation of K_Ga with liquid rate confirms that Intalox structured packings are wetted to a greater extent at low liquid rates than random packings.

EXAMPLE PROBLEM

A 72-in. ID tower currently is used to scrub air containing 2,500 ppm by vol. of acetic acid vapor. The air from two process operations enters this scrubber at 86°F and atmospheric pressure. The scrubbing liquid is a 0.37 wt% aqueous solution of sodium hydroxide. The present scrubber is packed with a 15-ft bed of 1-in. metal Pall rings. Only 110 gpm of scrubbing solution is available. Because of the tendency of the liquid to foam, the present scrubber handles only 3,600 CFM from each of the two parallel trains in order to restrict the pressure drop to 0.30 in. H_2O/ft. Can the vent from a third new operation also be handled in this scrubber by use of a different tower packing without loss of absorption efficiency?

Because Intalox structured packing 2T has an absorption efficiency greater than 1-in. metal Pall rings, this packing will be evaluated. At a fixed liquid rate, the mass transfer coefficient will increase at the 0.75 power of the gas rate for this gas-film-controlled absorption (see Chapter 3). At 10,800 CFM air flow, the mass transfer coefficient for Intalox structured packing 2T will be more than sufficient to handle the absorption of an additional 50% of acetic acid vapor with the same mass transfer driving force and packed depth. The inlet air has a density of 0.0728 lb/ft^3, while the inlet liquid has a density of 62.2 lb/ft^3 and a viscosity of 0.81 cps. Because only 232 lb/h of acetic acid vapor for three trains must be removed by the scrubber, the physical properties of the gas and liquid streams do not change from top to bottom of this tower. The flow parameter at the bottom of the scrubber will be:

$$X = \frac{55,111}{47,174}\left[\frac{0.0728}{62.2}\right]^{0.5} = 0.0400 \tag{2-A}$$

As a quick approximation, the pressure drop will be calculated for the new rates using the Generalized Pressure Drop Correlation. Because the liquid rate is less than 4 gpm/ft^2, a packing factor of 15.5 will be selected from Table 2-2.

The ordinate value for Figure 1-15 is:

$$Y = \frac{(0.4635)^2 \, (15.5) \, (0.81)^{0.10}}{32.2 \, (0.0728) \, (62.2 - 0.0728)} = 0.0224 \tag{2-B}$$

This method predicts a pressure drop for the Intalox structured packing 2T of 0.17 in. H_2O/ft at the new rates.

Because this scrubber will operate at the new rates below the loading region of the packing, the pressure drop can be calculated using the method of Bravo et al. [10]. For this calculation, the packing equivalent diameter is 0.0602 ft, from the dimensions given in Table 2-3, and the void fraction is 0.97. The value of constant C_3 is 3.08, the same as for other structured packings of similar surface areas (see Table 2-1). The superficial gas velocity is:

$$V = \frac{47.174}{3600 \, (28.3) \, (0.0728)} = 6.36 \text{ ft/s} \tag{2-C}$$

The effective gas velocity from Equation 2-5 is:

$$Ve = \frac{6.36}{0.707 \, (0.97)} = 9.27 \text{ ft / s} \tag{2-D}$$

Now, the Reynolds number for the gas phase can be determined.

$$Re = \frac{0.0602 \, (9.27) \, (0.0728)}{12.3 \times 10^{-6}} = 3303 \tag{2-E}$$

The friction factor from Equation 2-3 is:

$$f = 0.219 + \frac{73.3}{3303} = 0.241 \tag{2-F}$$

Next, the Froude number for the liquid phase is determined from Equation 2-7.

$$Fr = \left[\frac{0.541}{62.2}\right]^2 \left[\frac{1}{0.0602 \, (32.2)}\right] = 3.90 \times 10^{-5} \tag{2-G}$$

The value of h_T from Equation 2-6 is:

$$h_T = 3.08 (3.90 \times 10^{-5})^{0.5} = 0.01923 \tag{2-H}$$

The liquid holdup correction term becomes:

$$\left[\frac{1}{1 - 0.01923} \right]^5 = 1.102 \tag{2-I}$$

The pressure drop now can be calculated from Equation 2-1.

$$\Delta P = \frac{0.193 (0.241)(0.0728)(9.27)^2 (1.102)}{(0.0602)(32.2)}$$

$$= 0.165 \text{ in. } H_2O/ft \tag{2-J}$$

Finally, we will check against the maximum capacity of this packing as given in Figure 2-8. The operating capacity factor at the new rates is:

$$\frac{6.36 (0.0728)^{0.5}}{(62.2 - 0.0728)^{0.5}} = 0.218 \text{ ft/s} \tag{2-K}$$

This gas rate represents only 53% of the maximum operational capacity at a flow parameter of 0.0400. Therefore, the replacement of the 1-in. Pall Ring packing with Intalox structured packing 2T easily should permit an increase of 50% in the air rate through this scrubber.

NOTATION

C_s	Capacity factor (ft/s)
D_p	Packing equivalent diameter (ft)
f	Friction factor
Fr	Froude number
F_s	Vapor capacity factor ($lb^{0.5}/ft^{0.5} \cdot s$)
g_c	Gravitational constant (32.2 ft/s^2)
HETP	Height equivalent to a theoretical stage (ft)
h_T	Total liquid holdup (ft^3/ft^3)
HTU	Height of a transfer unit (ft)
$K_G a$	Mass transfer coefficient (lb-mol/h·ft^3·atm)
L^*	Liquid mass velocity (lb/ft$^2 \cdot$ s)
Re	Reynolds number
V	Superficial gas velocity (ft/s)
Ve	Effective gas velocity (ft/s)
ΔP	Pressure drop (in. H$_2$O/ft)
ε	Void fraction

μ_G Gas viscosity (lb/ft·s)
ρ_G Gas density (lb/ft^3)
ρ_L Liquid density (lb/ft^3)

REFERENCES

1. Scofield, R. C., *Chemical Engineering Progress,* Vol. 46, No. 8, 1950, p. 405.
2. Leva, M., *Tower Packings and Packed Tower Design,* 2nd ed., United States Stoneware, 1953, p. 17.
3. Huber, M. and Hiltbrunner, R., *Chemical Engineering Science,* Vol. 21, No. 7, 1966, p. 819.
4. Billet, R. *et al., Institution of Chemical Engineers Symposium Series No. 32,* 1969, p. 4:42.
5. Bravo, J. L. *et al., Hydrocarbon Processing,* Vol. 64, No. 1, 1985, p. 91.
6. Meier, W. *et al., Chemical Engineering Progress,* Vol. 73, No. 11, 1977, p. 71.
7. Meier, W. *et al., Institution of Chemical Engineers Symposium Series No. 56,* 1979, p. 3.3/1.
8. Billet, R., "Theory and Practice of Packed Columns," Korea Institute of Energy and Resources, 1988, p. 70.
9. McGlamery, G. G., "Liquid Film Transport Characteristics on Textured Metal Surfaces," Ph.D. Dissertation, University of Texas at Austin, May, 1988.
10. Bravo, J. L. *et al., Hydrocarbon Processing,* Vol. 65, No. 3, 1986, p. 45.
11. Fair, J. R. and Bravo, J. L., *Chemical Engineering Progress,* Vol. 86, No. 1, 1990, p. 19.
12. Fair, J. R. and Bravo, J. L., "Prediction of Mass Transfer Efficiencies and Pressure Drop for Structured Tower Packings in Vapor/Liquid Service," University of Texas at Austin, 1987.
13. Stichlmair, J. *et al., Gas Separation & Purification,* Vol. 3, 1989, p. 19.
14. Rocha, J. A. and Bravo, J. L., "New Holdup, Pressure Drop, and Efficiency Models for Structured Packings," University of Texas at Austin, 1990.
15. Fair, J. R. and Bravo, J. L., *Institution of Chemical Engineers Symposium Series No. 104,* 1987, p. A183.
16. Spiegel, L. and Meier, W., *Institution of Chemical Engineers Symposium Series No. 104,* 1987, p. A203.
17. Strigle, R. F. and Rukovena, F., *Chemical Engineering Progress,* Vol. 75, No. 3, 1979, p. 86.
18. Martin, C. L. *et al.,* "Performance of Structured Packings in Distillation Service," A.I.Ch.E. Meeting, New Orleans, March, 1988.
19. Rukovena, F. and Strigle, R. F., "Effect of Pressure on Structured Packing Performance," A.I.Ch.E. Meeting, Houston, March, 1989.
20. Chen, G. K. and Chuang, K. T., *Hydrocarbon Processing,* Vol. 68, No. 2, 1989, p. 37.

3

GAS ABSORPTION

In order to illustrate the use of packed columns in absorption opera-tions, it is necessary to refer to mass transfer theory. The initial part of this chapter has been devoted to a review of the fundamental principles of mass transfer that need to be understood to design absorption and strip-ping columns.

Absorption refers to the physical transfer of a solute from the gas phase to the liquid phase. Generally, the solute enters the column in a gas that is either insoluble or only slightly soluble in the liquid phase. While some of the liquid phase may be vaporized into the gas phase, this is incidental to the absorption operation.

The absorbed solute may form a simple solution in the liquid phase, or it may react chemically with a component in the liquid phase. If the concentration of solute in the liquid phase is small and the solute forms a simple solution, Henry's Law applies:

$$p^* = Hx \quad \text{liquid phase} \tag{3-1}$$

The partial pressure of solute in the gas phase is a function of the gas composition:

$$p = yP \quad \text{gas phase} \tag{3-2}$$

Combining Equations 3-1 and 3-2 we obtain:

$$y^* = \frac{Hx}{P} = \frac{p^*}{P/y} = \frac{p^*y}{p} \quad \begin{array}{l} \text{gas composition in} \\ \text{equilibrium with liquid} \\ \text{phase} \end{array} \tag{3-3}$$

for the vapor-phase concentration in equilibrium with the liquid phase. Absorption will take place whenever the partial pressure of solute in the vapor phase (Equation 3-2) exceeds the vapor pressure of solute above the liquid phase (Equation 3-1).

As the temperature of the liquid phase increases toward its boiling point, its vapor pressure approaches the system pressure. Thus, at the liq-uid-phase boiling temperature the solubility of the solute is reduced toward zero. The vapor pressure of the solute gas also increases with increasing temperature. Therefore, the Henry's Law constant increases with increasing liquid-phase temperature. As shown by Equation 3-3, at a constant gas-phase composition and pressure the solubility of a solute in the liquid phase is inversely proportional to the value of the Henry's Law constant.

Equation 3-1 permits calculation of the vapor pressure of the solute only for low concentrations of the solute in the liquid phase. The value of H must be modified in order that Equation 3-1 can be used at higher concentrations of solute in the liquid phase. Also, when the system pressure exceeds 150 psia a correction for the effect of pressure may be required.

TWO-FILM THEORY

The two-film theory still is widely employed to explain mass transfer operations. The boundary between the gas phase and the liquid phase is presumed to consist of a gas film adjacent to a liquid film. Flow in both of these films is assumed to be laminar or stagnant. The main-body gas phase, as well as the main-body liquid phase, are assumed to be completely mixed in turbulent flow so that no concentration gradient exists in the main body of either phase. Further, the solute concentration in the gas film at the interface is assumed to be in equilibrium with the solute concentration in the liquid film at the interface, and there is no resistance to mass transfer across the interface. There is a solute concentration gradient across both the gas film and the liquid film.

The derivation of equations to permit the use of mass transfer coefficient approach for design of packed towers has been described in detail in many texts. Thus, the mass transferred per unit time from the main-body gas phase through the gas film is indicated by this equation:

$$N \propto k_G \, (p - p') \tag{3-4}$$

for a small section of the interfacial area over which $p - p'$ essentially is constant. The driving force $(p - p')$ at any point is the difference between the partial pressure of solute in the main-body gas phase and that in the gas film at the interface.

Similarly, the solute transferred per unit of time through the liquid film to the main-body liquid phase is given by this expression:

$$N \propto k_L \, (x' - x) \tag{3-5}$$

for a small part of the interfacial area over which $x' - x$ is practically constant. The driving force $(x' - x)$ at any point is the difference between mol fraction of solute in the liquid film at the interface and that in the main-body liquid phase.

In a practical application three main problems must be solved:

1. the overall transfer coefficient depends partly on the nature of the gas film and partly on the nature of the liquid film
2. the driving force for mass transfer changes throughout the tower, and this must be taken into account
3. the interfacial area available for mass transfer must be adjusted for changes.

Mass transfer theory considers that the gas-film and liquid-film resistances are in series. The distribution of the overall resistance to mass transfer between the gas-film and liquid-film, as described by the two-film theory, results in these equations:

$$\frac{1}{K_G} = \frac{1}{k_G} + \frac{m}{k_L} \tag{3-6}$$

$$\frac{1}{K_L} = \frac{1}{mk_G} + \frac{1}{k_L} \tag{3-7}$$

The terms on the right side of Equations 3-6 and 3-7 are the individual film coefficients, and m is the slope of the equilibrium curve that relates the concentration of solute in the gas phase to the concentration of solute in the liquid phase at equilibrium. For low values of m the liquid film resistance is small, and the k_L term may be insignificant. Thus, the system is considered gas-film-controlled as K_G is almost equal to k_G. Similarly, for large values of m, the gas film resistance is small and the k_G term of little importance. Such a system is considered liquid-film-controlled, as K_L is about equal to k_L.

In allowing for the changes in the driving forces for mass transfer from the bottom to the top of a tower two things must be considered:

1. the change in equilibrium concentration in the liquid film due to the change of concentration of solute in the gas film
2. the changes of solute concentrations in the gas and liquid phases set by the mass balance.

A considerable amount of effort is needed to determine methods to take these considerations into account for many different situations. If the amount of solute transferred is small and the concentrations are low, the gas and liquid flows are practically constant. In this case the operating line is almost straight. If the system follows Henry's Law (see Equation 3-1), the equilibrium curve will be straight. For this situation the driving force may be predicted by the logarithmic mean of the driving forces at the ends of the tower. There also are other cases where an irreversible chemical reaction in the liquid reduces the equilibrium partial pressure of the solute over the liquid to zero.

It is necessary to allow for changes in the interfacial area between the gas and the liquid. This interfacial area not only is a function of the type and size of tower packing chosen, but also it may vary with flow rates. The interfacial area is accounted for by the use of a volumetric overall mass transfer coefficient (K_Ga or K_La). Note that this interfacial area is the same for the gas film as for the liquid film as applied to Equations 3-6 and 3-7.

The driving force for absorption involving highly soluble solutes usually is considered in terms of the partial pressure of solute in the vapor phase minus the vapor pressure of solute above the liquid phase. In other words, the calculation involves the solute concentrations in the main-body gas phase and in the main-body liquid phase, rather than the solute concentrations at the interface. Thus, the driving force is $p - p^*$ or $p - Hx$ where Henry's Law applies. The greater this driving force, the faster will be the rate of mass transfer if there are no other influences.

$$N = AZ \, K_Ga \, (p - p^*) \qquad\qquad (3\text{-}8)$$

The driving force for stripping operations involving slightly soluble solutes is considered in terms of liquid-phase composition minus the composition of a liquid in equilibrium with the gas phase. Thus, the driving force is $x - x^*$ or $x - p/H$ where Henry's Law applies. For practical purposes, again we have resorted to overall terms. The overall liquid-phase mass transfer coefficient in volumetric terms (K_La) is represented by the equation:

$$N = AZ \, K_La \, (x - x^*) \qquad\qquad (3\text{-}9)$$

GAS-FILM MASS TRANSFER COEFFICIENT

The gas-film mass transfer coefficient (k_G) does not change greatly with temperature. Initially k_G was believed to be related to the gas-phase Schmidt number to the 0.67 power [1]. This dimensionless number is:

$$Sc = \frac{u'}{\rho D} \qquad\qquad (3\text{-}10)$$

Due to the fact that mass transfer in packed beds is not totally controlled by molecular diffusion the exponent for the Schmidt number later was changed to 0.5 [2].

The gas-film mass transfer coefficient, however, is significantly influenced by the pressure. It has been reported that the mass transfer coefficient is a function of the pressure of the gas phase raised to the -0.32 power [3]. Thus, at twice the absolute system pressure, the mass transfer coefficient is increased only by 80%; however, the pressure difference driving force will increase in direct proportion to the system pressure at the constant gas-phase composition. For many absorption systems (such as those following Henry's Law), increasing the pressure will increase the solubility of the solute in the liquid phase.

LIQUID-FILM MASS TRANSFER COEFFICIENT

The liquid-film mass transfer coefficient (k_L) is markedly affected by temperature. Several investigators have proposed that this coefficient is proportional to the liquid-phase diffusivity to the 0.5 power [4, 5]. More recent investigators have reported this coefficient to be related to the liquid-phase Schmidt number to the -0.5 power [6, 7]. This mass transfer coefficient increases as the temperature increases, probably as a result of reduced liquid viscosity and increased diffusivity.

It is expected that a change in system pressure, and therefore the partial pressure of the solute, should have little effect on the liquid-phase coefficient. Although the solubility in the liquid phase is reduced with temperature increase, and the Henry's Law constant is greater, the liquid-film coefficient (k_L) may increase rapidly with temperature. Thus, there may exist an optimum temperature for a particular absorption system, which is not the lowest temperature, where solubility of the absorbed solute is greatest in the liquid phase.

OVERALL MASS TRANSFER COEFFICIENTS

The overall gas-phase mass transfer coefficient is related to the individual film coefficients in the following manner:

$$\frac{1}{K_G aP} = \frac{1}{k_G aP} = \frac{m}{k_L a} \qquad (3\text{-}11)$$

For systems following Henry's Law, the value of the slope of the equilibrium curve (m) equals H/P.

The reciprocal of the individual film mass transfer coefficient is the resistance to mass transfer exhibited by that film. Some examples of typical absorption systems indicating the controlling phase resistance are shown in Table 3-1.

In systems that are gas-film-controlled, the solute either will be highly soluble in the liquid phase or will react rapidly with a component in the

Table 3-1

Typical Absorption Operations

Solute	Absorbent Liquid	Controlling Phase
Oxygen	Water	Liquid
Chlorine	Water	Liquid
Carbon Dioxide	Water	Liquid
Carbon Dioxide	4% NaOH	Liquid
Carbon Dioxide	12% MEA	Liquid
Water Vapor	Water	Gas
Water Vapor	93% H_2SO_4	Gas
Ammonia	Water	Gas
Ammonia	10% H_2SO_4	Gas
Sulfur Dioxide	4% NaOH	Gas
Hydrogen Chloride	Water	Gas
Chlorine	5% NaOH	Gas
Sulfur Trioxide	98% H_2SO_4	Gas

liquid phase. In liquid-film-controlled systems the solute either has a low solubility in the liquid phase or reacts with a component in the liquid phase at a slow rate. In some cases, depending on the value of m, one may approximate the overall coefficient by neglecting the smaller resistance to mass transfer. In reality this is an extremely simplifying assumption because the percentage of gas and liquid-film control varies with the concentration of solute as well as the physical properties that change the solubility of the solute in the liquid phase.

In stripping operations we can relate the overall liquid-phase mass transfer coefficient to the individual film coefficients as follows:

$$\frac{1}{K_L a} = \frac{1}{m k_G a P} = \frac{1}{k_L a} \qquad (3\text{-}12)$$

The interfacial area (a) should not be confused with the geometric surface area of the tower packing. Shulman *et al.* demonstrated that the interfacial area is not directly related to the wetted area [8]. The increase in overall mass transfer coefficient for ceramic Intalox saddles compared to ceramic Raschig rings could, at least in part, be attributed to increased surface area per unit volume. However, metal Pall rings show a substantial increase in mass transfer coefficient compared to metal Raschig rings, yet both packings have the same surface area for the same size packing.

Modern tower packing shapes tend to be permeable, so that the gas and liquid can flow through the center of the packing element as well as around the shape. The increased mass transfer rates associated with these packings are due in part to increased interstitial transfer within the internal void.

For absorption operations it is customary to use K_Ga values because we usually are concerned about the composition of the gas phase. The overall mass transfer coefficients in absorption are considered to be a function of the gas and liquid flow rates:

$$K_Ga \propto L^bG^c \qquad\qquad \text{plot } K_G \text{ a vs } L \text{ \& } G \qquad (3\text{-}13)$$

In liquid-film-controlled systems the value of K_Ga primarily is a function of the liquid flow rate. For most random dumped tower packings the value of the exponent b in Equation 3-13 lies between 0.22 and 0.34; the exact value is characteristic of the type of packing employed. If data on the particular packing are not readily available, it is suggested that this exponent be assumed as 0.30 for preliminary designs. In such liquid-film-controlled systems there is a very small effect of gas rate. The value of the exponent c in Equation 3-13 normally is only 0.06 to 0.08. Thus, if a standard K_Ga value for such a system is determined to be 6.0 lb-mol/h · ft³ · atm at a liquid rate of 5,000 lb/ft² · h, the K_Ga value for this same tower packing at a liquid rate of 20,000 lb/ft² · h would be about 9.1 lb-mol/h · ft³ · atm.

In gas-film-controlled absorption systems the value of K_Ga is a function of both the liquid and the gas flow rates. The value of the exponent b for the effect of liquid flow rate in Equation 3-13 is the same for gas-film-controlled systems as for liquid-film-controlled systems. However, the value of the exponent c for the effect of gas flow rate in Equation 3-13 for a gas-film-controlled system has increased to between 0.67 and 0.80. In the absence of data on a specific system, it is suggested that the value of exponent c be taken as 0.75. In any event, the sum of exponents b and c should be greater than 1.0. Therefore, if the foregoing system were gas-film-controlled and the gas rate was increased from 900 lb/ft² · h to 1200 lb/ft² · h along with the preceding liquid rate increase, the new K_Ga would have a value of about 11.3 lb-mol/h · ft³ · atm.

In gas-film-controlled systems the value of K_Ga is much greater than in liquid-film-controlled systems. This is because the liquid-film resistance reduces the value of the overall coefficient in liquid-film-controlled systems, while it has only a small effect on this value in gas-film-controlled systems. In absorption operations carried out at a constant liquid-to-gas ratio, the number of mols of solute to be absorbed will increase in direct proportion to the gas rate at a fixed gas composition. The K_Ga value for a liquid-film-controlled system, however, will increase only as about the 0.37 power of the flow rates at a constant G/L ratio (b + c = 0.37). Thus, increasing the flow rates in such a system will either reduce the absorption efficiency or increase the packed depth required. For a gas-film-controlled system, the $K_G a$ will increase faster than the flow rates ($b + c > 1.0$); therefore, the absorption efficiency will not be reduced with an increase in flow rates.

The pressure driving force difference must be determined at the bottom of the packed bed (Δp_B) as well as at the top of the packed bed (Δp_T) in an absorber. For a gas stream containing a low concentration of solute, L/G is almost constant and the operating line of the absorber is straight. Also, if there is negligible heat of solution in the liquid phase, the value of H or m may be constant. Under these conditions the pressure difference driving force is the logarithmic mean average of the driving forces at the bottom and top of the packed bed.

$$\Delta p_{LM} = \frac{\Delta p_B - \Delta p_T}{\ln (\Delta p_B / \Delta p_T)} \tag{3-14}$$

The volume of tower packing required for the absorber can be calculated as follows:

$$AZ = \frac{N}{K_G a \Delta p_{LM}} \tag{3-15}$$

TRANSFER UNITS AND THEORETICAL STAGES

Frequently, it is convenient to calculate the packed height required by means of theoretical stages or transfer units. This is due to the fact that the height equivalent to a theoretical stage for a particular system tends to be constant. Further, the height of a transfer unit varies less with flow rates than do the mass transfer coefficients.

First, we will consider the transfer unit approach because it relates directly to the mass transfer coefficient. Where the gas flow does not change significantly over a short packed depth:

$$N = G_m (y_i - y_o) \tag{3-16}$$

G_m = gas phase flow
A = cross-sectional area
K_G = overall mass transfer coefficient

therefore, Equation 3-15 becomes:

$$Z = \frac{G_m (y_i - y_o)}{A K_G a \Delta p_{LM}} \quad \text{or} \quad \frac{G_m}{A K_G a P} \left[\frac{P(y_i - y_o)}{\Delta p_{LM}} \right] \tag{3-17}$$

∂ = interfacial area
P = total pressure

The overall height of a transfer unit is:

$$H_{OG} = \frac{G_m}{A K_G a P} \tag{3-18}$$

which is a function of flow rates and packing properties. The addition of resistances according to the two-film theory, as previously shown for mass transfer coefficients, also applies to the heights of transfer units.

$$H_{OG} = H_G + \lambda H_L \tag{3-19}$$

where

$$H_G = \frac{G_m}{Ak_G aP} \tag{3-20}$$

and

$$H_L = \frac{L_m}{Ak_L a} \tag{3-21}$$

Lambda is the ratio of the slope of the equilibrium curve to the slope of the operating line:

$$\lambda = \frac{mG_m}{L_m} \tag{3-22}$$

The number of transfer units required is:

$$N_{OG} = \int_{y_o}^{y_i} \frac{dy}{y^* - y} \tag{3-23}$$

y* = equil. mol fraction in gas phase
y = mol fraction in gas phase

In Equation 3-17, N_{OG} is represented by the term

$$\frac{P(y_i - y_o)}{\Delta p_{LM}}$$

In the transfer unit concept there is a clear separation between the number of transfer units (N_{OG}), which is based on driving forces, and the height of a transfer unit (H_{OG}), which represents the rate of mass transfer. Thus, the specification for the amount of solute transferred from the gas phase determines the number of transfer units required. The height of a transfer unit depends mainly on the choice of tower packing.

The logarithmic mean driving force used in Equations 3-14 and 3-17 is applicable only when both the operating line and the equilibrium curve are straight. However, the transfer unit method is not restricted to this situation. A method for determining the number of transfer units required when the equilibrium curve is not straight is illustrated in Chapter 6.

An alternative method uses a theoretical stage concept. This method is similar to the transfer unit method in that the specification for solute removal defines the number of theoretical stages required, while the choice of tower packing sets the height of a theoretical stage (HETP). There is a simple relationship between the height of theoretical stage and the height of a transfer unit (see Chapter 7). In gas absorption operations, however, either mass transfer coefficients or the transfer unit method normally is used for column design.

SIMPLIFIED DESIGN PROCEDURES

Kremser generally is credited with development of a procedure of calculation using the absorption factor [9]. However, this method does not estimate vapor and liquid compositions or temperature profiles in the column [10]. It assumes a straight operating line and an equilibrium curve of constant slope. The slope of the equilibrium curve is represented by the equilibrium ratio (K), which is the ratio of the mol fraction of solute in the vapor phase to the mol fraction of solute in the liquid phase. The absorption factor A* is the ratio of the slope of the operating line to the slope of the equilibrium curve.

$$A* = \frac{L_m}{KG_m} \tag{3-24}$$

The absorption factor can be used to calculate around each theoretical stage by the following equation:

$$y_n = \frac{y_{n+1} + A*Kx_{n-1}}{1 + A*} \tag{3-25}$$

Once the number of theoretical stages has been determined, it is necessary to estimate stage efficiency in order to calculate the packed depth required.

In an attempt to obtain more consistency with mass transfer theory, the transfer unit concept has been proposed. The number of gas-phase transfer units (N_{OG}) can be calculated by the Souders and Brown procedure using the absorption factor [11]. This equation assumes linear, although not parallel, operating line and equilibrium curve.

$$N_{OG} = \frac{\ln\left[\frac{y_i - Kx_i}{y_o - Kx_i}\left(1 - \frac{1}{A*}\right) + \frac{1}{A*}\right]}{1 - \frac{1}{A*}} \tag{3-26}$$

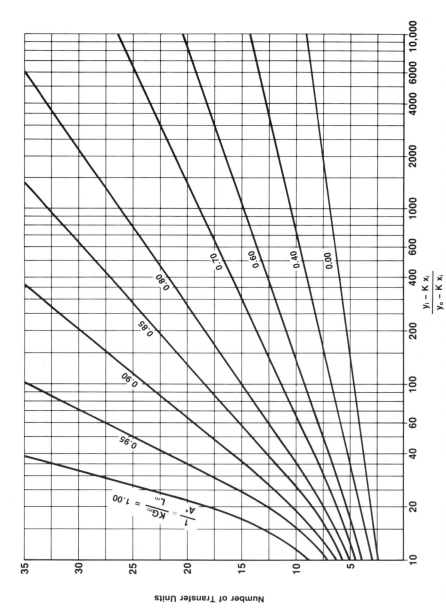

Figure 3-1. Colburn correlation for absorber design (From Colburn [12]. Reprinted with permission from *Industrial and Engineering Chemistry*, Vol. 33, 1941, p. 459, American Chemical Society.)

In order to do a preliminary absorber design, the Colburn correlation shown in Figure 3-1 can be used [12]. To determine the number of gas-phase transfer units, it merely is necessary to calculate the ratio of inlet to outlet gas compositions, $(y_i - Kx_i)/(y_o - Kx_i)$, and the absorption factor from Equation 3-24.

Once the number of transfer units has been calculated, the height of a transfer unit must be determined to ascertain the packed depth required. The height of a transfer unit is that depth of packing that produces a change in composition equal to the mass transfer driving force causing that change. The overall volumetric mass transfer coefficient and height of a transfer unit are related as given in Equation 3-18 for the gas phase and as follows for the liquid phase:

$$H_{OL} = \frac{L_m}{AK_L a} \tag{3-27}$$

The height of a transfer unit varies inversely with the value of the overall mass transfer coefficient and directly with the gas or liquid molar flow rate.

GENERAL DESIGN CONCEPT

Unfortunately, many commercially important absorption operations do not follow Henry's Law for equilibrium values and do not operate at constant gas rates or liquid rates. The concentration of solute in the entering gas stream may represent a significantly large percentage of that stream, so that after absorption of solute, the exit gas flow rate is reduced. Likewise, the liquid rate leaving the tower exceeds the entering liquid rate by the amount of solute absorbed. This statement assumes no vaporization of the solvent and zero solubility of the inert gas phase in the solvent. Equation 3-28 gives the mass balance across such an absorber:

$$y_i G_i + x_i L_i = y_o G_o + x_o L_o \tag{3-28}$$

This equation applies regardless of whether the equilibrium curve and operating line are straight. Rather than use an overall mass transfer coefficient analysis of the absorption operation, we can consider it as a series of theoretical stages. Such a theoretical stage is visualized as a mass transfer stage in which the liquid and gas are in equilibrium with each other leaving the stage. The equilibrium ratio for that stage is defined as the slope of the equilibrium curve:

$$K = \frac{y_n}{x_n} \tag{3-29}$$

For any theoretical stage n, the material balance becomes

$$y_{n+1} G_{n+1} + x_{n-1} L_{n-1} = y_n G_n + x_n L_n \qquad (3\text{-}30)$$

where $n + 1$ is the theoretical stage below, and $n - 1$ is the theoretical stage above. Over the entire column for any theoretical stage Equation 3-30 becomes:

$$y_i G_i + x_i L_i = y_n G_n + x_n L_n \qquad (3\text{-}31)$$

This equation can be rearranged as follows:

$$y_i = x_n \frac{L_n}{G_i} + y_n \frac{G_n}{G_i} - x_i \frac{L_i}{G_i} \qquad (3\text{-}32)$$

If the solute transferred per theoretical stage is small compared to total gas and liquid flows, then:

$$\frac{G_n}{G_{n+1}} \cong 1.0 \qquad (3\text{-}33)$$

and

$$\frac{L_{n-1}}{L_n} \cong 1.0 \qquad (3\text{-}34)$$

In this event, Equation 3-31 for absorption of solute from a lean entering gas stream becomes approximately:

$$y_i = x_n \frac{L_n}{G_n} + y_n - x_i \frac{L_i}{G_i} \qquad (3\text{-}35)$$

Equation 3-35 represents a straight operating line with a slope of L_n/G_n and an intercept of $y_i + x_i(L_i/G_i)$. An overall equation for the entire column permits calculation of the outlet gas composition (y_o) as follows:

$$y_o = y_i + x_i \frac{L_i}{G_i} - x_o \frac{L_n}{G_n} \qquad (3\text{-}36)$$

In those cases in which the solute constitutes a large percentage of the inlet gas stream, the gas flow rate will decrease from the bottom to the top of the absorber. In other cases, when dealing with a highly soluble solute, it may be desired to produce a concentrated solution of solute leaving the absorber. In this latter case inlet solvent flow will be restricted by the material balance, and the liquid rate will increase substantially from the top to the bottom of the absorber.

The example problem in Chapter 1 represents a case of a rich inlet gas stream containing 7.3 mol % solute. The gas flow rate is reduced from an inlet flow of 241,600 lb/h to an exit flow of 219,800 lb/h, due to solute absorption. The 30 wt % DEA flow rate, likewise, is increased from an inlet liquid flow of 504,200 lb/h to an outlet liquid flow of 526,000 lb/h.

In order to simplify a calculation of the number of theoretical stages required for systems with a rich gas stream, we can replace the usual abscissa value of mol fraction solute in the liquid phase with a value that shows mols CO_2 per mol DEA. The flow of DEA through the absorber is constant, since this solvent is not volatile at the operating temperature. The usual ordinate value of mol fraction solute in the gas phase can be replaced with a value that represents mols CO_2 per mol inert gas. The inert gas flow is almost constant, increasing only by the small amount of water evaporated.

On such a plot, the abscissa value at the bottom of the absorber is 0.45 mol CO_2 per mol DEA, and the ordinate value is 0.07875 mol CO_2 per mol inert gas. At the top of the absorber, the abscissa value is 0.10 mol CO_2 per mol DEA, and the ordinate value is 0.00503 mol CO_2 per mol inert gas. The slope of the operating line varies from 0.2080 mol DEA per mol inert gas at the bottom of the tower to 0.2074 mol DEA per mol of inert gas at the top of the tower. The operating line, therefore, essentially is straight.

The equilibrium curve can be constructed on such a plot from data on the vapor pressures of CO_2 above 30 wt % DEA solutions. A correction should be made for any change in temperature of the liquid, due to heat released by the solute and sensible heat absorbed by the gas. The number of theoretical stages required then can be stepped-off in the usual manner.

The number of theoretical stages for systems with nonlinear operating or equilibrium lines can be calculated by the methods described in Chapter 7. The relationship between HETP and H_{OG} is discussed in that chapter.

CHOICE OF SOLVENT

In absorption operations the inlet gas flow rate, solute concentration, and operating pressure are known, as is the desired solute concentration in the outlet gas stream. The solvent liquid may be low cost (such as water) and, therefore, used on a once-through basis when gas purification, rather than solute recovery, is required. On the other hand, the solvent may be expensive; thus, it must be recycled through a regenerator. This especially is the case where solute recovery is the goal. Since the outlet gas stream will be saturated with solvent vapor, the cost of solvent losses by evaporation should be evaluated. Additionally, the solvent selected should be chemically stable, noncorrosive, nontoxic, nonpolluting, and of low flammability.

The designer first must select the solvent liquid to be used and then specify its circulation rate. The greater the solubility of solute in the solvent, the lower will be the necessary liquid rate. The minimum solvent rate possible is that flow which produces a concentration of solute in the effluent liquid which is in equilibrium with the solute concentration in the entering gas stream. Of course, an infinite number of theoretical stages is required at minimum solvent flow. The economic optimum design results from a balance between the solvent circulation rate and the depth of packing in the absorber.

In the design of a new column the diameter can be adjusted based on the solvent flow rate, and the packed depth can be specified based on the number of theoretical stages required to meet the outlet gas solute content at the operating liquid-to-gas ratio. In the revamp of an existing column, either the maximum solvent flow rate or the maximum solute removal can be specified, but not both. The available height defines the maximum number of theoretical stages obtainable, while the column diameter controls the maximum liquid rate.

SELECTION OF COLUMN DIAMETER

Once the solvent rate is fixed, the designer can proceed to calculate the column diameter. The column cross-sectional area usually is specified by the pressure drop produced as a result of the design gas and liquid flow rates. Absorbers normally are specified to give a pressure drop between 0.10 to 0.40 in. H_2O/ft of packed depth. In non-foaming systems the design pressure drop usually is between 0.25 and 0.40 in. H_2O/ft. For systems that tend to foam moderately, the design pressure drop should be reduced to a maximum of 0.25 in. H_2O/ft at the point of greatest loading. Such a design will avoid imparting energy from the gas stream to the liquid phase, which can promote additional foaming.

Because high liquid flow rates frequently are encountered in absorption operations, the size of packing should be chosen as shown in Table 3-2 to avoid hydraulic overload. These liquid rates apply to mobile liquids and should be reduced at higher liquid viscosities as discussed in Chapter 1 under "High Liquid Rate Performance." At very high L/G ratios (exceeding 20), the calculated pressure drop still may fall within the above allowable design limits; however, in these situations, the gas rate should not exceed 85% of the rate that would give the pressure drop at flooding as defined by Equation 1-5 (see Chapter 1).

In some cases, the solute is absorbed from the gas stream to produce a specific liquid effluent concentration, such as for an HCl absorber. In this case, the liquid flow rate is fixed by the mass balance. Such operations may exhibit a very low L/G ratio (less than 1.2). In these cases, it usually is advisable to use a larger size random packing or a structured

Table 3-2

Maximum Recommended Liquid Loading for Random Packings

Packing Size (in.)	Liquid Rate (gpm/ft²)
¾	25
1	40
1½	55
2	70
3½	125

packing in order to reduce column diameter and thus increase the liquid irrigation rate. However, such a design may increase the packed depth required. The gas velocity at the top of the column should be kept low enough to avoid entrainment of liquid, which would represent loss of solvent and contamination of the outlet gas stream. The maximum capacity as limited by liquid entrainment is discussed in Chapter 7.

PHYSICAL ABSORPTION

After the column diameter and packing size have been selected, the required packed depth must be specified. This calculation requires a knowledge of the equilibrium values for the system involved. First, we will consider a system that uses a pure physical solvent in which there is a low heat of solution of the solute, such as the absorption of CO_2 into Selexol® solvent (trademark Union Carbide Corp.). This small heat release plus the high liquid-to-solute ratio means that the liquid temperature changes very little in the absorber. In such a system, the Henry's Law constant can be used to provide the equilibrium relationship. The inlet gas composition is known, and the desired outlet gas concentration is specified. The liquid circulation rate normally is fixed so that the equilibrium partial pressure of solute above the effluent liquid is about 80% of the partial pressure of solute in the entering gas stream. Assuming that the solvent is recirculated, the regenerated solvent feed to the absorber must have an equilibrium partial pressure of solute less than the specified partial pressure of solute in the exit gas stream. Because driving forces at the top of the absorber may be quite small, in order to avoid excessive packed depths, the solvent should be regenerated so that the equilibrium partial pressure of solute above the lean solvent is no more than 50% of the solute partial pressure specified for the exit gas stream.

Although acid gases may have a high solubility in Selexol solvent, this system is considered liquid-film controlled. Absorption is limited by diffusion in the liquid phase due to the high viscosity of Selexol solvent; therefore, liquid properties are important in determining the mass transfer rate. The height of a liquid-phase transfer unit increases with increasing liquid viscosity and with increasing Henry's Law constant. Within a given type of packing, at high liquid rates that completely wet the packing surface, the height of a liquid-phase transfer unit varies to about the 0.5 power of packing size.

SOLVENT ABSORPTION

Next, we will consider a system that uses a solvent into which the solute vapor is condensed. This operation will release a significant quantity of heat, which in turn will raise the solvent temperature as it flows down the absorption column. In this case, the effect of temperature on the equilibrium ratio (K) must be allowed for in the calculations. The solubility of solute normally will decrease with increasing solvent temperature (the K value will increase). To obtain high solute removal from the gas stream, a large solvent flow rate can be used in order to limit the temperature rise. If solvent flow is to be kept low, the heated liquid phase must be removed from the column, cooled externally, then returned to the absorber.

Mihm performed a study on the absorption of propane from a natural gas stream at a pressure of 650 psig using a hydrocarbon absorption oil [13]. With a lean oil feed rate of 10 gpm, 42% propane absorption was obtained using inlet gas and lean oil temperatures of 32°F. With the same gas and lean oil rates the propane absorption was reduced to 20% when the inlet gas and lean oil temperatures were raised to 70°F. When the lean oil rate was increased to 20 gpm, 72% of the propane was absorbed with inlet gas and lean oil temperatures of 32°F.

In recovery of light hydrocarbons by use of an absorption oil as the solvent, no chemical reactions occur, and the liquid phase is an ideal solution for practical purposes. Fortunately, in a refinery gas absorber, the K values usually are available for all major components of the gas stream. The heat load imparted to the solvent primarily represents the latent heat of vaporization of the absorbed light hydrocarbons. In addition, there may be a sensible heat load due to the temperature difference between the entering gas stream and the solvent feed.

Usually the solvent temperature will be reduced as low as practical before entering the absorber in order to provide the greatest possible hydrocarbon removal from the gas stream. As hydrocarbon is absorbed in the top of the column, the liquid temperature increases, as does the K value. As hydrocarbon is absorbed in the bottom of the column, the mol fraction and the partial pressure of solute in the gas phase decrease. In order to avoid an equilibrium pinch in the center of the absorber, the partially enriched solvent is collected on a trap tray and withdrawn from the column. This liquid is cooled in an external heat exchanger and returned to the absorber below the trap tray. Normally a sufficient solvent feed rate is used so that only a single liquid removal and cooling operation is required.

The calculation of such a column must be done by an iterative procedure around each theoretical stage until the mass balance, heat balance, and equilibrium ratios are satisfied simultaneously. By working down from the top of the absorber, the optimum liquid withdrawal point can be located. Next the cooled solvent return temperature can be fixed by working from the bottom up to the liquid withdrawal point. This system usually is considered to be liquid-film controlled; however, in operations at very high pressures and with low concentrations of solute in the gas phase, the gas-film resistance also can become significant.

NATURAL GAS DEHYDRATION

Natural gas is dehydrated using a glycol in order to reduce the water content of the gas so as to prevent formation of solid hydrates. At 90°F and 1,000 psia, natural gas saturated with water contains 45 lb H_2O per MMSCF (60°F & 14.7 psia) of gas. At a 10°F dew point this gas will have a water content of only 3 lb H_2O per MMSCF. Because of the cost of regeneration of the glycol drying agent, the flow of glycol usually is specified at 3 to 5 gallons of glycol per lb of water removed. Thus, in the above case, 1 MMSCFH of natural gas would be contacted in an absorber with only about 168 gph of glycol. If the lean absorber feed is 98.5 wt% triethylene glycol, the absorber effluent will be 96.0 wt % TEG.

Because of the very low quantity of liquid compared to the gas flow, bubble-cap trays have been widely employed in such contactors. For each 1 MMSCFH of gas flow, at least 4.9 ft^2 of bubbling area is required for such trays. With 7% downcomers on these trays, the liquid irrigation rate is less than 30 gph/ft^2 of column cross-sectional area. Such low liquid rates generally have discouraged the use of random packings in these contactors. The advent of structured sheet metal packings has significantly changed this situation. The high capacity of such packings, with a surface area of 50 to 55 ft^2/ft^3 in the large sizes, permits the use of as little as 3.0 ft^2 of column cross-sectional area for a gas flow of 1 MMSCFH at 90°F and 1,000 psia. Thus, the liquid irrigation rate will be increased to 56 gph/ft^2 of column area. This liquid rate is well within the efficient operational range of such structured packings, as is discussed under "Vacuum Distillation" (see Chapter 8).

Due to the high liquid viscosity, this system is liquid-film controlled; therefore, tray efficiency is in the order of 25% [14]. In practice, only 6 to 8 actual trays may be used in such a contactor. The efficiency of the large size structured packing is well within the HETP value of 6.8 ft allowed by the usual number of trays on 24-in. spacing. An HETP value of 4.2 ft has been reported for moderate dew point depressions with structured packings [15]. This efficiency will permit replacement of trays with a reduction of at least 40% in mass transfer height.

GAS DRYING

As another case of absorption, we will consider the drying of an insoluble gas by contact with a dehydrating liquid. Due to the high heat of vaporization of water, plus its high heat of solution in the dehydrating liquid, there can be a large heat load imparted to the liquid phase. As the dehydrating liquid is diluted by the condensed water, and as the liquid temperature increases, the vapor pressure of water above the liquid phase will increase. Usually a high liquid circulation rate is used in each stage of drying to minimize both the temperature rise and the dilution of the liquid dehydrating agent. When the amount of water vapor to be removed is large, a number of towers, each recycling cooled liquid, may be operated in series.

In the drying of chlorine, the hot cell gas typically is cooled to about 60° to 65°F before entering the first drying tower. The inlet gas stream at atmospheric pressure will contain 2 mol % maximum water vapor. Usually three drying towers in series will produce an exit chlorine gas containing no more than 40 mol ppm water vapor. Because only 20 lb of 98 wt% sulfuric acid is consumed per ton of dry chlorine, each column must be recirculated to provide a liquid rate of 4 to 6 gpm/ft^2 of cross-sectional area. The first tower and the third tower (with respect to gas flow) normally will use coolers on the recirculated acid stream to keep the outlet acid from each tower to 95°F maximum temperature.

The three towers usually are sized to a common diameter that will give a pressure drop of 0.10 in. to 0.15 in. H$_2$O/ft of packed depth, because the overall pressure drop desired for the entire drying system is only 4 in. to 5 in. H$_2$O. This process largely is gas-film-controlled, as expected. It is desirable to keep the packed depth in each of the three columns the same. To accomplish this configuration, an iterative design procedure is necessary. The driving force for mass transfer is the difference between the partial pressure of water vapor in the gas stream and the vapor pressure of water above the liquid phase. Because of the high liquid flow rate, as a first approximation, the acid concentration and temperature in each tower can be assumed constant in order to establish the amount of water vapor removed in each column, and thereby the acid concentration.

When super-dry chlorine (having a maximum water content of 10 mol ppm) is required, a fourth drying tower is used. This column removes very little water vapor, so that the liquid recirculated will be about 96 wt % sulfuric acid. Because of the high liquid-phase viscosity (greater than 15 cps), the absorption in this tower will be substantially liquid-film controlled.

SULFURIC ACID MANUFACTURE

The production of sulfuric acid uses some of the largest diameter packed towers in chemical plant process trains. Column diameters up to 30 ft have been used for both the drying tower and the SO_3 absorber. However, since the middle 1960s, with the acceptance of newer tower packings and advanced design procedures, column diameters seldom approach this size in modern plants. In a sulfur-burning plant, the hot gas stream entering the SO_3 absorber usually contains 8 to 10 mol % SO_3, which must be almost completely absorbed so the gas leaving the tower will contain only 30 to 40 mol ppm SO_3. The SO_3 is absorbed into 98 wt % sulfuric acid, in which it is highly soluble. The acid enters the absorber at a temperature of 170° to 180°F and leaves the column 50° to 60°F hotter. This temperature rise in the acid is due both to the heat of solution of SO_3 and the sensible heat removed by cooling the inlet gas stream. The large heat of formation of H_2SO_4 is not released in the absorption column, but in the subsequent water dilution tank, and removed in acid coolers.

This system is almost a pure gas-film-controlled absorption. The sum of the exponents b and c in Equation 3-13 is greater than unity. Thus, an increase in gas flow rate at constant gas composition will increase the mols of SO_3 to be absorbed in direct proportion. By holding a constant liquid-

Figure 3-2. Sulfuric acid plant using Intalox® Saddle (ceramic) tower packing.

to-gas ratio while increasing flow rates, the overall mass transfer coefficient will increase even faster than the quantity of SO_3 to be absorbed.

The design of the absorber first involves fixing the diameter so that the exit gas stream velocity is not so high as to entrain liquid sulfuric acid out of the column. The use of a design pressure drop of 0.25 to 0.30 in. H_2O/ft at the bottom of the absorber is common practice. This pressure drop may double in nine to ten years of operation due to an accumulation of sulfation products in the packed bed. To minimize blockage of the packed bed, a 2-in. or 3-in. size ceramic packing normally is specified. As a result of the use of modern tower packings, as well as the development of improved packing support systems and liquid distributor design, the superficial gas velocity within the column has been increased almost two-fold from designs common in the late 1950s.

The design of the SO_3 absorber is relatively straightforward for the packed depth required. The driving force for mass transfer is the difference between the partial pressure of SO_3 in the gas stream and the vapor pressure of SO_3 above the sulfuric acid. The overall mass transfer coefficients are very high, in the order of 20 lb mol/h · ft^3 · atm for 2-in. ceramic Intalox saddles at a liquid rate of 7.5 gpm/ft^2 and a gas rate of 1200 lb/ft^2 · h. This high value for K_Ga indicates that there is very little liquid-film resistance.

Because of the materials of construction necessary to resist corrosion, the uniformity of gas and liquid distribution may be less than current best practice. The designer should allow for this situation in specifying the packed depth, which may be up to 50% greater than the theoretical depth required.

FORMALDEHYDE ABSORPTION

Often, a fixed composition of the effluent liquid is required for the product to be marketed. In such a case, the feed liquid rate to the absorber is set by a material balance. As an example, we will consider the absorption of formaldehyde from a gas stream to produce a 50 wt % aqueous solution. Although, HCHO is highly soluble in water, it releases 27,000 BTU/lb mol HCHO of heat when absorbed into water [16]. Because the vapor pressure of HCHO above its solutions increases with both concentration and temperature, it is necessary to withdraw and cool the liquid phase repeatedly.

Commercial absorbers normally use countercurrent packed beds in externally cooled pumparound sections to remove the heat of absorption. This system is complicated by the tendency of HCHO solutions to produce a solid phase if the concentration is too high or the temperature too low. Thus, the 50 wt % HCHO solution must be discharged from the absorber at a temperature greater than 131°F [17].

The feed gas to the absorber is at a temperature of about 260°F; therefore, the bottom bed serves to cool the feed gas and reduce its volume [18]. Structured packing should be considered for this bed in order to reduce the diameter of the absorber. The other packed sections in the main absorber can use either structured packing or random packing. About two-thirds of the gas stream leaving the top bed of the main absorber is recycled. The remaining one-third of the gas is scrubbed free of HCHO in a smaller diameter tower irrigated by the feed water. Because of the low liquid irrigation rate in this vent gas scrubber (about 0.5 gpm/ft^2), a structured packing often is chosen.

ABSORPTION WITH CHEMICAL REACTION

Many absorption operations of great commercial importance involve a reaction between the solute and a component present in the liquid phase. Of course, the solute first must be dissolved into the liquid phase before a reaction can take place. As an example, organic sulfides are easily oxidized; however, they are not removed from pulp mill vent gases by contact with aqueous solutions of oxidizing agents simply because of the very low solubility of these sulfides in water.

Chemical reactions in the liquid phase are either reversible or irreversible. Typical reversible reactions are involved in the absorption of H_2S into ethanolamines, or the absorption of CO_2 into alkali carbonate solutions. These reversible reactions permit the resultant solution to be regenerated so that the solute can be recovered in a concentrated form. Some irreversible reactions are the absorption of NH_3 into dilute acids and the absorption of CO_2 into alkaline hydroxides. The solute in such absorptions is so tightly bound in the reaction product that there is no appreciable vapor pressure of solute above the liquid phase. Under these conditions, regeneration of the solute is not possible, and the reacting component in the liquid is consumed. The purpose of such a reactant is to increase the solubility of the solute in the liquid phase and/or reduce the liquid-film resistance to mass transfer. Much theoretical work has been conducted since the 1950s to study diffusion and reaction in the liquid phase [19]. To calculate the effect of the rate of chemical reaction on the mass transfer requires the prediction of physical/chemical constants of salt solutions, such as equilibrium constants, reaction velocities, solubilities, and diffusion coefficients. Often, these constants must be available at elevated temperatures and/or pressures.

In practical cases, the difficulty of obtaining the required data leads the designer to use a simplified procedure using the physical absorption equations previously described together with mass transfer coefficients obtained from past experience. Despite the fact that the chemical reaction defines processes in the liquid phase, it is common practice to use partial pressure driving forces and empirically determined overall mass transfer coefficients.

The absorption of CO_2 into a sodium hydroxide solution has been used to characterize the relative performance of tower packings. Most of the available data are based on atmospheric pressure operation in which the inlet gas phase contains 1 mol % CO_2 in air and the gas mass flow rate is constant at a superficial velocity of 3.5 ft/s. The liquid phase is one normal aqueous sodium hydroxide at a temperature of 75°F. The conversion to soda ash is kept low (25% conversion of the NaOH) to ensure the availability of sufficient free hydroxyl ions, so as to provide an excess over that required for combining with the absorbed CO_2.

In this system, the reaction of hydrolyzed CO_2 with hydroxyl ions is moderately rapid, and the partial pressure of CO_2 in equilibrium with the bulk liquid is zero for practical purposes. The effect of the liquid-phase reaction is to reduce substantially the liquid-film resistance, because the distance the absorbed solute must diffuse is only about 10% of that customary for a simple physical absorption. The liquid-film mass transfer coefficient is a function of liquid flow rate [4]. The liquid-film mass transfer coefficient is constant at any fixed percentage carbonation and almost independent of gas flow rate below the loading region. This system, therefore, is used to measure the relative interfacial area for different packings as influenced by the liquid flow rate.

Tables 3-3 through 3-6 show the overall K_Ga values obtained for this system at a liquid rate of 10 gpm/ft² and a gas rate F_s value of 0.9413

Table 3-3

Overall Mass Transfer Coefficient
CO_2/NaOH System

Metal Tower Packings

Packing	K_Ga (lb-mol/h · ft³ · atm)
#25 IMTP® Packing	3.42
#40 IMTP® Packing	2.86
#50 IMTP® Packing	2.44
#70 IMTP® Packing	1.74
1 in. Pall Rings	3.10
1½ in. Pall Rings	2.58
2 in. Pall Rings	2.18
3½ in. Pall Rings	1.28
#1 Hy-Pak® Packing	2.89
#1½ Hy-Pak® Packing	2.42
#2 Hy-Pak® Packing	2.06
#3 Hy-Pak® Packing	1.45

Table 3-4

Overall Mass Transfer Coefficient
CO_2/NaOH System

Plastic Tower Packings

Packing	K_Ga (lb-mol/h · ft³ · atm)
#1 Super Intalox® Packing	2.80
#2 Super Intalox® Packing	1.92
#3 Super Intalox® Packing	1.23
Intalox® Snowflake® Packing	2.37
1 in. Pall Rings	2.64
1½ in. Pall Rings	2.25
2 in. Pall Rings	2.09
3½ in. Pall Rings	1.23

Table 3-5

Overall Mass Transfer Coefficient
CO_2/NaOH System

Ceramic Tower Packings

Packing	K_Ga (lb-mol/h · ft³ · atm)
1 in. Intalox® Saddles	2.82
1½ in. Intalox® Saddles	2.27
2 in. Intalox® Saddles	1.88
3 in. Intalox® Saddles	1.11
1 in. Raschig Rings	2.31
1½ in. Raschig Rings	1.92
2 in. Raschig Rings	1.63
3 in. Raschig Rings	1.02

Table 3-6

Overall Mass Transfer Coefficient
CO_2/NaOH System

Structured Tower Packings

Packing	K_Ga (lb-mol/h · ft³ · atm)
Intalox® Structured Packing 1T	4.52
Intalox® Structured Packing 2T	3.80
Intalox® Structured Packing 3T	2.76

$lb^{0.5}/ft^{0.5} \cdot$ s with different sizes and types of metal, plastic, and ceramic random packings, as well as sheet metal structured packings. These overall mass transfer coefficients are calculated from the following equation:

$$K_G a = \frac{y_i G_i - y_o G_o}{AZ \, \Delta p_{LM}} \qquad (3\text{-}37)$$

The logarithmic mean partial pressure driving force is:

$$\Delta p_{LM} = \frac{P(y_i - y_o)}{\ln(y_i / y_o)} \qquad (3\text{-}38)$$

In Equation 3-38, no vapor pressure of CO_2 is assumed above the liquid phase.

In this system, the $K_G a$ will increase with liquid rate in accordance with Equation 3-13. However, the $K_G a$ value reaches a maximum, as the liquid rate is increased at constant gas rate, when a pressure drop of about 0.75 in. H_2O/ft is achieved for 2-in. and smaller sizes of random packings. This increase in $K_G a$ value primarily is due to variation of the interfacial area with liquid rate because of an increase in liquid holdup. This effect is verified by data on oxygen desorption as well as by data on CO_2 absorption [20, 21]. However, liquid entrainment at a gas rate of 3.5 ft/s makes absorption measurements invalid at liquid rates above those listed in Table 3-2.

CRACKED GAS SCRUBBING

In an olefins plant, the gas stream at a pressure of 140 to 180 psia is washed with a caustic soda solution to remove all acidic components present. Typically, the inlet gas contains 300 to 1,000 ppm of H_2S plus CO_2. The exit gas specifications will be 1 to 5 ppm by volume total acid gases in order to prevent freeze-up in the cold section fractionators. This caustic scrubber usually has been constructed with 30 to 50 total trays. The top three to five trays serve as a water-wash section to prevent caustic carry-over in the exit gas stream. The remaining trays constitute two or three pumparound sections. Fresh caustic solution is fed to the upper section along with the pumparound return liquid. Excess partially spent solution overflows a trap tray at the bottom of the section and goes to the next lower section where it is mixed with pumparound return liquid from the bottom of that section. The liquid effluent from the bottom of the column is a salt solution from which 65% to 75% of the sodium hydroxide has been consumed. The pressure drop through such a trayed column normally is 5 to 8 psi.

The capacity of a trayed column in this service is limited by caustic carry-over in the exit gas stream and by solution foaming in the column. The use of #50 IMTP random packing to revamp such a column can increase the capacity by 40% over trays on 24-in. spacing. Even at this greater throughput, pressure drop will be only 40% to 50% that of the trayed column at the original lower capacity. The use of #50 IMTP packing requires only 80% of the mass transfer height of the trays to achieve the same acid gas removal efficiency. A three-stage packed scrubber can be designed to use 80% to 85% of the sodium hydroxide in the feed; thus, chemical costs as well as spent caustic disposal problems would be reduced. Further, the lower pressure drop provided by a packed scrubber reduces power requirements on the compressors that follow this scrubber.

AMINE SYSTEMS

One of the most widely used commercial absorption processes is the removal of CO_2 or H_2S from a gas stream by contacting it with a solution of monoethanolamine or diethanolamine. Both of these solutions are alkaline and combine chemically with ½ mol of acid gas per mol of amine. Although a chemical combination exists, still even at equilibrium, the acid gas exhibits a vapor pressure above the solution. Because this vapor pressure of the absorbed acid gas increases rapidly with temperature increase, it is possible to regenerate the rich amine solution by stripping the heated solvent.

In the past, about 3 normal (18 wt%) MEA solutions have been used as solvents for acid gases. It is desirable to operate with a high solution strength so as to reduce the liquid circulation requirement. However, the vapor pressure of CO_2 above the rich solution at constant CO_2/MEA ratio increases with increasing MEA concentration. Also, the boiling point for regeneration increases at higher MEA concentrations, which greatly increases the rate of corrosion of common metals. Because of the higher vapor pressures of CO_2 produced at elevated temperatures, regeneration of the rich amine solution at several atmospheres pressure would be more easily accomplished; however, actual regenerator pressures in many cases are kept about 10 psig in order to minimize corrosion. Further, MEA tends to degrade as the temperature increases, which incurs the expense of replacement of this solvent and removal of the degradation products.

The basic equipment arrangement for an amine acid gas removal system is shown in Figure 3-3. It consists of an absorber in which cooled lean solvent flows downward in contact with the upwardly flowing gas to be treated. Before leaving the absorber, the purified gas may be washed with water to recover any vaporized MEA. The rich solvent at the bottom of the absorber is in contact with the entering gas stream, thus provid-

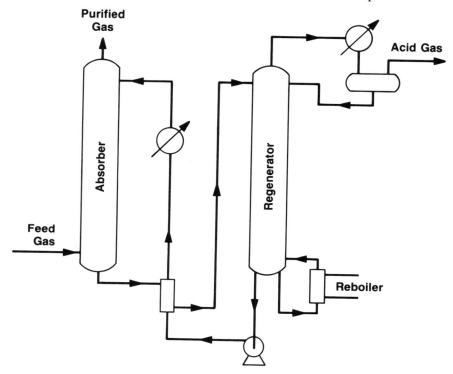

Figure 3-3. Typical amine gas treatment system.

ing the greatest mass transfer driving force. Due to the heat of solution and heat of reaction of the acid gas with the amine, the rich liquid effluent will be at a higher temperature than the lean liquid feed, unless cooled by the gas stream. The rich liquid flows through a heat exchanger where it is heated by the regenerator bottoms liquid. The hot rich amine is fed to the top of a reboiled stripping column. The overhead stripped acid gas is cooled to remove water vapor, and the condensate is returned to the system to maintain the water balance. The stripped, hot lean bottoms solution first is cooled against the rich stripper feed liquid and then against cooling water, before being returned to the top of the absorber. If the gas stream to be treated contains condensable hydrocarbon vapors, the lean solvent temperature should be above the dew point temperature of these vapors in order to prevent condensation of an immiscible hydrocarbon liquid, which promotes foaming of the liquid phase in the absorber.

Amines are considered to be moderately foaming systems in absorbers; therefore, the absorber diameter is specified so that the pressure drop for the packed bed does not exceed 0.25 in. H_2O/ft at the point of greatest loading. The pressure drop is restricted to avoid the gas phase doing excessive work on the liquid phase, which would produce a greater degree of foaming by the amine solution. There will be a different tower diameter required for different size tower packings. Generally, as absorber operating pressure increases, the size of packing used is increased. Because the thickness of the vessel shell is a function of operating pressure and diameter, at high pressures usually it is less expensive to increase the packed height as a result of the use of larger size packing rather than to increase the diameter and, therefore, the shell thickness.

The gas flow rate and inlet composition are known, and the outlet gas composition is specified for the absorber. Normally the lean solvent feed will contain 0.12 to 0.15 mol of CO_2 per mol MEA. This will allow absorption of 0.30 to 0.35 mol of CO_2 per mol of MEA in the lean solvent feed. The solvent flow rate now can be fixed from the material balance. For absorbers that process an inlet gas stream with a CO_2 partial pressure greater than 20 psia, the rich effluent liquid could contain more than 0.50 mol of CO_2 per mol of MEA, based on the equilibrium condition. However, the absorption of CO_2 at these high solution concentrations involves complicated mechanisms, all of which result in slower absorption rates than at concentrations below 0.50 mol of CO_2 per mol of MEA [22]. Further, corrosion rates increase with acid gas loading, which may necessitate the use of stainless steel for the rich amine piping.

The effects of liquid and gas flow rates for this absorption are given by Equation 3-13 using the exponents applicable to liquid-film-controlled systems. Because 1-normal sodium hydroxide for the standard test system has been replaced with a 3-normal MEA solution as the liquid phase, the values of the overall mass transfer coefficients will be twice those shown for the standard system in Tables 3-3 through 3-6 for lean solvent containing 0.15 mol CO_2 per mol MEA. These values are based on a liquid rate of 10 gpm/ft^2 and a gas capacity factor (F_s) of 0.94 lb$^{0.5}$/ft$^{0.5} \cdot$ s.

The K_Ga values are for a solvent temperature of 75°F. They will increase as $e^{0.013 \, (T - 75)}$ at higher liquid temperatures [23]. These K_Ga values apply for a partial pressure of CO_2 in the gas stream of 0.01 atm. The K_Ga is reduced as the partial pressure of solute in the gas stream increases. As previously stated, the K_Ga value is a function of the system pressure to the -0.32 power [3]. Of course, the driving force for mass transfer is increased at the higher partial pressure. Although the solubility of CO_2 in the liquid phase would be expected to increase at higher pressures, the mass transfer coefficient is restricted by diffusion of the reactive amine.

The K_Ga value decreases as the ratio of mols acid gas per mol MEA in the solvent increases. This effect on the K_Ga value is given by $K_Ga \propto$

1.375 − 2.5C, where C is the number of mols of acid gas per mol of MEA. Increasing the concentration of MEA in the solvent normally would be expected to increase the K_Ga value because of increased diffusion of reactive amine into the liquid film. However, increasing the MEA concentration also increases the viscosity of the liquid phase, which reduces the rate of diffusion. The K_Ga value shows an overall decrease of 5% for a 1-normal increase in the MEA concentration above 3-normal. Many CO_2 absorption systems have been designed using the above rules for modifying the mass transfer coefficient.

The driving force for mass transfer is the difference between the partial pressure of CO_2 in the gas phase and the vapor pressure of CO_2 above the liquid phase. A mass and heat balance across the absorber will fix the outlet rich solvent temperature and composition, enabling the vapor pressure of CO_2 above the effluent liquid to be determined. For purposes of initial heat balance calculations, the exit gas stream temperature can be assumed to be the same as the inlet lean solvent temperature.

Usually both the equilibrium line and the operating line for such an absorption operation are curved; still it is normal practice to use a logarithmic mean average of the partial-pressure difference driving forces at the top and bottom of the absorber as the overall driving force. The mass transfer coefficients are corrected empirically, as has been described, from the values obtained for the standard test system. To accommodate the use of the logarithmic average overall driving force, a logarithmic average of the K_Ga values at the top and bottom of the absorber is used as the overall mass transfer coefficient. The packed depth required then can be calculated from Equation 3-15.

When H_2S is the solute to be removed from the gas stream, the design of an amine system is similar to that just described for CO_2 absorption. However, the K_Ga value for CO_2 absorption into MEA is only about 40% of the K_Ga value for H_2S absorption into the same MEA solution. The K_Ga value for H_2S absorption is influenced by the same variables in the same manner as for CO_2 absorption, with the exception of the temperature influence. The K_Ga for H_2S absorption decreases with increasing solvent temperature, probably because of reduced H_2S solubility in the liquid phase. The K_Ga value applicable at 75°F will be reduced to $e^{0.0079(75 - T)}$ at higher liquid temperatures.

Diethanolamine solutions find wide use in treating sulfur-bearing gas streams. This is because MEA forms a nonregenerable, stable chemical compound with carbonyl sulfide and carbon disulfide. In the past, usually a 2.5 normal (26 wt %) DEA solution has been used as a solvent for H_2S in treating natural gas and refinery gas streams.

Again, the design of the treating system is similar to that using an MEA solvent. However, the K_Ga value for absorption into a DEA solvent is only 50% to 60% of that for an MEA solution of the same normality. Because of the lower vapor pressure of DEA above its solutions, a water wash normally is not required at the top of the absorber.

Recently, higher strength amine solutions, containing 45% to 55 wt % total amine, have been introduced for CO_2 removal from synthesis gas streams used in the production of ammonia and hydrogen. Many of these solvents are proprietary blends of MDEA and other amines. Also, these solvents contain special chemical additives to inhibit corrosion of metals and reduce amine degradation. Because of the greater strength of these amine solutions, the solvent flow rate required for each lb of CO_2 absorbed can be reduced.

Although the heat of solution of CO_2 in these solvents can be 15% to 20% lower than for an MEA solution, because of the reduced liquid rate the temperature rise in the absorber will be greater than for a 3-normal MEA solvent. Thus, for an inlet lean solvent temperature of 100°F, the outlet rich solvent temperature may be 180°F.

These proprietary solutions still exhibit some foaming tendencies; therefore, the column diameter should be chosen for a maximum pressure drop of 0.25 in. H_2O/ft with the packing selected. The physical properties of these solvents can be obtained from the process licensor.

The vapor pressure of CO_2 above these proprietary solvents is different than that above MEA or DEA solutions and varies with the composition of the solvent. Thus, the process licensor must provide this information in order to permit calculation of the partial pressure driving force for absorption. Due to the high temperature of the rich solvent effluent, the liquid flow rate must be great enough to avoid a driving force limitation at the bottom of the absorber.

The mass transfer coefficients for these high-strength amine systems usually are similar to those for 2.5 normal DEA solutions. These systems do provide a reduction in energy consumption due to the lower heat of solution of CO_2 as well as the reduced liquid heating and cooling requirements.

Although the vapor pressure of these proprietary solvents may be almost as low as that of a DEA solution, a water wash bed at the top of the absorber may be desirable. A loss of only a few ppm of costly solvent in the treated gas stream due to vaporization or entrainment can result in a large annual replacement expense. Systems that operate in cold climates should be designed to prevent freeze-up due to the high solidification temperature of most amine solutions.

HOT CARBONATE SYSTEMS

Another very widely used commercial absorption process involves the removal of CO_2 or H_2S by contacting the gas stream with a hot potassium carbonate solution. This process was developed to operate at a constant liquid temperature, thereby eliminating the heat required to raise the temperature of an amine solution to permit regeneration. Absorption and release of acid gases using this process depend largely on the difference in operating pressure in the absorber compared to the pressure in the regenerator. Normally the hot carbonate process is useful only when the partial pressure of the acid gas in the gas stream to be treated is at least 18 psi. Because the solvent is an aqueous inorganic salt solution, hydrocarbon solubility is very low. This process is widely used to purify high-pressure natural gas, as there is no loss of fuel gas by coabsorption with the acid gas.

The absorbed CO_2 reacts with the alkaline solvent as follows:

$$K_2CO_3 + CO_2 + H_2O = 2KHCO_3 \tag{3-39}$$

When H_2S is absorbed the reaction is:

$$K_2CO_3 + H_2S = KHCO_3 + KHS \tag{3-40}$$

Although the first hydrogen ionization constant for H_2CO_3 is more than six times that for H_2S, CO_2 is absorbed into an alkaline carbonate solution at a slower rate than H_2S. Note that Equation 3-39 shows a mol of water in the reaction, while Equation 3-40 shows the acid gas reacting directly with the carbonate. It is believed that the absorbed CO_2 first reacts with water to form H_2CO_3, which subsequently combines with the alkaline carbonate. Thus, the overall rate of absorption is controlled by the relatively slow chemical reaction between CO_2 and H_2O. Much effort has been devoted to the development of catalysts that promote the rate of hydrolysis of CO_2. Conventional amines, such as DEA, can be used to increase the rate of CO_2 absorption. Even at low concentrations of an amine, the concentration of free amine is greater than that of hydroxyl ion, thus enhancing the rate of chemical reaction of CO_2 in solution [24]. Proprietary hot carbonate systems using such promoters develop overall mass transfer coefficients for CO_2 absorption, which typically are 2.5 to 3 times those exhibited by unpromoted hot carbonate systems.

The basic arrangement of a hot carbonate acid gas removal system is shown in Figure 3-4. It consists of an absorber in which hot lean solvent flows downward contacting the upwardly flowing gas stream to be purified. The rich solution from the bottom of the absorber flows through a pressure reduction valve into the top of the regenerator where the solution flashes at the lower regenerator operating pressure. The overhead vapor stream from the regenerator is cooled to condense water vapor. This condensate is used to wash the outlet gas free of entrained K_2CO_3. The regenerator is reboiled to provide steam to strip the acid gas from the solvent. The lean bottoms from the regenerator is returned by

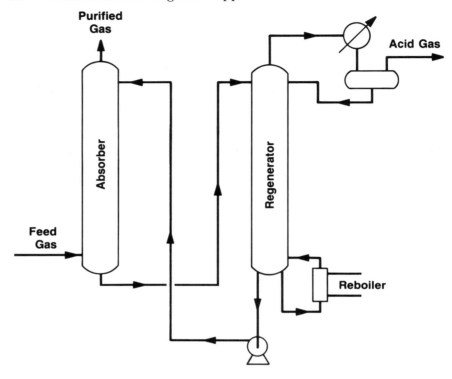

Figure 3-4. Typical hot carbonate gas treatment system.

means of high pressure pumps to the top of the absorber as feed. Because the solvent is circulated hot, the sensible heating load required by an amine system is eliminated; however, the reboiler on the regenerator still must provide the heat of reaction of the solute with the carbonate, as well as the steam in the overhead vapor stream.

Although this process originally was developed using a 40 wt % K_2CO_3 solution strength, most commercial processes use a 24 to 30 wt % solution. Solvent concentrations greater than 30 wt % K_2CO_3 are avoided because of the possibility of $KHCO_3$ precipitation. The rich solution from the absorber is up to 80% converted to bicarbonate by CO_2 absorption. The rich solution CO_2 concentration, of course, is limited by the equilibrium between the partial pressure of CO_2 in the inlet gas stream and the vapor pressure of CO_2 above the rich solvent. The lean solution normally is regenerated so that it contains no less than 20% of the carbonate in the form of bicarbonate. This lean solvent strength will give an equilibrium concentration of about 2,000 mol ppm CO_2 in the gas, leaving an absorber operating at a pressure of 300 psia [25]. Regeneration of the solvent to a lower bicarbonate content would require considerably more stripping steam, and thus a greater reboiler duty.

To reduce the CO_2 content of the absorber exit gas stream, the majority of the lean solvent can be fed to the absorber to irrigate the second packed bed down from the top. A portion of the lean solvent will be cooled to about 190°F and fed to the top of the absorber as shown in Figure 3-5. The cooler solvent in contact with the exit gas stream at the top of the absorber has a lower equilibrium vapor pressure of CO_2. However, this modification does add a sensible heat load to the system that somewhat increases the regenerator reboiler duty.

In an effort to produce a low CO_2 content in the absorber exit gas, as well as to minimize energy consumption, a split stream process has been developed. As Figure 3-6 illustrates, the rich solvent flows downward through about 70% of the total packed depth in the regenerator at which point it is intercepted by a trap tray. The majority of the solvent, which has been partially regenerated, is withdrawn at that level. The balance of the solvent continues down the column where it now is stripped

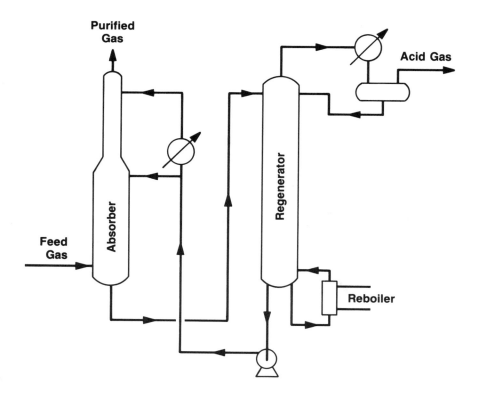

Figure 3-5. Modified hot carbonate gas treatment system.

with three to four times the pounds of steam per gallon of solvent as the ratio in the upper part of the column. The resultant very lean solvent from the bottom of the regenerator is cooled and fed to the top of the absorber. The partially stripped solvent that had been withdrawn from the side of the regenerator is fed to the absorber about half-way down the total packed depth. This arrangement will permit reducing the CO_2 content of the exit gas to 1,000 mol ppm for an absorber operating at a pressure of 400 psia.

A hot carbonate absorber is considered to be a slightly foaming system. The diameter of the column and the packing size should be selected so that the design pressure drop is restricted to about 0.30 in. H_2O/ft at the point of maximum loading. In such systems liquid loadings tend to be very high, so that the packing size should be selected to accommodate

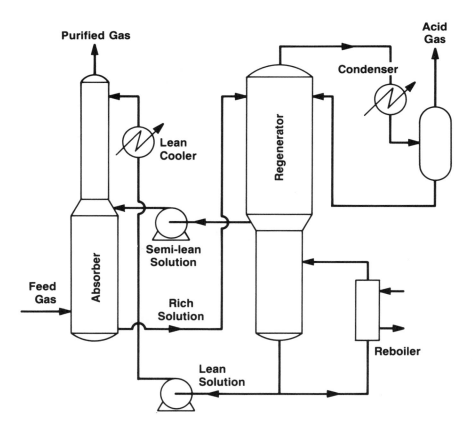

Figure 3-6. Split-stream hot carbonate gas treatment system.

the irrigation rate in accordance with the recommendations in Table 3-2. In a split-stream system (Figure 3-6), because the liquid flow is lower in the upper section and the gas flow has been reduced by absorption of some of the solute, the upper section of the absorber may be of a smaller diameter than the lower section. Because the liquid flow in the lower section of the regenerator is only about 30% of that in the upper section, either a smaller column diameter or a smaller size of packing can be used there.

The inlet gas flow rate and composition will be known. The absorber exit gas composition will be related to the bicarbonate content and temperature of the lean solvent. The rich liquid composition leaving the absorber will be related to the partial pressure of acid gas in the inlet gas stream. Once these terminal stream compositions have been determined, a mass balance will be used to set the solvent flow rate.

The effects of liquid and gas flow rates for this process are given by Equation 3-13 using the exponents for liquid-film-controlled systems. For an unpromoted 25 wt % K_2CO_3 solution at a liquid rate of 40 gpm/ft^2 with a gas capacity factor (F_s) of 0.94 lb$^{0.5}$/ft$^{0.5} \cdot$ s, industrial experience indicates that the overall K_Ga values will be approximately one-sixth of the values for the standard CO_2/NaOH system given in Tables 3-3 through 3-6. These values apply for 20% conversion to bicarbonate in the solvent at a temperature of 235°F. The K_Ga value decreases as the percent conversion to bicarbonate increases at the rate of $K_Ga \propto 1.207 - 1.08 B$, where B is the mol fraction of K_2CO_3 present as bicarbonate.

These K_Ga values also apply for a CO_2 partial pressure of 1.3 atm in the inlet gas stream. At higher CO_2 partial pressures, the K_Ga value will be lower by the -0.32 power of the system pressure expressed in atmospheres. However, the driving force for mass transfer increases at higher CO_2 partial pressures. Although, at a CO_2 partial pressure of 0.7 atm, the K_Ga value will increase by 20%, normally the hot carbonate process is not useful at such low pressures.

The hot carbonate system has been promoted with organic materials, which not only increase the rate of CO_2 hydrolysis, but also alter the equilibrium to lower the CO_2 vapor pressure above the lean solvent. Because this process operates at a continuous high temperature, organic materials may degenerate to produce corrosive by-products; therefore, a corrosion inhibitor usually is used in combination with the organic promoter. When H_2S is being absorbed, oxidative-type inhibitors must be avoided because of the possible production of solid sulfur in the solution.

The calculation of packed depth required is similar to the procedure used for an amine absorber. The number of mols of acid gas to be absorbed is calculated by material balance from the gas flow rate and the concentrations of solute in the inlet and outlet gas streams. The liquid flow rate is fixed by mass balance, which depends on carbonate strength, the degree of regeneration, and the extent of carbonation of the solvent. The driving force is considered to be the logarithmic mean average of the solute partial-pressure differences at the top and bottom of the absorber. The design overall mass transfer coefficient is the logarithmic average of the coefficients for the terminal ends of the absorber or section between feeds for split-stream operations. Because of some inconsistencies in the data, it is suggested that individual K_Ga values not exceed those applicable to a partial pressure for CO_2 of 0.7 atm. The packed depth required then can be calculated from Equation 3-15.

Because the bulk of the solvent is recirculated without cooling, there is only a small sensible heat load. The heat of reaction with K_2CO_3 is only 270 Btu/lb of CO_2 absorbed. This is one-third the heat of reaction of CO_2 with MEA; therefore, the heat load on a hot carbonate system per pound of CO_2 absorbed and regenerated is lower than for an amine solvent system.

Generally, the hot carbonate process is much less corrosive to common metals than amine solvent systems. Potassium carbonate is a very stable compound that is not degraded at the usual high operating temperatures or by oxidizing agents. Hot carbonate systems, therefore, are used to remove CO_2 from recycle gas streams in organic oxidation reactions.

When H_2S is to be removed from the gas stream, the mass transfer coefficient for this absorption is only slightly higher than for CO_2 absorption [26]. This is due to the high temperature of the recirculated solvent, as a colder carbonate solution would absorb H_2S much more rapidly than CO_2. Because CO_2 is a stronger acid than H_2S, it is more securely bound in the alkaline solvent; therefore, because of the higher vapor pressure of H_2S above the carbonate solution, it is more readily regenerated than is CO_2. The hot carbonate process is capable of treating natural gas to meet pipeline specifications of 0.25 grains H_2S per 100 std ft^3 of gas. Also, this process can be expected to remove carbonyl sulfide from the gas stream. It is believed that the hot alkaline solution hydrolyzes the COS to H_2S and CO_2, which subsequently are absorbed.

MULTICOMPONENT ABSORPTION

In many applications there is more than one solute that can be transferred from the gas phase to the liquid phase. Generally, the absorption efficiency required is specified for one solute, which is the key component. The depth of packing necessary and solvent flow rate required are calculated to meet the specification set for this key component. However, the effect of simultaneous absorption of other solutes also must be considered, because that may affect the economics of the process or require design modifications.

The number of theoretical stages is fixed by the packed depth used and is the same for all solutes. The rate of absorption (K_Ga), as well as the driving force for absorption (Δp_{LM}), can vary considerably from one solute to another. In general, the removal of solutes from the gas phase has the effect only of reducing the partial pressure of that solute; however, transfer of solutes to the liquid phase can have two quite different effects. If the absorbed solutes do not change the liquid phase to a significant degree, the absorption of each solute can be considered as progressing independently. However, if the absorption of these solutes contribute to a change in the liquid phase, then the effect of the liquid phase on the absorption of each solute must be evaluated. These points will be illustrated by the following examples.

First, consider a 75°F vent stream from pulp bleaching that is contaminated with 120 mol ppm ClO_2 that is scrubbed with 4 wt % sodium hydroxide solution to remove 95% of this ClO_2. The 8-ft 6-in. ID available column will be operated at a superficial gas velocity of 6.5 ft/s and a liquid recirculation rate of 6 gpm/ft^2. Because the inlet air stream also contains 800 mol ppm CO_2, which can be absorbed, calculate the required 20 wt % NaOH feed added to the recirculated liquid to maintain this operation.

As this is a scrubber involving two liquid-film-controlled systems, and the absorption of these small quantities of solutes will have a minimal effect on the liquid phase, we will use Figure 5-3 for this design (see Chapter 5). The basic K_Ga value for absorption of ClO_2 into either water or caustic is 4.4 lb-mol/h · ft^3 · atm, while similarly the basic K_Ga value for absorption of CO_2 is 1.5 lb-mol/h · ft^3 · atm using a 4 wt % NaOH scrubbing liquid for 2-in. plastic Super Intalox packing (see Table 5-3). These basic K_Ga values must be multiplied by a factor of 1.13 (from Table 5-6) to adjust them for a liquid rate of 6 gpm/ft^2. From Figure 5-3 using an adjusted K_Ga value of 5.0 lb-mol/h · ft^3 · atm, a 36-ft depth of 2-in. plastic Super Intalox packing is required to obtain the ClO_2 removal desired.

Next, a calculation of the amount of CO_2 absorbed simultaneously is needed. With an adjusted K_Ga value of 1.7 lb-mol/h · ft^3 · atm, Figure 5-3 indicates that 64% of the CO_2 will be absorbed in a 36-ft deep packed bed. Thus, a total of 0.39 lb-mol/h of ClO_2, plus 1.74 lb-mol/h of CO_2 will be absorbed. Because two mols of NaOH are required to react with each mol of acid gas, 4.26 lb-mol/h of NaOH will be consumed. Thus, 852 lb/h of 20 wt % sodium hydroxide feed is needed to maintain this scrubbing operation.

Secondly, design a DEA absorber that treats 65 MMSCFD (60°F) of natural gas at a pressure of 1,020 psia. The inlet gas contains 1.6 mol % H_2S, which must be reduced to 16 mol ppm in the treated gas. The inlet gas also contains 6.6 mol % CO_2, which must be reduced to not more than 1.7 mol % in the outlet gas. The 26 wt % DEA solvent enters this 6-ft 0-

in. ID absorber at 100°F containing 0.012 mols H_2S and 0.070 mols CO_2 per mol DEA. The rich solution to the regenerator is to contain 0.43 mols total acid gas per mol DEA.

By material balance, 114.1 lb-mols/h of H_2S and at least 357.8 lb-mols/h of CO_2 must be absorbed. Thus, the lean solution feed rate will be 549,000 lb/h. The basic K_Ga values for 2.5 normal DEA should be $2(0.55)$ times the values given in Table 3-3; thus, for #40 IMTP packing, the basic K_Ga would be 3.15 lb-mol/h $\cdot$ ft^3·atm for CO_2 absorption. The K_Ga value for H_2S would be 2.5 times that for CO_2 or a basic K_Ga of 7.87 lb-mol/hr $\cdot$ ft^3 $\cdot$ atm. These basic K_Ga values would be increased by a factor of 1.49 to account for the effect of 37.7 gpm/ft^2 liquid rate. There is negligible correction needed for gas rate because both H_2S and CO_2 represent liquid-film-controlled absorptions.

Both H_2S and CO_2 combine with two mols of DEA in the solvent. To allow for the reduction of K_Ga values with absorption, the total consumption of DEA must be considered. Thus, in the rich solution containing a total of 0.43 mols acid gas per mol of DEA, the relative K_Ga values are only $1.375 - 2.5(0.43) = 0.300$; therefore, they are reduced by 70%. For the lean solution containing only 0.082 mols total acid gas per mol DEA, the relative K_Ga values are $1.375 - 2.5(0.082) = 1.170$. Thus, they are increased by a factor of 1.17.

There also is a temperature effect to be considered that is different for H_2S than for CO_2 absorption. By heat balance, the rich solution will leave the absorber at a temperature of 125°F. The K_Ga values for CO_2 will be greater by factors of $e^{0.013(25)}$, or 1.38 times at 100°F, and by $e^{0.013(50)}$, or 1.92 times at 125°F. However, the K_Ga values for H_2S will be reduced by factors of $e^{0.0079(-25)}$, or 0.82 times at 100°F for the lean feed, and $e^{0.0079(-50)}$, or 0.67 times at 125°F for the rich effluent.

Finally, there is an effect of pressure on the K_Ga values. These values at atmospheric pressure will be reduced by the -0.32 power of the system pressure expressed in atmospheres. Thus, these K_Ga values are lower by a factor of 0.258.

In summary, the K_Ga for CO_2 absorption after making all the previously outlined corrections is 0.70 lb mol/h $\cdot$ ft^3 $\cdot$ atm at the bottom and 1.96 lb mol/h $\cdot$ ft^3 $\cdot$ atm at the top of the absorber. Likewise, the K_Ga for H_2S absorption after corrections is 0.61 lb mol/h $\cdot$ ft^3 $\cdot$ atm at the bottom and 2.90 lb mol/h $\cdot$ ft^3 $\cdot$ atm at the top. For design purpose, we will use a logarithmic mean average of the K_Ga values at the bottom and top of the column. Thus, the design K_Ga for CO_2 absorption is 1.22 lb mol/h $\cdot$ ft^3 $\cdot$ atm, and for H_2S absorption it is 1.47 lb mol/h $\cdot$ ft^3 $\cdot$ atm.

The partial pressure driving forces at the bottom of the tower must be calculated from the partial pressures of both CO_2 and H_2S in the inlet gas stream and the equilibrium partial pressure of each solute above the rich DEA solution at 125°F. Likewise, the partial pressure driving forces at the top of the tower must be determined from the partial pressures of CO_2 and H_2S in the treated gas and the equilibrium partial pressures of each solute above the lean DEA solution at 100°F. The ln mean partial pressure driving force for each solute then can be calculated. The depth of packing required for absorption of each solute is determined separately using Equation 3-15. The actual packed depth should be specified as the larger of these two independently calculated values.

REBOILED ABSORBERS

In the treatment of a natural gas stream with lean oil, the less volatile components (lower K values) primarily are absorbed in the lower part of the column, while the more volatile components (higher K values) primarily are absorbed in the upper part of the column [27]. Thus, in a column treating a 470 psia natural gas stream to remove all of the C-5 and heavier components, one-sixth of the ethane also will be absorbed. While the rich oil could be deethanized in a separate column, there is an advantage to the use of a single column called a "reboiled absorber." This compound column really consists of an upper section, which acts as an absorber, and a lower section, which acts as a stripper. By incorporating a reboiler at the bottom of the column, the ethane can be liberated from the heated rich oil and caused to leave the system at the top of the absorption section. In this case, the absorption section acts as a rectifier for the stripped vapor to prevent the loss of less volatile components in the overhead gas stream.

EXAMPLE PROBLEM

A 7-ft 0-in. ID CO_2 absorber in an ammonia plant presently is equipped with 20 valve trays on 24-in. spacing. The gas to the absorber is 79,400 lb/h at 130°F with a density of 0.792 lb/ft^3. The inlet gas contains 18.2 mol % CO_2, which must be reduced down to 90 mol ppm CO_2 in the outlet gas stream. The absorber operates at a top pressure of 325 psia. The liquid feed is 30.2 wt % monoethanolamine solution at a temperature of 110°F. This lean solution flow is 575,000 lb/h, which contains 0.12 mol CO_2 per mol MEA. It is desired to increase the rates by 35%, which the present trays will not accommodate. Can the existing column handle these higher rates with tower packing?

By material balance, there are 994.2 lb-mol/h of CO_2 present in the inlet gas and 0.4 lb-mol/h of CO_2 present in the outlet gas; thus, 993.8 lb-mol/h of CO_2 are absorbed. The rich liquid flow is 618,800 lb/h containing 0.47 mol CO_2 per mol MEA. This rich liquid has a density of 65.7 lb/ft^3 and a viscosity of 1.09 cps.

First we will determine whether #2 Hy-Pak packing could be used with respect to the capacity of the packing and then with respect to its absorption efficiency. The point of greatest loading normally is at the bottom of an absorber. The flow parameter here from Figure 1-15 is:

$$X = \frac{618,800}{79,400} \left[\frac{0.792}{65.7} \right]^{0.5} = 0.856 \qquad (3\text{-}A)$$

The inlet gas mass velocity is 0.573 lb/ft^2·s. The ordinate value for the present flow is:

$$Y = \frac{(0.573)^2 (26)(1.04)^{0.1}}{32.2(0.792)(65.7 - 0.792)} = 0.00518 \qquad (3\text{-}B)$$

Thus, the pressure drop at the bottom of the absorber for #2 Hy-Pak packing would be 0.08 in. H$_2$O/ft at the present flow rates.

If the gas and liquid rates are increased by 1.35 times, then at the bottom of the absorber the flow parameter still will be X = 0.856.

However, the ordinate value will increase to:

$$Y = \frac{(0.774)^2 (26)(1.04)^{0.1}}{32.2(0.792)(65.7 - 0.792)} = 0.00945 \qquad (3\text{-}C)$$

From Figure 1-15, the pressure drop for #2 Hy-Pak packing now has increased to 0.22 in. H$_2$O/ft. Thus, the #2 Hy-Pak packing can handle the increased hydraulic flows without exceeding a pressure drop of 0.25 in. H$_2$O/ft. That is the maximum design basis for amine absorbers, which are considered moderately foaming systems.

Next, we will check the operation at increased rates to determine the depth of packing required. From Table 3-3, the standard K_Ga value for #2 Hy-Pak packing is 2.06 lb-mol/h · ft^3 · atm. For a 5-normal MEA solution, the base K_Ga value would be 3.72 lb-mol/h · ft^3 · atm. This K_Ga value must be modified for the flow rates, the liquid temperatures and mols of CO$_2$ per mol MEA in both the lean and rich solvents, as well as the partial pressures of CO$_2$ in the inlet and outlet gas streams.

The 35% increased flow rates will require that 1,342 lb-mol/h of CO$_2$ are absorbed. The CO$_2$ concentration in the inlet and outlet gas streams, as well as the CO$_2$ concentration in the inlet and outlet MEA solutions, will be the same as at the original lower rates. The logarithmic mean partial-pressure driving force also will be unchanged.

The partial pressure of CO$_2$ at the bottom of the column is 4.024 atm, while at the top of the column it is 0.00199 atm. After reduction of these values by the equilibrium partial pressure of CO$_2$ above the MEA solutions, the logarithmic mean-pressure driving force is 0.522 atm. The logarithmic mean average of the modified K_Ga values is 2.32 lb-mol/h · ft^3 · atm at flow rates 135% of present rates.

The packed depth required can be calculated from Equation 3-15:

$$Z = \frac{1342}{38.5(2.32)(0.522)} = 28.8 \text{ ft} \tag{3-D}$$

Because there is 38 ft of vertical height available from the bottom tray to the top tray, #2 Hy-Pak packing can handle the absorption requirement at the desired higher flow rates.

In summary, the 20 trays can be replaced with a 31.5-ft deep bed of #2 Hy-Pak packing using only 16 tray spaces to facilitate optimum use of the existing tray support rings. This revamped column will accommodate a 35% increase in gas and liquid flow rates while providing at least the same CO_2 removal efficiency as the present trays.

NOTATION

A	Column cross-sectional area (ft^2)
A*	Absorption factor
a	Interfacial area (ft^2/ft^3)
D	Diffusivity (ft^2/h)
F_s	Vapor capacity factor (lb$^{0.5}$/ft$^{0.5}$ · s)
G	Gas mass velocity (lb/ft^2 · h)
G_i	Inlet gas flow (lb-mol/h)
G_m	Gas phase flow (lb-mol/h)
G_o	Outlet gas flow (lb-mol/h)
H	Henry's Law constant (atm/mol fraction)
HETP	Height equivalent to a theoretical stage (ft)
H_{OG}	Overall height of gas phase transfer unit (ft)
H_{OL}	Overall height of liquid phase transfer unit (ft)
K	Equilibrium ratio
K_G	Overall gas-phase mass transfer coefficient (lb-mol/h · ft^2 · atm)
K_L	Overall liquid-phase mass transfer coefficient (lb-mol/h · ft^2 · mol/mol)
k_G	Gas-film mass transfer coefficient (lb-mol/h · ft^2 · atm)
k_L	Liquid-film mass transfer coefficient (lb-mol/h · ft^2 · mol/mol)
L	Liquid mass velocity (lb/ft^2 · h)
L_i	Inlet liquid flow (lb-mol/h)
L_m	Liquid phase flow (lb-mol/h)
L_o	Outlet liquid flow (lb-mol/h)

m	Slope of equilibrium curve
N	Solute transferred (lb-mol/h)
N_{OG}	Number of overall gas phase transfer units
n	Stage number
P	Total system pressure (atm)
p	Partial pressure in gas phase (atm)
p*	Vapor pressure of solute (atm)
p'	Partial pressure of solute in gas film (atm)
Sc	Schmidt number
T	Temperature (°F)
u'	Viscosity (lb/ft · h)
x	Mol fraction in liquid phase
x*	Equilibrium mol fraction in liquid phase
x'	Mol fraction in liquid film at interface
x_i	Mol fraction solute in inlet liquid
x_o	Mol fraction solute in outlet liquid
y	Mol fraction in gas phase
y*	Equilibrium mol fraction in gas phase
y_i	Mol fraction solute in inlet gas
y_o	Mol fraction solute in outlet gas
Z	Packed depth (ft)
Δp_{LM}	ln mean partial pressure driving force (atm)
Δp_B	Partial pressure driving force at bottom (atm)
Δp_T	Partial pressure driving force at top (atm)
λ	Lambda factor
ρ	Density (lb/ft³)

REFERENCES

1. Chilton, T. H. and Colburn, A. P., *Industrial and Engineering Chemistry,* Vol. 26, 1934, p. 1183.
2. Cornell, D. *et al., Chemical Engineering Progress,* Vol. 56, No. 7, 1960, p. 68.
3. Eckert, J. S., *Canadian Gas Journal,* March/April, 1972, p. 2.
4. Sherwood, T. K. and Holloway, F. A. L., *Transactions of American Institute of Chemical Engineers,* Vol. 36, 1940, p. 39.
5. Huckabay, H. K. and Garrison, R. L., *Hydrocarbon Processing,* Vol. 48, No. 6, 1969, p. 153.
6. Onda, K. *et al., Journal of Chemical Engineering, Japan,* Vol. 1, 1968, p. 56.
7. Bolles, W. L. and Fair, J. R., *Chemical Engineering,* Vol. 89, No. 14, 1982, p. 109.
8. Shulman, H. L. *et al., A.I.Ch.E. Journal,* Vol. 6, No. 1, 1960, p. 174.

9. Kremser, A., *National Petroleum News,* Vol. 22, No. 21, 1930, p. 45.

10. Maddox, R. N., *Process Engineer's Absorption Pocket Handbook,* Gulf Publishing, 1985, p. 2.

11. Souders, M. and Brown, G. G., *Industrial and Engineering Chemistry,* Vol. 24, 1932, p. 519.

12. Colburn, A. P., *Industrial and Engineering Chemistry,* Vol. 33, 1941, p. 459.

13. Mihm, J. C., *Petroleum Engineer,* Vol. 45, No. 2, 1973, p. 66.

14. Campbell, J. M., *Gas Conditioning and Processing,* Vol. II, Campbell Petroleum Series, Norman, OK, 1978.

15. Kean, J. A. *et al., Hydrocarbon Processing,* Vol. 70, No. 4, 1991, p. 47.

16. Walker, J. F., *Formaldehyde,* 2nd ed., Reinhold Publishing, 1953, p. 90.

17. Walker, J. F., *Formaldehyde,* 2nd ed., Reinhold Publishing, 1953, p. 96.

18. Petrochemical Handbook '89, *Hydrocarbon Processing,* Vol. 68, No. 11, 1989, p. 104.

19. Danckwerts, P. V. and Alper, E., *Transactions Institute of Chemical Engineers,* Vol. 53, 1975, p. 34.

20. Yoshida, F. and Konayagi, T., *Industrial and Engineering Chemistry,* Vol. 50, No. 3, 1958, p. 365.

21. Shulman, H. L. *et al., A.I.Ch.E. Journal,* Vol. 1, No. 2, 1955, p. 259.

22. Butwell, K. F. *et al., Chemical Engineering Progress,* Vol. 75, No. 2, 1979, p. 75.

23. *Regression of Operating Data from 11 Plants,* Norton Company, 1977.

24. Say, G. R. *et al., Chemical Engineering Progress,* Vol. 80, No. 10, 1984, p. 72.

25. Bocard, J. P. and Mayland, B. J., *Hydrocarbon Processing,* Vol. 41, No. 4, 1962, p. 128.

26. Kohl, A. L. and Riesenfeld, F. C., *Gas Purification,* McGraw-Hill, 1960, p. 145.

27. Sherwood, T. K., *Absorption and Extraction,* McGraw-Hill, 1937, p. 113.

4

LIQUID STRIPPING

Stripping is a mass transfer operation that involves the transfer of a solute from the liquid phase to the gas phase. This operation may use an insoluble inert gas phase or a gas that is only slightly soluble in the liquid phase. Some of the liquid solvent also may be evaporated into the gas phase; however, this is incidental to the stripping operation. The stripping operation also may use a saturated vapor, such as steam, as the gas phase that will be totally or partially condensed into the liquid phase. This condensate need not be soluble in the liquid phase. Finally, the gas phase can be generated by reboiling the solvent liquid. In any case, for a successful stripping operation, the solute must be more volatile than the solvent.

In the most simple case, the entering liquid is a solution of solute in the liquid phase that follows Henry's Law. The vapor pressure of solute above the liquid phase is given by:

$$p^* = Hx \qquad (4\text{-}1)$$

The partial pressure of solute in the vapor phase is a function of the composition:

$$p = yP \qquad (4\text{-}2)$$

Stripping of solute will continue as long as the vapor pressure of solute above the liquid phase exceeds the partial pressure of solute in the gas phase.

Solute solubility in the liquid phase is inversely proportional to the value of the Henry's Law constant. From Equation 4-1 anything that increases the value of H will enhance the stripping operation. Because the Henry's Law constant increases with temperature, a commonly used stripping method involves heating the liquid phase.

It is convenient to use liquid-phase concentrations in calculations involving stripping of solute from a solvent. The driving force for stripping operations is the difference between the solute concentration in the main-body liquid phase and the concentration of solute in equilibrium with the gas phase. This driving force is:

$$\Delta x = x - x^* \tag{4-3}$$

The mass transferred per unit time is expressed by:

$$N = AZ \, K_La \, (x - x^*) \tag{4-4}$$

The interfacial area (a) is not the geometric surface area of the packing, but it is the mass transfer area between the gas and liquid phases. Thus, the product of a and AZ represents the total interfacial area within the entire packed bed. As stated in Chapter 3, the value of this interfacial area can be influenced by gas and liquid flow rates as well as the type and size of tower packing employed; therefore, overall terms have been used. The interfacial area is combined with the liquid-phase mass transfer coefficient to produce an overall volumetric coefficient (K_La).

To facilitate the calculation, the overall driving force is based on the liquid-phase and gas-phase compositions. For systems following Henry's Law, Equation 4-3 can be written [1]:

$$\Delta x = x - \frac{yP}{H} \tag{4-5}$$

Or, when Henry's Law does not apply to the system, the equilibrium ratio (K) can be used to express the overall driving force:

$$K = \frac{y}{x} \tag{4-6}$$

This equilibrium ratio is a function of temperature, pressure, and composition, even in a simple hydrocarbon system [2]. Thus, Equation 4-3 can be written as:

$$\Delta x = x - \frac{y}{K} \tag{4-7}$$

The mass transfer equation, in overall terms, becomes:

$$N = AZ \, K_La \, \Delta x_{LM} \tag{4-8}$$

The compositional overall driving force is the logarithmic mean average of the driving forces at the bottom and top of the packed bed:

$$\Delta x_{LM} = \frac{\Delta x_T - \Delta x_B}{\ln(\Delta x_T / \Delta x_B)} \tag{4-9}$$

Equation 4-9 assumes a straight operating line and equilibrium curve. This is valid for systems where the solute mass transferred is small compared with the liquid and gas mass flows, and the value of H or K is independent of solute concentration in the liquid phase.

DESIGN THEORY

The overall liquid-phase mass transfer coefficient is related to the individual gas and liquid-film mass transfer coefficients as:

$$\frac{1}{K_L a} = \frac{1}{m k_G a P} + \frac{1}{k_L a} \tag{4-10}$$

where m is the slope of the equilibrium curve. For systems that obey Henry's Law, m is equal to H/P. Equation 4-10 is analogous to Equation 3-11 for gas absorption (see Chapter 3).

The Henry's Law constant, as given in Table 4-1, usually is applied to slightly soluble gases such as aqueous solutions of oxygen, chlorine, carbon monoxide, hydrogen, ethylene, hydrogen sulfide, methane, nitrogen, and carbon dioxide [3]. For solutes of greater solubility, such as C-3 and C-4 hydrocarbons dissolved in light naphtha, the operating line slope (m) equals the equilibrium ratio (K). This ratio (K) generally is applicable to ideal liquid-phase solutions at pressures up to about 10 atm.

Table 4-1

Solubilities of Gases in Water
Henry's Law Constants

Compound	H @ 50°F (atm/mol fraction)	H @ 68°F (atm/mol fraction)
Acetylene	960	1,210
Carbon Dioxide	1,040	1,420
Carbon Monoxide	44,200	53,600
Carbonyl Sulfide	1,480	2,190
Chlorine	404	548
Ethane	18,900	26,300
Ethylene	7,680	10,200
Hydrogen	63,600	68,300
Hydrogen Sulfide	367	483
Methane	29,700	37,600
Nitrogen	66,800	80,400
Oxygen	32,700	40,100
Ozone	2,480	3,760
Propylene	4,460	—

Overall mass transfer coefficients show similar variations with gas and liquid flow rates as in absorption (see Chapter 3). The effects of temperature and pressure are expected to be the same for the gas-film and liquid-film mass transfer coefficients as in absorption operations. Because liquid-film mass transfer coefficients, as well as the Henry's Law constant (H) and the equilibrium ratio (K), increase with rising temperature, stripping is facilitated by heating the liquid phase.

The transfer unit method may be more convenient for use in calculating the packed depth required. The height of a transfer unit tends to vary less with flow rates than the overall liquid-phase mass transfer coefficient. Using this method, the packed depth is:

$$Z = N_{OL} H_{OL} \tag{4-11}$$

When the solute mass transferred is small compared to the liquid mass flow:

$$N = L_m (x_i - x_o) \tag{4-12}$$

The height of a liquid-phase transfer unit is:

$$H_{OL} = \frac{L_m}{AK_L a} \tag{4-13}$$

SIMPLIFIED DESIGN PROCEDURES

The stripping factor can be used to calculate the number of theoretical stages in a stripping operation in a manner analogous to the use of the absorption factor in absorption processes, as described in Chapter 3. The stripping factor S* is the ratio of the equilibrium curve slope to the operating line slope:

$$S* = \frac{KG_m}{L_m} \tag{4-14}$$

The stripping factor is the reciprocal of the absorption factor described in Chapter 3.

The Colburn correlation, shown in Figure 4-1, can be used to determine the number of liquid-phase transfer units (N_{OL}) [4]. For this calculation, first it is necessary to calculate the abscissa value

$$\frac{x_i - y_i / K}{x_o - y_i / K}$$

and secondly the stripping factor from Equation 4-14. These calculations assume that the equilibrium curve and the operating line are linear, although not necessarily parallel. These conditions are fulfilled in the stripping of low concentrations of solute where H or K are constant, and the amount of solute transferred does not materially change the gas and liquid flow rates.

COLUMN DIAMETER SELECTION

In stripping operations, the inlet liquid flow rate, inlet solute concentration, and column operating pressure are known, while the desired solute concentration in the outlet liquid stream will be specified. The solvent liquid may be low cost or a waste product that will be stripped on a once-through basis. On the other hand, if the solvent is expensive, it will be recycled through an absorber. This latter type of operation usually is the case when solute recovery is the primary purpose of the operation. The designer first must select the stripping gas to be used, then determine its flow rate. The greater the solubility of solute in the solvent, the larger will be the required stripping gas flow. Solutes that are highly soluble in the liquid phase exhibit low H or K values, thus gas-phase concentrations of solute are low. Because the outlet gas stream will be saturated with solvent, the gas stream usually is cooled to condense the solvent vapor if the solvent is costly. A condenser commonly is employed for a steam-stripping operation and this condensate used as reflux to a wash section above the stripper feed.

After the stripping gas flow rate is determined, the designer can calculate the column diameter needed and then the packed depth. The column cross-sectional area usually is set to produce a pressure drop between 0.15 in. to 0.50 in. H_2O/ft of packed depth at the point of maximum loading. For systems that are known to foam the design pressure drop should not exceed 0.25 in. H_2O/ft in operations using inert gas stripping. Where steam or reboiled solvent vapor is the stripping gas, the design pressure drop can be a maximum of 0.30 in. H_2O/ft for a moderately foaming liquid. To assure good gas and liquid contact, a minimum pressure drop of 0.15 in. H_2O/ft is suggested.

Usually, liquid irrigation rates in strippers are only about 60% of those in companion absorbers. In single-pass strippers, the liquid irrigation rate should not exceed the values shown in Table 3-2 to avoid aspiration of the gas phase down the column with the liquid (see Chapter 3). Such a gas recycle increases the solute concentration in the gas stream entering the packed bed and reduces the mass transfer driving force at the column bottom. These liquid rates in Table 3-2 apply to mobile liquids. For liquids with viscosities of 50 cps or greater, 1½-in. or larger-size packings normally should be specified.

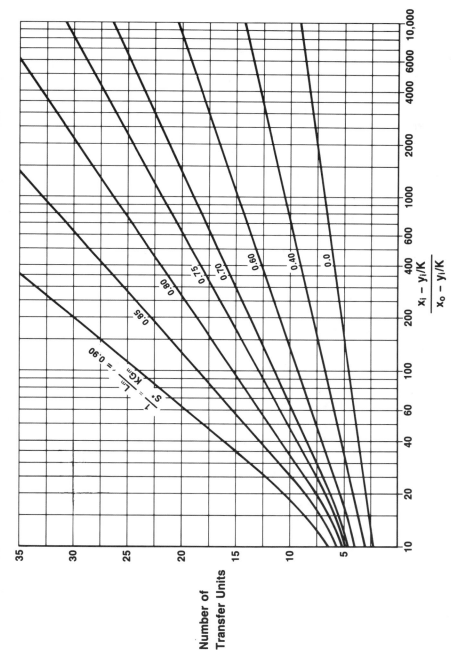

Figure 4-1. Colburn correlation for stripper design. (From Colburn [4]. Reprinted with permission from *Industrial and Engineering Chemistry*, American Chemical Society, Vol. 33, 1941, pg. 459.)

WATER DEAERATION

A common stripping operation that obeys Henry's Law is illustrated by the removal of dissolved oxygen from water. This can be accomplished by stripping the water with steam, a method commonly used for boiler feed-water treatment. The Henry's Law constant for this system is 75% greater at 212°F water temperature than at 68°F, which results in increased vapor pressure of oxygen above the liquid. In addition, the pure steam stripping vapor contains no oxygen; therefore, the maximum possible driving force for mass transfer is available at the column bottom.

Frequently, it is not desirable to have boiling water as effluent from the deaeration column. Normally it is not cost effective to use the large flow of inert gas required for stripping oxygen down to the desired low concentration in the effluent liquid. Under these conditions, vacuum deaeration usually is used.

When water is fed into a column under vacuum, a portion of the liquid will flash to vapor. The water then drops in temperature until its vapor pressure, plus those of the dissolved gases, equals the column pressure. A water feed at a temperature of 68°F will contain 9.3 ppm by wt. oxygen and 15.3 ppm by wt. nitrogen at equilibrium with the atmospheric air. In addition, the water may contain carbon dioxide, which will be stripped if the CO_2 is released from chemical combination by acidifying the water. The concentration of dissolved gases can be reduced significantly by use of a vacuum deaerator. Thus, if air-saturated, decarbonated water at 68°F is the feed to a deaerator operating at a pressure of 23.5 mm Hg absolute, 95% of the oxygen and over 99% of the nitrogen will be removed. The nitrogen is removed to a greater extent because its Henry's Law constant is twice that of oxygen (see Table 4-1). Further, the flashed water vapor will cause the liquid effluent to be cooled to a temperature of 63.5°F. At this lower temperature, the Henry's Law constant for dissolved oxygen is reduced by only 4%, as compared to water at 68°F.

The partial pressure of oxygen in the gas phase is the product of a larger mol fraction (y) and a lower total system pressure. The actual stripping gas in this operation is water vapor. Because the water flashes to the lower temperature in one equilibrium stage, there is very little stripping vapor available in the lower part of the column. Even if the liquid and vapor were to reach equilibrium at the column bottom, the amount of stripped oxygen is so small that there is almost no upward movement of the vapor phase. The high liquid flow used in these deaerators tends to drag the small vapor phase out of the vacuum column where the oxygen is reabsorbed quickly.

If a second-stage column is operated in series with the first column with respect to the liquid flow, but at a lower absolute pressure, additional flashed water vapor is generated for stripping the oxygen to a lower concentration. Thus in a second-stage deaerator, operated at 12 mm Hg absolute pressure, the water flashes further and is cooled to a temperature of 55°F. This additional water vapor will serve to sweep the stripped oxygen out of the packed bed. Such a two-stage deaerator can produce an effluent containing a minimum of 0.1 ppm by wt O_2 and that is virtually nitrogen free.

A small amount of inert gas added to the bottom of the vacuum column causes a substantial reduction in the effluent water oxygen content. Thus, the use of 0.24 SCF of methane per 100 gallons of water can reduce the effluent oxygen content by an additional 66% [5]. Adding a small amount of steam per gallon of water also is effective in reducing the oxygen content, compared to straight vacuum deaeration. The steam both heats the water at the interface to reduce oxygen solubility and acts as a stripping vapor.

A vacuum deaerator diameter typically is specified to give a liquid irrigation rate of about 40 gpm/ft^2 of column cross-sectional area. Originally, vacuum deaerators used ceramic packings and operated at lower liquid rates; however, most modern columns use 2-in. or larger-size plastic packings with a packed bed typically 7-ft to 15-ft deep.

This operation is so highly liquid-film controlled that the gas-film resistance, for practical purposes, can be neglected. Therefore, the number of transfer units required is:

$$N_{OL} = \ln\left[\frac{x_i}{x_o}\right] \qquad (4\text{-}15)$$

The overall height of a liquid-film transfer unit (H_{OL}) is a function of the liquid flow rate and the temperature. The H_{OL} for #2 plastic Super Intalox packing is 2.6 ft at a liquid rate of 40 gpm/ft^2 and temperature of 68°F. The H_{OL} increases as the water temperature is lowered. The H_{OL} value varies with temperature for this packing as:

$$H_{OL} \propto 1 + 0.002 (68 - T)^{1.3} \qquad (4\text{-}16)$$

Thus, at 53°F the H_{OL} is 2.8 ft, while at 41°F the H_{OL} is 3.0 ft for #2 plastic Super Intalox packing at a liquid rate of 40 gpm/ft^2. The value of the height of a liquid phase transfer unit in the stripping of oxygen was found to vary as the 0.22 power of the liquid rate for ring packings and the 0.28 power of the liquid rate for saddle-shaped packings [6]. It has been demonstrated that the value of H_{OL} increases with increasing liquid irrigation rate as the 0.25 power of that rate [7]. At a liquid rate of 24 gpm/ft^2, the H_{OL} is reduced to 2.3 ft compared to the value at 40 gpm/ft^2. As an example, assume 68°F water saturated with air is fed to a vacuum deaerator operated at a pressure of 23.5 mm Hg absolute. To obtain 95% oxygen removal using #2 plastic Super Intalox packing operating at a liquid rate of 40 gpm/ft^2, slightly less than an 8-ft deep bed is required.

Once the height of a transfer unit has been determined and the number of transfer units calculated from Equation 4-15, the packed depth required can be obtained from Equation 4-11.

In some cases a 3-in. or 3½-in. size plastic packing is specified. The H_{OL} for this larger size packing will be about 3.3 ft at 40 gpm/ft^2 liquid rate and 68°F.

WATER DECARBONATION

Prior to deaeration of water in a vacuum column, the dissolved carbon dioxide can be removed using an air stripping operation. Of course, only free CO_2 can be stripped, so that CO_2 combined in the form of carbonates or bicarbonates must be disassociated by acidification of the water using a nonvolatile acid.

The liquid irrigation rates used are similar to those for deaerators. The air flow normally used is a maximum of 120 CFM per 100 gpm of water feed; therefore, pressure drop is less than 0.1 in. H_2O/ft. Precautions should be observed to assure uniform gas distribution at this low pressure drop (see Chapter 10). However, 2-in. or larger-size plastic packings normally are specified and packed depths of 8 ft to 14 ft commonly used. Again, the liquid film resistance is controlling, and the gas-film resistance is negligible. Figure 4-1 can be used to determine the number of transfer units required; however, the abscissa value should be corrected to allow for a small amount of CO_2 in the stripping air.

In this service, the H_{OL} for #2 plastic Super Intalox packing is 2.8 ft at a liquid rate of 40 gpm/ft^2 and a temperature of 68°F. The H_{OL} value increases at lower water temperatures in the same manner as for water deaeration. Thus, H_{OL} is 3.0 ft at 53°F and 3.2 ft at 41°F at a liquid rate of 40 gpm/ft^2. The same investigators found that the height of a liquid phase transfer unit for CO_2 stripping increased in a similar manner with liquid rate as for oxygen desorption [6]. At a liquid rate of 30 gpm/ft^2 the H_{OL} is 2.6 ft, while at a liquid rate of 53 gpm/ft^2 the H_{OL} is 3.0 ft for #2 plastic Super Intalox packing at a water temperature of 68°F.

For the higher liquid rates, 3-in. or 3½-in. size packings usually are specified. The H_{OL} value for these larger packings is 27% greater than for the 2-in. size of the same type packing.

AMMONIA STRIPPING

Many industries generate liquid streams that contain from 0.01 to 2 wt% ammonia nitrogen that have an adverse effect when discharged into lakes or streams. While ion exchange and biological processes can be employed to remove ammonia nitrogen from aqueous solutions, ammonia stripping is the simplest method and easiest to control [8]. In an aqueous solution dissolved ammonia reacts as follows:

$$NH_3 + H_2O = NH^+_4 + OH^- \tag{4-17}$$

At a pH of 7 or lower, the ammonia is present as NH_4^+ ions. As the pH is increased, the reaction in Equation 4-17 is driven toward the left. At a pH of 12 or greater, free NH_3 (as a dissolved gas) is present in solution.

Because only free NH_3 can be stripped from solution, the pH of the liquid discharge first must be increased to above 11 by the addition of an alkali. This feed then is stripped of ammonia in a countercurrently operated packed column using air. A minimum of 240 CFM of air is required per gpm of liquid feed at 68°F; however, in practice 300 to 400 CFM of air per gpm of feed may be used. It must be realized that the air will cool the feed liquid toward the air temperature. Because a reduction of 18°F in the temperature of the water will reduce the vapor pressure of ammonia by about 40%, the use of steam injection to heat the air may be needed to obtain the required ammonia removal in cold climates (below 52°F).

The design of an air stripping column first requires selection of the ratio of air-to-water feed. The values for the equilibrium constant (K) for ammonia above its aqueous solutions at various temperatures are given in Table 4-2 [9]. These values apply to dilute solutions (below 12 wt% NH_3) at atmospheric pressure. The stripping factor then is calculated using Equation 4-14. If the liquid temperature changes significantly through the stripper, the value of K will be reduced for the liquid effluent while the value of G_m/L_m will increase, due to evaporation of water. In such a case, a logarithmic mean value of S* should be used. Because the inlet air contains no ammonia, the value of the abscissa in Figure 4-1 equals x_i/x_o. The number of transfer units required can be determined from this Colburn correlation.

Because of the high ratio of gas to liquid, the liquid irrigation rate will be low. To avoid high gas-phase pressure drop, a high-capacity packing usually is selected in order to minimize the column cross-sectional area needed. Because the CO_2 normally present in the stripping air will be absorbed into the alkaline solution, precipitation of calcium carbonate may occur in the packed bed. In order to reduce scaling, plastic packing usually is specified. In some cases, scale-inhibiting polymers are added to the feed liquid.

below 12%
at
$P = 1 atm$

Table 4-2

Equilibrium Constant for Ammonia Solutions

Temperature (°F)	Equilibrium Constant (y/x)
40	0.460
50	0.632
60	0.840
70	1.10
80	1.41
90	1.81
100	2.28

Because of its low pressure drop (F=13), Intalox Snowflake packing represents a typical plastic random packing used in such services. This packing will develop an H_{OL} value of 2.2 ft when operated at a liquid rate of 1.5 gpm/ft². To obtain 96% ammonia removal from water at 62°F, a 12-ft deep bed is needed using an air rate of 360 CFM per gpm.

A modification of this technology has been used to treat solutions of ammonium salts and free ammonia. The stripped ammonia in the exit air stream subsequently is absorbed into a dilute sulfuric acid solution in a packed column. The air leaving this absorber is ammonia-free, thus it is recycled back through the stripping column in a closed cycle. Such a system is described in U.S. patent 3,920,419 [10]. This process is operated at a temperature range of 140 to 180°F in order to raise the vapor pressure of the dissolved ammonia. At such temperatures only 50 to 100 CFM of air per gpm is needed to remove 99% of the ammonia from the feed. By minimizing the recycled air flow, the diameters of the stripper and absorber are reduced.

AMINE REGENERATION

One of the most common stripping operations is the regeneration of an amine solution that has been used to absorb CO_2 or H_2S. Typically, a 3-normal monoethanolamine solution containing 0.42 to 0.50 mol CO_2 per mol MEA is fed to the stripper. The rich solvent is preheated to a temperature of 190° to 210°F by heat exchange against the hot, lean stripper bottoms liquid. The stripper typically operates at a top pressure not greater than 10 psig, and the overhead vapor will contain 25 to 33 mol% CO_2, with the balance being water vapor. The stripped vapor passes through a condenser to reduce the water vapor content. The condensate is returned to the column to irrigate a wash bed at the top of the stripper to prevent loss of MEA vapor in the overhead gas stream.

The stripper is heated by a reboiler that typically requires 0.9 to 1.1 lb of heating steam per gallon of solvent to be regenerated. Lean solvent leaves the stripper bottom at a temperature of 235° to 245°F and contains 0.12 to 0.15 mol CO_2 per mol MEA. Reboiler energy must be sufficient to provide 820 Btu/lb of CO_2, representing the heat of reaction with MEA, the sensible heat load to raise the solvent temperature, and the steam present in the overhead vapor.

Amines are considered moderately foaming systems; therefore, the column diameter is specified to limit the pressure drop to 0.30 in. H_2O/ft of packed depth at the point of greatest loading. The complex of CO_2 and MEA must be chemically decomposed in the stripper. The rate of this decomposition reaction is increased by raising the stripper temperature. However, the MEA itself tends to decompose thermally, producing by-products that are corrosive to common metals. Regeneration temperatures, therefore, usually are limited to a maximum of 250°F. If the overhead CO_2 gas is used in the process rather than vented, a compressor can be used to increase the CO_2 pressure. This can be a lower-cost alternative to raising the stripper pressure and requiring nickel alloy construction for the column and internals. Because CO_2 release is a function of the decomposition rate of the CO_2/MEA complex, it is necessary to provide sufficient liquid residence time in the stripper. A column for this reaction normally has tower packing no larger than 2-in. size and operates at a pressure drop of no less than 0.10 in. H_2O/ft. Maximum liquid irrigation rate typically is 30 gpm/ft^2.

The vapor pressure of CO_2 above the MEA solvent varies with the molar ratio of CO_2 to MEA, as well as with the temperature. The equilibrium curve representing this stripping operation is a plot of the mol fraction of CO_2 in the vapor in equilibrium with the mol fraction of CO_2 in the liquid phase. The operating line on this same plot is determined by a heat and material balance. The number of liquid-phase transfer units (N_{OL}) usually varies from five to nine, depending on the ratio of mols of liquid to mols of stripping vapor. The lower the steam consumption per gallon of solvent, the greater the number of liquid-phase transfer units required. However, because of the equilibrium curve shape, use of a larger number of transfer units does not substantially reduce reboiler duty [11].

Because of the liquid-phase reaction to liberate CO_2, this stripping operation is highly liquid-film controlled. For practical purposes, the gas-film resistance can be neglected. The H_{OL} for 1½-in. ceramic Intalox saddle packing is 3.1 ft at a liquid rate of 10 gpm/ft^2. If the liquid rate is raised 25 gpm/ft^2, the H_{OL} increases to 4.1 ft for the same packing. Using Equation 4-13, then the K_La value for regeneration is increasing as the 0.7 power of the liquid flow rate. However, in absorption the K_Ga value increases only as about the 0.3 power of the liquid rate.

The mass transfer rate is influenced significantly by the operating temperature. This is in large part due to the effect of temperature on the decomposition rate of the CO_2/MEA complex. The K_La value will, therefore, increase about 14% for a 10°F rise in liquid temperature. This temperature effect on the K_La value in the regenerator is similar to the effect of temperature on the K_Ga value in the absorber.

Because of the volatility of MEA, a wash bed of 4- to 6-ft packed depth usually is installed above the feed point. This bed is irrigated with condensate and the liquid rate is low; therefore, a smaller size packing than used in the stripping bed may be selected.

The stripping of diethanolamine solutions is similar to MEA regeneration. In this case, although the heat of reaction of CO_2 with DEA is 20% lower than with MEA, the regeneration still requires 1.0 to 1.2 lb of steam per gallon of solvent regenerated. The 2.5-normal solution of DEA typically used requires a higher solvent flow rate for the same acid gas absorption than 3-normal MEA solvent.

DEA solutions are used when a sulfur-bearing gas stream is being purified, because MEA forms nonregenerable compounds with COS and CS_2. The DEA system should be followed by a caustic wash if 10 ppm or less COS concentration is specified in the purified gas stream. Even though H_2S is absorbed faster than CO_2, the equilibrium favors stripping of H_2S more rapidly than CO_2, because CO_2 forms a more stable complex with the amine solvent.

Although the rate of absorption of CO_2 and H_2S into a DEA solvent is less than into an MEA solvent, the DEA solution is somewhat easier to strip than an MEA solution. Usually the same H_{OL} value is used to design DEA strippers as is used for the design of MEA strippers. The DEA solvent, however, can be regenerated to a lower acid gas concentration—about 0.07 to 0.08 mol CO_2 per mol DEA—than is typical for an MEA solvent. Because of the low vapor pressure of DEA, a wash bed may not be required at the top of the stripper.

DEA solutions degrade thermally in operation. Purification of a small sidestream of DEA solvent by vacuum distillation formerly was employed. Currently, decomposition products are deactivated by the addition of an alkali carbonate to the solvent. In addition, a small sidestream liquid flow continuously is passed through an activated carbon filter. The filter adsorbs degradation products as well as dissolved hydrocarbons that may promote foaming.

HOT CARBONATE REGENERATION

Another widely used stripping operation is the regeneration of a rich potassium carbonate solution from an absorber that removes H_2S or CO_2 from a gas stream. This process typically uses a 25 wt% K_2CO_3 aqueous solution that enters the stripper 70% to 80% converted to bicarbonate. The liquid feed comes from the absorber bottom at a temperature of about 240°F and at a high pressure.

The equilibrium CO_2 concentration in solution decreases rapidly as the partial pressure of CO_2 in the gas phase is reduced, thus regeneration at low pressure is desirable. The stripper usually operates at a top pressure up to 25 psia; therefore, the liquid feed undergoes a large flash on entering this column. The rich liquid throttle valve should be located as close to the stripper feed inlet nozzle as possible. Sometimes this high-pressure rich liquid is passed through a power recovery turbine that drives the lean carbonate booster pump to reduce the plant energy consumption. The feed liquid in the fully flashed condition may have a velocity of 100 to 150 ft/s through the regenerator feed nozzle. Special design of the feed liquid distributor in the regenerator is required to dissipate this energy.

The CO_2 is stripped from rich solvent by a combination of flashing and steam stripping. As much as 40 to 60% of the total CO_2 stripped can be released during the flashing operation. The remaining CO_2 is released by stripping the solution with steam. The overhead vapor from the stripper usually contains about 28 mol % CO_2; the balance is steam. The vapor passes through a condenser to reduce the water vapor content. The condensate returns to the system to maintain the water balance. This condensate usually irrigates a wash section at the top of the stripper to prevent loss of K_2CO_3 by entrainment in the vapor stream.

The stripping steam required is provided by a reboiler that is heated with steam or with hot process gas feed to the absorber. The lean solution leaves the regenerator at about the same temperature as the feed-liquid temperature. This lean solution still is 20% to 25% converted to bicarbonate. Because the solvent is circulated hot through the system, there is very little sensible heat load. The reboiler must supply enough energy to provide the 270 Btu/lb of CO_2 heat of reaction with the K_2CO_3, plus the heat to vaporize the additional water contained in the overhead gas stream. Regeneration usually requires about 0.6 lb of steam per gallon of solvent. If regeneration of the lean solvent is carried out to less than 20% bicarbonate content, the stripping steam requirement increases considerably. Data has been developed by British Gas Corporation demonstrating the increase in steam consumption as conversion to bicarbonate is reduced [12]. In systems where a portion of the lean solvent is cooled before it returns to the absorber, an additional sensible heat load is added to the reboiler duty.

Hot carbonate systems are considered slightly foaming; therefore, the stripper diameter should be selected to give a pressure drop no higher than 0.40 in. H_2O/ft of packed depth at the point of maximum loading. In a split-stream system (see Chapter 3) a smaller packing can be specified for the bottom bed than is used in the upper section of the regenerator, or the bottom section of the stripper can be of a smaller diameter. This is possible because the liquid rate is much lower in the bottom bed after withdrawal of the semi-lean solution. However, for mechanical reasons, the regenerator usually has the same diameter throughout the entire column height. In hot carbonate systems, the liquid loading can be very high; therefore, packing size should be selected in accordance with the recommendations in regard to maximum liquid irrigation rate (see Table 3-2). Any vapor that is aspirated in the liquid phase and carried to the bottom of the column results in a stripping efficiency loss.

The regeneration of a hot carbonate solution requires reversal of Equation 4-18 or 4-19:

$$K_2CO_3 + CO_2 + H_2O = 2KHCO_3 \qquad\qquad (4\text{-}18)$$

$$K_2CO_3 + H_2S = KHCO_3 + KHS \qquad\qquad (4\text{-}19)$$

Because acid gas release is a function of the $KHCO_3$ or KHS decomposition rate, sufficient liquid residence time must be provided in the packed bed. The regenerator packing usually is no larger than the 2-in. size, and the pressure drop at minimum loading is at least 0.15 in. H_2O/ft of packed depth. Where a high turndown ratio is necessary for processing the gas stream in the absorber, the solvent circulation rate should be reduced to not less than 50% of design flow. This is recommended even though the gas flow to the absorber is less than one-half the design rate.

The solvent flow rate and composition of rich and lean solutions are known from the absorber design or operation. Because regeneration normally is carried out at an absolute pressure of less than 2 atm, the boiling temperature for the lean solvent is only 230° to 250°F. The stripper usually is designed on the basis of an overall liquid-phase mass transfer coefficient ($K_L a$) because this operation is substantially liquid-film controlled. Data released by Norton Company in 1968 demonstrated that the $K_L a$ for steam stripping K_2CO_3 solutions increases as the liquid rate to the 0.90 power [13]. Thus, the $K_L a$ at 22 gpm/ft^2 is 50% greater than at 14 gpm/ft^2 liquid rate. The number of mols of CO_2 to be stripped, however, is 57% greater at the higher liquid flow rate. Higher liquid irrigation rates, therefore, require slightly greater packed depths to regenerate the solvent to the same lean solution concentration.

The $K_L a$ also is a function of the percentage conversion to bicarbonate as shown in Figure 4-2. At 60% conversion, the $K_L a$ is 33% lower than at 75% bicarbonate; while at 40% bicarbonate, the $K_L a$ is 70% lower. The $K_L a$ used to calculate the packed depth required is the logarithmic average of the $K_L a$ values at the top and bottom of the stripper or section of substantially uniform liquid flow for a split-stream system.

The $K_L a$ value for stripping CO_2 at a liquid rate of 20 gpm/ft² for a solution of 75% conversion to bicarbonate is 37 to 43 lb-mol/ h · ft³ · mol/mol for 2-in. ceramic Intalox saddles, #2 Hy-Pak packing, or 2-in. metal Pall rings. The $K_L a$ value for 2-in.-size packings is about 75% of $K_L a$ for 1 in.-size packings of the same type.

The mol fraction CO_2 in the lean solvent normally will be 0.008 to 0.010 for a 25 wt% K_2CO_3 solution. The CO_2 content in the vapor from the reboiler fixes the equilibrium liquid-phase solute concentration from the K value. This value can be calculated from the data compiled by Bocard and Mayland for the vapor pressure of CO_2 above hot carbonate solutions as a function of K_2CO_3 concentration, CO_2 absorbed, and the temperature [14]. Solute concentration in the solution leaving the packing is one theoretical stage richer than the lean solvent when the regenerator is heated by a reboiler. Thus, the driving force (Δx_B) is determined for the bottom of the regenerator. From a mass balance, the concentration of CO_2 in the vapor phase at the stripping section top can be calculated. Again, the K value can be used to fix the equilibrium solute concentration above the feed liquid. The actual rich solution contains 0.028 to 0.033 mol fraction CO_2. The driving force (Δx_T) at the stripping section top is determined from the liquid composition, after the flash of the rich liquid feed. The overall driving force used in the calculation of the packed depth is the logarithmic mean average of the driving forces at the bottom and top of the stripper or for sections of similar liquid flow rates for split-stream operation.

The mols of CO_2 to be stripped can be calculated from a mass balance on the solvent. Then the total packed depth can be determined from Equation 4-8. The depth of each packed bed normally is a maximum of 30 ft when using metal or ceramic packings. With polypropylene packing, the maximum suggested bed depth is 24 ft because of the possibility of creep at elevated temperatures. If the operating temperature is 245°F or greater, polypropylene packing should be glass-reinforced to reduce the creep rate.

Hot carbonate systems are widely used for treating high-pressure natural gas to remove H_2S down to 4 mol ppm to meet pipeline requirements. The H_2S has a higher vapor pressure above the carbonate solution than CO_2; thus, it is more readily stripped from the solvent. This occurs because CO_2 forms a stronger acid, which is more tightly held in the alkaline solvent.

Generally it is uneconomical to regenerate a solvent down to a bicarbonate content so low that it permits reduction of the CO_2 in the absorber outlet gas below 1,500 mol ppm for a typical unpromoted hot carbonate system. Although some promoted systems claim to be able to

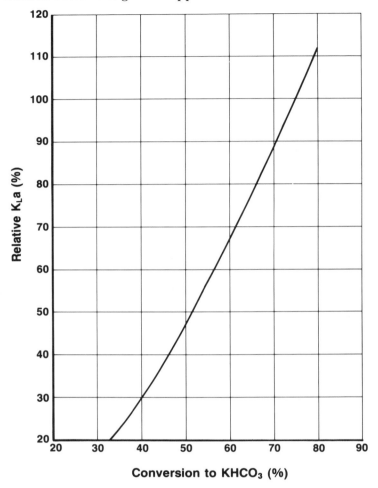

Figure 4-2. Relative K_La for 20% K_2CO_3 regeneration.

purify gas down to 500 mol ppm CO_2 content, the steam required for regeneration of the solvent may be up to 30% greater than with the higher CO_2 content in the treated gas stream.

When organic promoters are used with this system, the process licensor usually supplies a corrosion inhibitor as part of the package. The corrosion inhibitor is present only in the liquid phase because it is not volatile. Severe carbon steel corrosion due to the wet CO_2 has been experienced in the vapor phase areas. The use of austenitic stainless steels, therefore, is common practice at the top of the regenerator column.

SIDE STRIPPERS

In petroleum refining the atmospheric crude tower produces a number of products that are removed as liquid sidestreams. Each of these liquid sidestreams contains some quantity of light hydrocarbons present in the vapor that passes up the crude tower at the elevation of the sidestream removal. These light components must be removed in order to meet the initial boiling point specification for the product. Usually the liquid sidestream is fed to a stripper that uses either a reboiler or superheated steam to strip out these light components. The overhead vapor from this stripper is returned to the atmospheric crude tower, so that the side stripper operates at about the same pressure as the crude tower. The current preference is to use reboiled side strippers for the lower boiling products, rather than direct steam stripping.[1] This practice reduces the heat load on the crude tower condenser as well as the sour water stripper [15]. Typically, this side stripper requires only two or three theoretical stages so that four to six actual trays are used.

To illustrate this operation, consider a 5.0-ft ID side stripper equipped with 4 valve trays on 24-in. spacing. This stripper uses 3.7 lb. of 150 psig saturated steam to strip each barrel of diesel feed. The top stripper pressure is 23 psia and the liquid feed temperature is 395°F. The existing valve trays can handle a feed rate of 164,000 lb/h of liquid. In order to increase the capacity of this side stripper use of tower packing is considered; however, only 6 ft of height is available to provide the required two theoretical stages. Because of its high capacity and low HETP value, a structured sheet metal type of packing should be considered.

A check of the loadings indicates that 19.4% of the liquid feed is vaporized so that the liquid rate at the bottom of the tower is only 80.6% of that at the top. More significantly, the Cs factor at the bottom is only 21.6% of the C_s value at the top of the column. The use of a smaller size packing for the lower theoretical stage than for the upper theoretical stage should be investigated. From an efficiency consideration, two layers of the 2T-size Intalox Structured packing will provide over one theoretical stage, as will three layers of 3T-size of this same packing.

Because the available mass transfer height can accept six total layers of this structured packing, a replacement of the four trays with four layers of size 3T resting on two layers of Intalox Structured packing 2T is suggested. Such a packed bed configuration will permit a 35% increase in the liquid feed capacity at the same stripping steam ratio. As the pressure drop of the size 2T packing at the bottom is below 0.05 in. H_2O/ft, use of a stream sparger is recommended to obtain uniform flow of stripping steam into the bottom of the packed bed.

---

[1]From *Petroleum Refinery Distillation* by R.N. Watkins. Copyright 1979 by Gulf Publishing Company, Houston, TX. Used with permission. All rights reserved.

EXAMPLE PROBLEM

We will consider the stripping of 500 gpm of water at 68°F that contains 500 mol ppm H_2S in order to produce an effluent liquid containing only 2 mol ppm H_2S. The stripping gas will be atmospheric air at 68°F, which is H_2S free. The liquid feed first will be acidified with dilute sulfuric acid to assure all the H_2S is liberated from any salts present in solution. From Table 4-1, the Henry's Law constant (H) for H_2S at 68°F is 483 atm/mol fraction. In order to minimize the column size, a liquid irrigation rate of 40 gpm/ft^2 will be used; therefore, a 4.0-ft ID column will be specified.

Initially, we will try an air rate of 1,200 CFM per 1,000 gpm. Thus, G_m = 93.44 lb-mol/h, L_m = 13,870 lb-mol/h, and the stripping factor from Equation 4-14 will be 3.25. Because y_i is zero, the abscissa value for Figure 4-1 will be 250. Thus, N_{OL} will be 7.4 liquid transfer units required. Because of the small column size, #1 plastic Super Intalox packing will be specified. The H_{OL} is 2.7 ft at a liquid rate of 40 gpm/ft^2, so a 20.0-ft deep bed is required. Because the gas velocity is only 0.8 ft/s, the pressure drop is less than 0.05 in. H_2O/ft.

A 50% greater air rate of 1,800 CFM per 1,000 gpm will be tried. Thus, G_m = 140.2 lb-mol/h and S* = 4.88. N_{OL} now is 6.7 transfer units, which requires an 18.0-ft deep packed bed. The gas velocity has increased to 1.2 ft/s and the pressure drop is 0.06 in. H_2O/ft.

If the air rate is raised to 3,000 CFM per 1,000 gpm, which gives a gas velocity of 2.0 ft/s, then G_m = 233.6 lb-mol/h; and the value of the stripping factor will be 8.13. From Figure 4-1, N_{OL} will be reduced to 6.1 transfer units and the packed depth needed will be 16.5 ft. The pressure drop now has increased to 0.18 in. H_2O/ft.

From these calculations, the use of the largest air rate will provide the lowest column cost for this application. The pressure drop through a 16.5-ft depth of #1 plastic Super Intalox packing will total only 3.0 in. H_2O. The blower specified should deliver 1,500 CFM of air at an outlet pressure of 4 in. H_2O. Thus, the operating power requirement will be small.

NOTATION

A	Column cross-section area (ft^2)
a	Interfacial area (ft^2/ft^3)
F	Packing factor
G_m	Gas phase flow (lb-mol/h)
H	Henry's Law constant (atm/mol fraction)
H_{OL}	Overall height of liquid phase transfer unit (ft)
K	Equilibrium ratio

$K_L a$ Overall liquid-phase mass transfer coefficient (lb-mol/h $\cdot$ ft^3 $\cdot$ mol/mol)

k_G Gas-film mass transfer coefficient (lb-mol/h $\cdot$ ft^2 $\cdot$ atm)

k_L Liquid-film mass transfer coefficient (lb-mol/h $\cdot$ ft^2 $\cdot$ mol/mol)

L_m Liquid phase flow (lb-mol/h)

m   Slope of equilibrium curve

N   Solute transferred (lb-mol/h)

N_{OL} Number of overall liquid phase transfer units

P   Total system pressure (atm)

p   Partial pressure in gas phase (atm)

p^* Vapor pressure of solute (atm)

S^* Stripping factor

T   Temperature ($^\circ$F)

x   Mol fraction in liquid phase

x^* Equilibrium mol fraction in liquid phase

x_i Mol fraction solute in inlet liquid

x_o Mol fraction solute in outlet liquid

y   Mol fraction in gas phase

y_i Mol fraction solute in inlet gas

y_o Mol fraction solute in outlet gas

Z   Packed depth (ft)

Δp Partial pressure difference (atm)

Δx Mol fraction difference in liquid

Δx_B Mol fraction difference in liquid at bottom

Δx_{LM} ln mean mol fraction driving force

Δx_T Mol fraction difference in liquid at top

REFERENCES

1. Landolt-Boernstein, *Zahlenwerte und Funktionen ous Physik,* Vol. 4, Part 4, Band c, Springer-Verlag, 1976.
2. Maddox, R. N., *Process Engineer's Absorption Pocket Handbook,* Gulf Publishing, Houston, 1985, p. 9.
3. *International Critical Tables,* Vol. 3, McGraw-Hill, 1928, p. 256.
4. Colburn, A. P., *Industrial and Engineering Chemistry,* Vol. 33, 1941, p. 459.
5. Frank, W. J., "Efficient Removal of Oxygen in Waterflood by Vacuum Deaeration," American Institute of Mining, Metallurgical, and Petroleum Engineers, Paper SPE-4064, 1972.
6. Sherwood, T. K. and Holloway, F. A. L., *Transactions of American Institute of Chemical Engineers,* Vol. 36, No. 1, 1940, p. 21.

7. Society of Petroleum Engineers of American Institute of Mechanical Engineers, Paper SPE-4064.

8. Culp, R. L. and Culp, G. L., *Advanced Wastewater Treatment,* Van Nostrand Reinhold, 1971, p. 298.

9. Perry, R. H. *et al., Chemical Engineer's Handbook,* 4th ed, McGraw-Hill, 1963, p. 3-66.

10. Schroeder, J. W. and Naso, A. C., "Method of Removing Ammonia from Ammonia Containing Liquor," Republic Steel, 1975.

11. Kohl, A. L. and Riesenfeld, F. C., *Gas Purification,* McGraw-Hill, 1960, p. 57-61. (See also Kohl and Riesenfeld, *Gas Purification,* 4th ed., Gulf Publishing Company, Houston, 1985.)

12. Evans, L. J. P. and Siddique, Q. M., "CO_2 Removal Studies and Their Application to SNG Plant Conversions," Institution of Chemical Engineers, 41st Autumn Research Meeting, November 1975.

13. Eckert J. S. *et al.,* "Technical Data Related to Tower Packing," Norton Company, 1968, GR-274A Rev. 1.

14. Bocard, J. P. and Mayland, B. J., *Hydrocarbon Processing,* Vol. 41, No. 4, 1962, p. 128.

15. Watkins, R. N., *Petroleum Refinery Distillation,* 2nd Ed., Gulf Publishing, Houston, 1979, p.34.

5

POLLUTION CONTROL

Over the past two decades emissions from chemical and hydrocarbon processing operations have come under increasing scrutiny and regulation by various governmental agencies. As a result of public pressure, a number of rules and regulations have been promulgated to control both air and water discharges from manufacturing plants.

In this chapter first we will consider devices to control air pollution. Although primary emphasis will be placed on removing corrosive or toxic materials from vented gas streams, discharge of obnoxious compounds, which may be banned as a public nuisance, will also be discussed. In the future, even venting of inert gases such as CO_2 may be controlled. Secondly, we will discuss the problem of discharging aqueous liquid wastes, which contain low molecular weight volatile organic compounds. Not only are such emissions currently regulated but, because of the effect of materials discharged in the past on the aquifer, ground water supplies in many locations must be purified.

With increasing public awareness to changes in the environment, more rigorous enforcement of regulations covering plant discharges will occur. As a result, billions of dollars must be invested to control such discharges. The amortization of this investment plus the operating costs of such equipment will be added to the cost of products manufactured in the industrialized nations. In order for these countries to remain competitive, pollution control systems should be evaluated thoroughly before final selection and installation.

GAS PURIFICATION

Tower packing is used in the scrubbing of corrosive, obnoxious, or hazardous gases, vapors, and particulates from a gas stream. Packed scrubbers have low power requirements and occupy a reasonably small space. They can handle high-temperature and high-moisture content gas streams. Corrosion-resistant construction is readily available.

Packed fume scrubbers operate on the principle of presenting a large surface area wetted by a liquid (usually water) over which the air flows turbulently. Scrubbing is accomplished by impingement of particles on the wetted packing surface and by absorption of soluble gas or vapor molecules from the air by contact with the wetted surface.

GAS SCRUBBER TYPES

Packed scrubbers generally are arranged in one of four ways, based on the manner in which the liquid is contacted with the gas stream. Concurrent flow scrubbers make up two of these classifications. In both cases the liquid and gas flow in the same direction through the scrubber.

In a horizontal flow concurrent scrubber, the gas velocity carries scrubbing liquid into the packed bed and the device actually operates as a wetted entrainment separator. Normally, superficial gas velocity is limited to a maximum of 9.6 ft/s due to liquid reentrainment at higher velocities. Packed bed thickness is restricted because the depth of liquid penetration into the tower packing is limited by the allowable gas velocity.

A vertical flow concurrent scrubber can operate at very high gas velocities so that pressure drops from 1 in. H_2O/ft to as high as 3 in. H_2O/ft are common. There is no flooding limit of the packing because the liquid holdup in the packed bed decreases as the gas rate increases (see Figure 1-17). Contact time between gas and liquid is a function of bed depth as well as the gas velocity. Absorption driving forces are reduced because the exit gas is in contact with the highest concentration of contaminant in the liquid phase. The exit gas phase may contain substantial liquid entrainment that must be removed before this gas is discharged into the atmosphere.

The third class of scrubber is called cross-flow. This device contacts a horizontally flowing gas stream with a vertically descending liquid flow. Thus, cross-sectional area for gas flow is different from the area for liquid flow. Liquid flow rates can be 40% lower per 1,000 CFM of air than when the gas flow area is the same as the liquid flow area. Even at these reduced liquid rates satisfactory wetting of the tower packing is obtained.

Mass transfer driving forces are intermediate between vertical concurrent scrubbers and countercurrent scrubbers [1]. If the absorbed solute obeys Henry's Law in the liquid phase, the mass transfer driving force will limit maximum solute removal efficiency to about 90% of that obtained in a countercurrent scrubber for typical chemical fumes—assuming scrubbing water flow is limited. However, if the absorption of solute is followed by a rapid chemical reaction in the liquid phase, so that there is no appreciable vapor pressure of solute above the solution, the mass transfer driving force will be the same as for a countercurrent scrubber.

The most widely used type of scrubber operates with gas and liquid in countercurrent flow as the liquid flows vertically downward under the influence of gravity. Maximum gas flow rate is limited by liquid entrainment or by pressure drop. Packed bed depth, as well as gas velocity, controls contact time between the gas and liquid phases. Mass transfer driving forces are maximized because the exit gas stream contacts the entering liquid, which contains a minimum or zero solute concentration.

The pressure drop through the tower packing is very important because the cost of power to move the gas stream through the scrubber may be the largest operating cost factor. Most tower packing manufacturers can provide experimental pressure drop data specific to the air/water system. If this information is not available, the pressure drop can be determined from the generalized pressure-drop correlation shown in Figure 1-15 or Figure 1-16.

Countercurrent scrubbers generally have these characteristics:

- Designed to operate at a pressure drop between 0.25 in. and 0.60 in. H_2O/ft of packed depth.
- Air velocity normally between 5.0 and 8.0 ft/s if modern, high-capacity plastic tower packings are used.
- Inlet concentrations of contaminant in the gas stream normally do not exceed 5,000 ppm by volume.
- Liquid irrigation rates typically are from 2 to 8 gpm/ft^2 of column cross-sectional area.

Plastic packings have been used extensively in scrubbers because of their light weight, low cost, and resistance to mechanical damage. Such packings offer a wide range of resistance to chemical attack by acids, alkalis, and many organic compounds. However, it should be recognized that plastic packings can be deformed by excessive temperatures or by exposure to certain solvents.

PARTICULATE REMOVAL

Removal of a solid or liquid particulate involves a physical capture by wetting after the particle has penetrated the liquid surface. There is no limit to the amount of particulate capture that can be achieved, as long as the liquid-film properties remain unchanged during the scrubbing operation.

Wet packed scrubbers are highly efficient for removing particles of 10 micron or larger equivalent particle diameter. Removal efficiencies of 90% to 95% can be expected even on 6-micron size material. Generally, for a given type of wet scrubber, the greater the power applied to the system the higher the collection efficiency for the particulate material. For this reason, countercurrently operated packed scrubbers for particulate removal normally are designed to operate at a pressure drop not less than 0.40 in. H_2O/ft. However, in a countercurrent packed scrubber, the power applied (as reflected by pressure drop) is limited by hydraulic flooding of the packing or by the gas rate producing massive liquid entrainment.

To obtain impingement and capture of a particle, the liquid must wet the particulate and make it a part of the liquid phase as a means of removing it from the gas stream. The inertial effect (which depends on the mass of the particle and its velocity) must be sufficient to allow the particle to follow a different path than that of the gas stream. This causes it to impinge on the surface of the wetted packing elements. The optimum packing, therefore, should present an adequate impingement surface for particle capture, while producing a low pressure drop. The tower packing must have surfaces that can be continuously wetted and must resist entrainment of liquid into the gas phase. Table 5-1 shows a comparison of particulate removal efficiency by size obtained in scrubbers with packings vs. those with baffles.

Table 5-1

Wet Scrubber Particulate Removal Efficiency

Particulate Diameter	Wt. % Removal Efficiency	
(microns)	Packing	Baffles
12	99	85
10	97	82
8	95	80
6	93	75
5	90	70
3	87	60
2	75	50

Source: ASHRAE 1983 Equipment Handbook [2]

As the solids loading in the inlet gas stream increase, larger sizes of packings should be selected so as to avoid blockage with the recovered particulate. In addition, higher liquid irrigation rates should be employed in order to assure complete wetting of the packing surfaces, as well as to flush off deposited solids.

The removal efficiency depends on the kinetic energy possessed by the particle, which is:

$$KE = \frac{wV^2}{2g} \tag{5-1}$$

The mass at constant specific gravity is a function of the cube of the equivalent particle diameter. For example, to capture a 3-micron particle with the same efficiency as a 5-micron particle, the gas velocity must be increased by 2.15 times. Because pressure drop is proportional to the square of the gas velocity, the scrubber must operate at 4.62 times the pressure drop for the 3-micron particle to be captured with the same efficiency as 5-micron particle removal.

A concurrently operated vertical flow scrubber removes the restriction of power input with respect to hydraulic flooding of the packed bed. Therefore, this device can operate at higher gas velocities and greater pressure drops than a countercurrently operated scrubber. With increased power input possible, concurrently operated packed scrubbers are much more effective for the removal of particles from 1- to 3-micron equivalent diameter than countercurrent units. Table 5-2 shows typical size ranges for common particulate emissions [3]. Tobacco smoke has been included in this list to provide a comparison of size with commonly encountered particulates.

Table 5-2

Typical Industrial Particulate Emissions

Particulate	Size Range (microns)
Ground Limestone	40 to 900
Fly Ash	2 to 700
Cement Dust	3 to 80
Electroplating Mist	5 to 50
Sulfuric Acid Mist	0.5 to 30
Insecticide Dust	0.5 to 9
Alkali Fumes	0.1 to 5
Galvanizing Flux	0.1 to 1
Oil Smoke	0.03 to 0.90
Magnesium Oxide Smoke	0.01 to 0.40
Tobacco Smoke	0.01 to 0.40
Zinc Oxide Fumes	0.01 to 0.40

GAS SCRUBBING

Gas or vapor removal is more complex than particulate removal because the constituent removed from the air stream is dissolved in the liquid phase and may change the liquid properties. A solution of any volatile material exhibits a vapor pressure of the solute above the liquid phase. This vapor pressure increases with solute concentration and liquid temperature. Contaminant removal continues only as long as the partial pressure of that constituent in the gas phase exceeds the vapor pressure of that solute above the liquid phase. Contaminant removal rate is a function of this driving force pressure difference, as well as the mass transfer coefficient.

Calculating fume scrubber efficiency requires an understanding of mass transfer principles. The reader is referred to Chapter 3 for a more detailed discussion of the two-film theory of mass transfer.

The solute transferred in terms of the overall gas-phase mass transfer coefficient is:

$$N = AZ \, K_G a \, P(y - y^*) \tag{5-2}$$

Similarly, the solute transferred in terms of the overall liquid-phase mass transfer coefficient is:

$$N = AZ \, K_L a \, (x^* - x) \tag{5-3}$$

It can be assumed that over a small solute concentration change, a linear equilibrium relationship exists that relates the concentrations in the gas and liquid phases for at least one theoretical stage. The relationship between the solute concentrations in the two phases can be expressed in terms of the equilibrium curve slope m.

As previously stated in Chapter 3, the mass transfer rate is considered to be determined by the gas-film resistance operating in series with the liquid-film resistance. The film that offers the predominant mass transfer resistance is called the controlling film. Contaminants that have a limited solubility in the liquid phase (a high value of m) usually are considered to be a liquid-film-controlled system. Contaminants that are highly soluble in the liquid phase (a low value of m) usually are considered to be a gas-film-controlled system.

A calculation can be made for the solute transferred based on the compositions of the main-body gas phase and the main-body liquid phase. It requires only a knowledge of the equilibrium relationship between y and x. For low concentrations of a non-reacting solute in the liquid phase, the equilibrium partial pressure of solute above the liquid phase is expressed by Henry's Law:

$$p^* = Hx \tag{5-4}$$

At low concentrations of solute and constant temperature operation, the Henry's Law constant (H) can be considered a fixed value. Using the two-film theory requires a knowledge of the value of H to evaluate the driving force magnitude as well as the mass transfer coefficient.

In certain applications, where the dissolved solute would exhibit a high vapor pressure above the resultant solution, a reactive chemical is added to the liquid phase. One function of this reactant is to combine with the absorbed solute so as to eliminate, or substantially reduce, the vapor pressure of the solute above the liquid phase. In these situations, the mass transfer driving force is maximized. Further, the scrubbing solution can be recirculated while still obtaining a high fume removal efficiency. For example, the use of an alkaline scrubbing liquid for removal of chlorine from a gas stream is common practice.

At the bottom of the packed bed, the driving force for mass transfer is:

$$\Delta p_B = y_i P - H x_o \tag{5-5}$$

At the top of the packed bed, this driving force is:

$$\Delta p_T = y_o P - H x_i \tag{5-6}$$

Because the amount of solute transferred is very small, the values of G_m and L_m are practically unchanged. Thus, the slope of the operating line is constant. If there is no great change in liquid temperature, the value of H is constant and the operating line is straight. In practice, a logarithmic mean driving force is used to account for the change in partial pressure differences throughout the packed depth, just as though the equilibrium curve and operating line are straight.

$$\Delta p_{LM} = \frac{\Delta p_B - \Delta p_T}{\ln(\Delta p_B / \Delta p_T)} \tag{5-7}$$

The mass transferred may be expressed as:

$$N = K_G a \, AZ\Delta \, p_{LM} \tag{5-8}$$

SCRUBBER DESIGN METHODS

In fume scrubbing operations, often it is not possible to define the gas flow rate or contaminant concentration with great precision. In many practical cases there is an uncertainty about the value of H. Obviously, the scrubber design cannot be more exact than the definition of the scrubbing problem. However, there has been much experience in the scrubbing of many common contaminant gases, which permits the use of simplifying assumptions to provide a rapid design procedure. The empirical overall mass transfer coefficients derived from this experience allow for assumptions such as a small partial pressure of solute above the effluent liquid. Values typically obtained in this manner are shown in Tables 5-3 and 5-4.

Table 5-3

K_Ga Values for Liquid-Film Controlled Systems

Gas Contaminant	Scrubbing Liquid	Overall K_Ga Value (lb-mol/h · ft³ · atm)
Carbon Dioxide	4% NaOH	1.5
Hydrogen Sulfide	4% NaOH	4.4
Sulfur Dioxide	Water	2.2
Hydrogen Cyanide	Water	4.4
Formaldehyde	Water	4.4
Chlorine	Water	3.4
Bromine	5% NaOH	3.7
Chlorine Dioxide	Water	4.4

Note: K_Ga values apply to #2 plastic Super Intalox® packing as a gas velocity of 3.5 ft/s and a liquid rate of 4 gpm/ft².

Table 5-4

K_Ga Values for Gas-film Controlled Systems

Gas Contaminant	Scrubbing Liquid	Overall K_Ga Value (lb-mol/h · ft³ · atm)
Hydrogen Chloride	Water	14
Hydrogen Fluoride	Water	6.0
Ammonia	Dilute Acid	13
Chlorine	8% NaOH	10.8
Sulfur Dioxide	11% Na₂CO₃	8.9

Note: K_Ga values apply to #2 plastic Super Intalox® packing at a gas velocity of 3.5 ft/s and a liquid rate of 4 gpm/ft².

In many fume scrubbing operations, water is the absorbent, so that x_i in Equation 5-6 is zero. If a large excess of scrubbing water is used, solute concentration in the liquid phase (x) approaches zero, and Hx_o in Equation 5-5 is negligible. In either case, the mass transfer driving force approaches a value of y_oP or y_iP, respectively. Thus, Equation 5-7 can be simplified to:

$$\Delta p_{LM} = P\left[\frac{y_i - y_o}{\ln(y_i/y_o)}\right] \tag{5-9}$$

When very low concentrations of solute are being removed from the gas phase, the solute transferred from the gas stream is:

$$N = G_m (y_i - y_o) \tag{5-10}$$

Equations 5-8, 5-9, and 5-10 may be combined to give:

$$G_m (y_i - y_o) = K_G a \, AZP \left[\frac{y_i - y_o}{\ln (y_i / y_o)} \right] \tag{5-11}$$

Equation 5-11 can be simplified to produce:

$$G_m = \frac{K_G a \, AZP}{\ln (y_i / y_o)} \tag{5-12}$$

and then rearranged to:

$$\ln (y_i / y_o) = \frac{K_G a \, AZP}{G_m} \tag{5-13}$$

A rapid design can be carried out using a graphical procedure developed by Foote [4]. A semi-log plot of solute removal efficiency at constant G_m/A gas rate per unit of column area can be made against the packed depth with $K_G a$ as the parameter.

The percent removal efficiency of contaminant is:

$$E = 100 \, (1 - y_o/y_i) \tag{5-14}$$

This graphical design procedure will apply to most fume scrubbers that operate at atmospheric pressure.

LIQUID-FILM-CONTROLLED SYSTEMS

For a liquid-film-controlled system, the effect of gas rate on the overall $K_G a$ value is small and will not significantly alter graphical calculations. The plots in Figures 5-1, 5-2, and 5-3 permit rapid determination of the packed height required for fume scrubbers in such systems. As can be seen, the packed depth necessary for a given solute removal efficiency becomes greater with increasing gas rate.

Liquid-film-controlled systems usually provide low $K_G a$ values that are less than 6 lb-mol/h · ft^3 · atm. Table 5-3 shows the comparative base $K_G a$ values for various systems [5]. These base values apply to a gas rate of 3.5 ft/s superficial velocity, a liquid irrigation rate of 4 gpm/ft^2, and atmospheric pressure operation. Values shown are for #2 plastic Super Intalox packing. The packed depth required for other sizes or types of tower packings is a function of the ratio: $K_G a$ value for #2 plastic Super Intalox packing to $K_G a$ value for the other packing. Table 5-5 gives relative $K_G a$ values for tower packings commonly used in fume scrubbers.

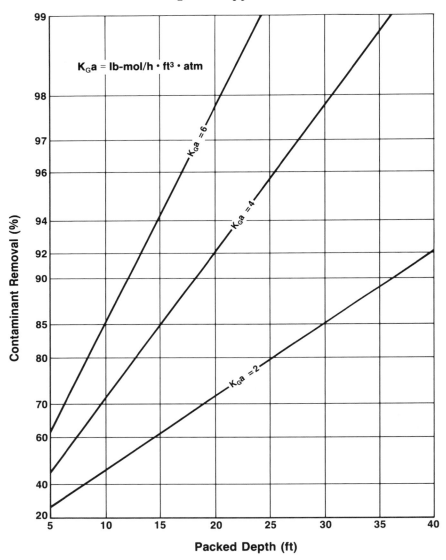

Figure 5-1. Packed depth requirements for liquid-film-controlled systems (3.5 ft/s gas rate). (From *1983 Equipment* [2]. Reprinted by permission from ASHRAE Handbook.)

Liquid flow rate has a significant effect on the overall K_Ga value. A doubling of the liquid irrigation rate typically will increase the overall K_Ga value by 23%. Table 5-6 gives the correction factor for the K_Ga value that applies to liquid rates other than the base value of 4 gpm/ft^2. The K_Ga

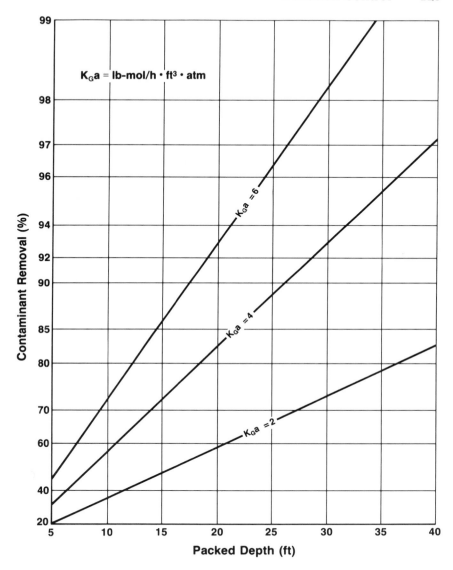

Figure 5-2. Packed depth requirements for liquid-film-controlled systems (5.0 ft/s gas rate). (From *1983 Equipment* [2]. Reprinted by permission from ASHRAE Handbook.)

values given in Table 5-3 are typical for liquid temperatures from 60° to 75°F. Higher liquid temperatures normally increase K_Ga values. However, a maximum rate of absorption may be achieved for the particular system. This occurs because at higher temperatures, the diffusion rate of the

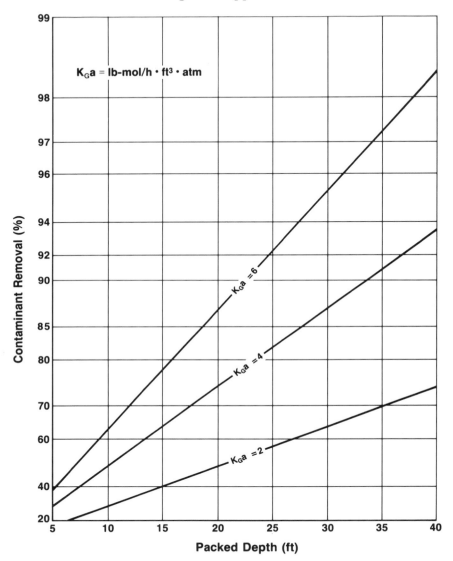

Figure 5-3. Packed depth requirements for liquid-film-controlled systems (6.5 ft/s gas rate). (From *1983 Equipment* [2]. Reprinted by permission from ASHRAE Handbook.)

solute dissolved in the liquid phase increases, but the solubility of a gaseous solute in the liquid phase usually decreases. Although the K_Ga value theoretically is independent of the driving force (Δp_{LM}), the effect of the solubility (m or H) is shown by Equation 3-11 (see Chapter 3).

Table 5-5

Relative K$_G$a Values for Tower Packings

Type of Packing	Size (in.)			
	1	1½	2	3 or 3½
Plastic Super Intalox® Saddles	1.49	—	1.00	0.63
Intalox® Snowflake® Packing	—	—	1.24	—
Metal Hy-Pak® Packing	1.52	1.28	1.08	0.76
Metal Pall Rings	1.62	1.32	1.13	0.65
Plastic Pall Rings	1.38	1.19	1.09	0.63
Ceramic Intalox® Saddles	1.46	1.19	0.99	0.57
Ceramic Raschig Rings	1.21	1.02	0.84	0.53
Plastic Tellerette Packing	1.52	—	1.38	1.18

GAS-FILM-CONTROLLED SYSTEMS

In a gas-film-controlled system, the effect of liquid rate on the overall K$_G$a value is essentially the same as for a liquid-film-controlled system, such as that shown in Table 5-6. In addition, in such a system the gas rate has a significant effect on the overall mass transfer coefficient. Similarly, Figures 5-4, 5-5, and 5-6 allow a rapid determination of the packed depth required for fume scrubbers in gas-film-controlled systems. In these plots, the overall K$_G$a value has been corrected for the effect of the gas flow rate. Because the K$_G$a value increases with an increasing gas flow rate, the solute removal efficiency drops only slightly for a fixed packed depth as the gas rate is increased in such a system.

Gas-film-controlled systems normally have higher K$_G$a values than liquid-film-controlled systems. Table 5-4 shows the base K$_G$a values for typical gas-film-controlled systems at 3.5 ft/s superficial gas velocity and 4 gpm/ft^2 liquid irrigation rate [5]. These values apply for #2 plastic Super Intalox packing and for liquid temperatures from 60° to 75°F. The packed depth required for other tower packings is a function of the ratio:

Table 5-6

Effect of Liquid Rate on Scrubber Efficiency

Liquid Rate (gpm/ft^2)	Relative K$_G$a Value
2.0	0.81
3.0	0.92
4.0	1.00
5.0	1.07
6.0	1.13
8.0	1.23
10.0	1.32

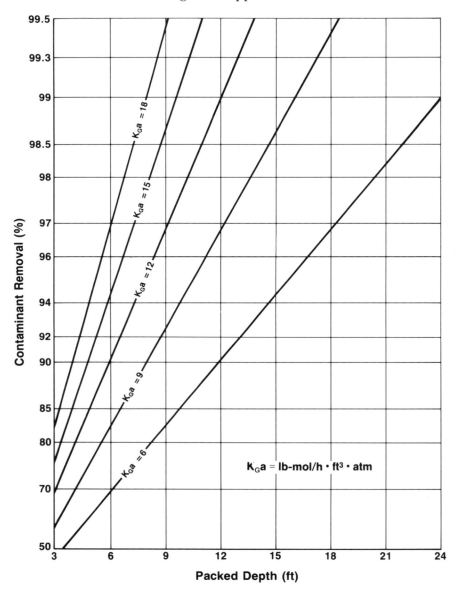

Figure 5-4. Packed depth requirements for gas-film-controlled systems (3.5 ft/s gas rate). (From *1983 Equipment* [2]. Reprinted by permission from ASHRAE Handbook.)

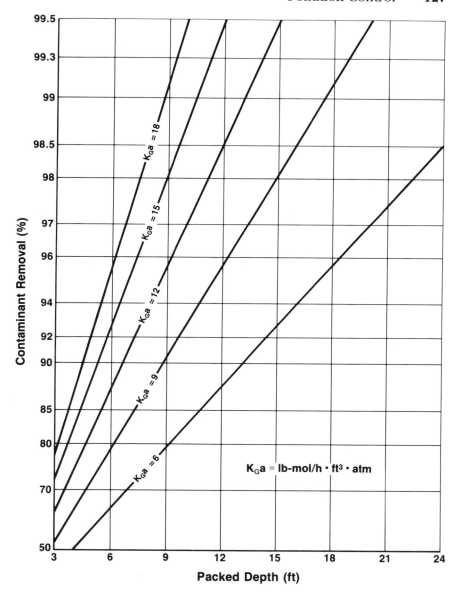

Figure 5-5. Packed depth requirements for gas-film-controlled systems (5.0 ft/s gas rate). (From *1983 Equipment* [2]. Reprinted by permission from ASHRAE Handbook.)

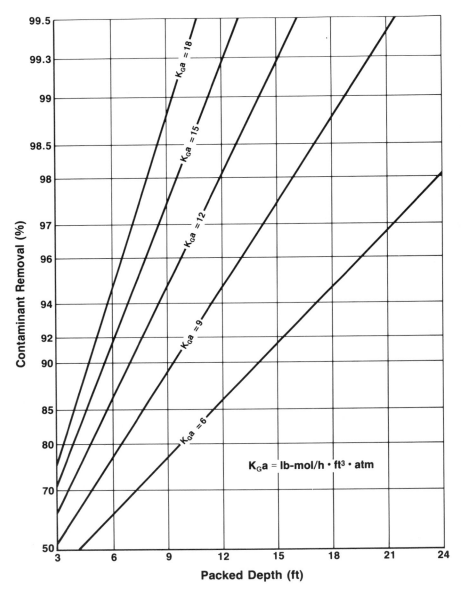

Figure 5-6. Packed depth requirements for gas-film-controlled systems (6.5 ft/s gas rate). (From *1983 Equipment* [2]. Reprinted by permission from ASHRAE Handbook.)

K_Ga value for #2 plastic Super Intalox packing to K_Ga value for the packing selected as shown in Table 5-5. The packed depth required also is inversely proportional to the relative K_Ga values corrected for liquid rate, as given in Table 5-6.

If the scrubbing liquid contains a chemical that reacts with the contaminant absorbed from the gas stream, at least 33% excess of this chemical over the amount theoretically required should be provided when determining the circulating liquid rate. Hydrogen chloride dissolved in water develops a negligible partial pressure of the contaminant when the solution has a concentration less than 8 wt% HCl. In this case, water is usually used as the scrubbing liquid. However, if ammonia is dissolved in water, there is an appreciable partial pressure of the contaminant above the resulting solution, even at 1 wt% NH_3 concentration. To use Figures 5-4, 5-5, and 5-6 in fume scrubber design for this system, the scrubbing liquid must contain enough dilute acid to keep the liquid phase pH below seven.

SCRUBBER SIZE DETERMINATION

To use Figures 5-1 through 5-6 in the design of a countercurrent scrubber, the column diameter first must be selected to fix the superficial gas velocity. Normal gas velocity varies between 5.0 and 8.0 ft/s for operations at atmospheric pressure using modern random packings. The maximum velocity should be limited to avoid entrainment and loss of the scrubbing liquid, even if the pressure drop is not excessive. Next, a convenient liquid irrigation rate between 2 and 8 gpm/ft^2 of column cross-sectional area is chosen. Most commercial scrubbers use liquid irrigation rates between 3 and 6 gpm/ft^2. However, the minimum liquid feed rate for scrubbing with water normally provides a solute concentration not greater than 0.002 mol fraction in the effluent liquid.

It is necessary to know the base K_Ga value for the solute to be removed by the scrubber. If experimental data or industrial experience is not available, the base K_Ga value should be selected from Tables 5-3 or 5-4 for the system that most closely resembles that under consideration. The percent removal efficiency is determined from the solute concentration in the inlet gas stream and the allowable concentration of that solute in the exit gas stream.

If the base K_Ga value for the system involved is less than 6.0 lb-mol/h $\cdot$ ft^3 $\cdot$ atm, Figures 5-1 through 5-3 usually apply. If the base K_Ga value is greater than 6.0 lb-mol/h $\cdot$ ft^3 $\cdot$ atm, Figures 5-4 through 5-6 normally should be used. The base K_Ga value chosen should be adjusted for the effect of liquid rate using the values shown in Table 5-6. The removal efficiency desired is located on the ordinate of Figures 5-1 through 5-6, and the packed depth required is read on the abscissa by interpolation between the parameters that enclose the adjusted K_Ga value.

The packed depth just determined applies for #2 plastic Super Intalox packing. For other types or sizes of tower packings this depth should be multiplied by the ratio: K_Ga for #2 plastic Super Intalox packing to K_Ga value for the packing selected as given in Table 5-5. This procedure is shown in detail in the illustrative problem at the end of this section.

If the packed depth just determined is excessive, the designer should increase the liquid rate and/or select a different tower packing. If the packed depth required still is too high, either the removal efficiency required must be reduced or two scrubbers should be operated in series.

After the initial design is fixed, the pressure drop should be calculated using Figure 1-15 or Figure 1-16 (see Chapter 1). The operating pressure drop should not exceed 0.60 in. H_2O/ft when water is used as the scrubbing liquid. When other liquids are used, the pressure drop normally is a maximum of 0.40 in. H_2O/ft, if the liquid specific gravity is at least 0.80. Some liquids containing dissolved salts or solid particulates tend to foam. This foaming of the liquid phase will be greater when the fume scrubber is operated at high pressure drops. For such foaming systems, the scrubber should be designed to produce a maximum pressure drop of 0.25 in. H_2O/ft of packed depth. If the calculated pressure drop for the scrubber exceeds the allowable value, then the design procedure must be repeated using a larger diameter column or a different tower packing.

OTHER DESIGN CONSIDERATIONS

One major cost of operation of a fume scrubber usually is the power required for the fan to move the gas stream. Moderate gas flows are conveniently handled by centrifugal blowers. Such systems commonly are designed for a maximum pressure drop of 6 in. of water for the scrubber, including the ductwork. Where large volumes of gas are handled, axial fans normally are used [6]. Because of fan pressure limitations, the overall pressure drop through such a system usually is designed to be a maximum 4 in. of water. The blower or fan commonly is located following the fume scrubber. This location protects the fan from severe corrosion by chemical fumes or erosion by solid particulates. However, such a location means that the fan will be handling a gas stream that is saturated with water vapor. The fan discharge should be designed to prevent any condensed water being returned to this fan.

It must be remembered that a fume scrubber merely removes a contaminant from a gas stream but does not destroy it. The scrubber liquid effluent will contain all of these scrubbed contaminants; thus, it will present a water pollution potential [7]. Particulates can be settled, or filtered, out of this discharged liquid for recovery or sludge disposal. Chemical

Figure 5-7. Fume scrubber fabricated of FRP.

contaminants must be neutralized, or otherwise reacted, to render them non-contaminating to surface water.

SO_2 SCRUBBING

One of the largest sources of air pollution is the SO_2 present in the flue gas produced by the combustion of fuels containing sulfur. In the United

States, the 1990 Clean Air Act requires reduction of SO_2 emissions from fuel combustion by 60% overall. Thus, flue gas desulfurization systems will represent large capital expenditures and operating costs for many utilities and manufacturing plants.

Packed columns provide a highly efficient wet-scrubber for SO_2 removal. Normally, any particulate in the flue gas will be removed using an electrostatic precipitator or Venturi scrubber prior to SO_2 removal. Generally, wet scrubbing systems can be separated into three categories as follows:

1. Simple alkaline scrubbing using slaked lime slurry, dilute caustic soda, or soda ash solution.
2. Dual alkaline scrubbing using a lime-regenerated sodium salt solution.
3. Regenerative processes in which the sulfur is recovered as a saleable by-product.

In simple alkaline scrubbing, a large portion of the liquid is recycled. When lime or limestone slurries are used as the scrubbing liquid, insoluble calcium sulfite and calcium sulfate are produced. The effluent from the scrubber must be settled, so that clarified liquid is returned to the scrubber. The solids removed then are sent to a landfill. When sodium hydroxide or soda ash solutions are used as the scrubbing liquid, soluble sodium sulfite and sodium sulfate are produced. A part of the scrubbing solution is withdrawn to purge these salts from the system before addition of more alkali to the scrubber feed. Thus, a large quantity of purged liquid waste must be treated before disposal.

In the dual-alkali process, a recycled alkaline solution of sodium salts is the scrubbing liquid. The scrubber effluent is treated with slaked lime to precipitate insoluble calcium sulfite and calcium sulfate, while regenerating the alkalinity of the solution. Then, the calcium salts are thickened and filtered from the recycled solution. This system requires only a small make-up of sodium alkali and produces a smaller amount of solids for disposal than a simple lime scrubbing system.

Although it is possible to convert the SO_2 removed from the flue gas to ammonium sulfate, sodium sulfate, or gypsum, the market for such by-products is quite restricted. More recently, interest has centered on processes that recover the SO_2 in concentrated form. One such system, the Wellman Lord Process (licensed by Davy-McKee/Davy Corp. Plc.) uses a solution of sodium or potassium sulfite to absorb SO_2. The liquid effluent contains a mixture of sulfites and bisulfites from which the less soluble bisulfites are crystallized. The recovered solids are heated to decompose the bisulfites to sulfites with the release of SO_2. These sulfites then are redissolved in the liquid recycled to the scrubber. Only a small quantity of sodium or potassium carbonate is required to make up for losses as sulfates formed by oxidizing the sulfite salts.

Because of the fan power required to move large volumes of flue gas through the scrubbing system, pressure drop is extremely important. While spray towers have low pressure drop, their efficiency is too low to meet a minimum of 90% SO_2 removal typically specified. Either countercurrent or cross-flow packed scrubbers will provide a low pressure drop while meeting the SO_2 removal required. Typically, a large size packing is used to minimize the cross-sectional area needed. Plastic packing is preferred; however, the inlet gas stream must be cooled to avoid distortion of such packing. Normally, these systems for utilities consist of a number of parallel modules plus a spare module, so as to assure achieving the 99.5% on-stream factor demanded.

From Table 5-4, it can be seen that the mass transfer coefficient for absorption of SO_2 into an alkaline solution is quite high. As an example, we will consider the scrubbing of a flue gas stream using a dual-alkali system. The gas entering the scrubber has a mol weight of 29.2 and contains 2,800 ppm by volume SO_2. Because the exit gas is to contain no more than 200 ppm by volume SO_2, the scrubber must be designed for 93% SO_2 removal. For 1,000,000 SCFH (60°F and 1 atm) of flue gas, 6.87 lb-mol/h of SO_2 must be absorbed in this scrubber. Using a 7-ft 0-in. ID scrubber, with the entering gas at 150°F and 15.0 psia, the inlet gas velocity will be 8.3 ft/s. We will operate with a liquid recycle of 230 gpm so that the K_Ga value for #3 plastic Super Intalox packing will be 12.1 lb-mol/h · ft^3 · atm. Thus, a 15-ft 0-in. deep packed bed is required giving a pressure drop of only 5.4 in. H_2O for the entire scrubber.

All wet scrubbing systems produce an exit gas stream that has been cooled and saturated with water. Usually, this exit gas must be reheated to reduce its density, thereby providing sufficient buoyancy for atmospheric dispersal.

NOx REMOVAL

A special design procedure is necessary for fume scrubbers intended to remove NOx from gas streams. The contaminant usually is a mixture of NO, NO_2 together with its dimer N_2O_4, and N_2O_5. NO is a relatively insoluble gas. It must be oxidized to NO_2 before it becomes soluble in water and allows effective absorption. The N_2O_5 is readily soluble in water to produce a nitric acid solution.

When NO_2 is dissolved in water, two-thirds of the mols react with water to form nitric acid. However, the other one-third of the mols are desorbed into the gas stream as NO:

$$3NO_2 + H_2O = 2HNO_3 + NO \hspace{3cm} (5\text{-}15)$$

The by-product, NO, then must be oxidized to NO_2 for it to be reabsorbed. Because this oxidation reaction in the gas phase is time dependent, NO_2 removal efficiency usually is limited to about 80% in a single fume scrubber when water is the scrubbing liquid.

When sodium hydroxide solutions are used for scrubbing NO_2, the resultant reaction produces equal mols of sodium nitrate and sodium nitrite:

$$2NO_2 + 2NaOH = NaNO_3 + NaNO_2 + H_2O \hspace{2cm} (5\text{-}16)$$

The NO_2 first must be absorbed by the water into the liquid film before it can react with the caustic. In such a liquid phase, two competing reactions take place: NO_2 with water and NO_2 with NaOH. If the NaOH concentration in the liquid film is deficient, NO gas is released back into the gas phase in accordance with Equation 5-15. The diffusion rate of NaOH into the liquid film is a function of the liquid-phase solution concentration. For this system, 3 normal (12 wt%) NaOH seems to provide optimum absorption efficiency. Higher solution concentrations are less effective because the associated greater liquid viscosity retards the diffusion rate of the NaOH, as well as the products of reaction.

Equations have been developed to predict the efficiency of NO_2 removal based on experience over many years with ceramic saddle-type packings. NO_2 removal efficiency, as defined by Equation 5-14, can be related to the gas retention time (i.e., the depth of the packed bed divided by the superficial gas velocity). Empirically, suitable designs for such scrubbers employing water as the liquid phase are produced using:

$$\ln\left[\frac{y_o}{y_i}\right] = -0.734 \ln\left[\frac{Z}{V}\right] - 0.141 \hspace{2cm} (5\text{-}17)$$

This relationship seems to apply as long as the NO_2 concentration in the exit gas (y_o) is not less than 200 ppm by volume. Such scrubbers usually use a 1-in. or 1½-in. size tower packing and employ a liquid irrigation rate of at least 4 gpm/ft^2.

Where an NaOH solution is used as the scrubbing liquid, the removal efficiency for NO_2 is substantially increased as compared to water scrubbing according to:

$$\ln\left[\frac{y_o}{y_i}\right] = -0.736 \frac{Z}{V} - 0.130 \hspace{2cm} (5\text{-}18)$$

Normally, these scrubbers are operated in a batch mode with respect to the liquid phase. A 12 wt% NaOH solution will be charged to the system and recirculated until there is 2 wt% free NaOH remaining. Equation 5-18 gives the average removal efficiency over one liquid batch. Initially the NO_2 removal efficiency is higher, then efficiency deteriorates as the free NaOH concentration becomes lower. Such scrubbers usually use a 2-in. size packing and a liquid recirculation rate of about 6 gpm/ft^2. However, the liquid circulation rate must be sufficient to provide at least 133% of the NaOH theoretically required to combine with the NO_2 in the gas stream at the lowest NaOH concentration (the end of the batch).

Usually the gas stream entering the scrubber contains other oxides of nitrogen in addition to NO_2. Any residual NO in the gas stream leaving the scrubber tends to oxidize on mixing with the outside air. A colorless exit stack cannot be assured by the use of simple liquid scrubbing of a gas stream containing NOx contaminants.

To meet increasing stringent regulations, Selective Catalytic Reduction of nitrogen oxides with ammonia is gaining favor where low NOx levels are required in the discharge. Such systems give removal efficiencies of 90% or greater with a pressure drop not exceeding 5-in. of water. Lim *et al.* discuss the problems of NOx production during the combustion of fuels [8]. These authors describe the use of Norton's NC-300® zeolite catalyst for reduction of NO and NO_2 using ammonia.

ORGANIC VAPOR CONTROL

Organic chemicals accounted for 80% of the toxic air releases in the United States in 1988 [9]. The most common methods for controlling such releases are incineration, adsorption, condensation, and absorption. Incineration is capable of handling even low concentrations of organic materials; however, the energy requirement per lb. of organic destroyed can be quite large. However, in recent years, progress has been made in heat recovery using ceramic Intalox saddle packing as a heat sink. Condensation also consumes a large amount of energy and is not efficient except for high concentrations of organics in the gas stream (i.e., at least 5,000 ppm by vol.). Carbon adsorption and absorption into a non-volatile solvent normally are selected where the concentration of organic materials is at least 1,000 ppm by vol, because such processes permit recovery of these organics.

Packed absorbers can remove over 95% of the entering organic vapors by contacting the gas stream with a solvent. This solvent should have a low vapor pressure to prevent its loss by evaporation and must be inert to the organic solutes being absorbed. Because many gas streams to be treated contain water vapor, the solvent must tolerate both water and the organic solutes without forming two liquid phases.

The absorption system consists of a packed absorber operating at the gas stream pressure and a solvent stripper. The lean solvent is fed to the absorber at as low a temperature as practical in order to minimize solute vapor pressure, as well as solvent losses. Due to the high boiling point of the solvent, regeneration usually is accomplished under vacuum. The rich solvent from the absorber is heated and then flashed under a reduced pressure to liberate the solute in vapor form. This solute vapor is condensed, and the lean solvent is cooled and recycled to the absorber.

The solvent circulation rate is selected so as to keep the vapor pressure of the solute above the rich solvent below the partial pressure of that solute in the entering gas stream. Obviously, this liquid rate should be sufficient to provide good wetting of the packing based on the column cross-sectional area required to handle the gas flow. The concentration of solute in the lean solvent will control the loss of solute in the exit gas stream from the absorber. The solute concentration in the lean solvent is determined by an equilibrium flash in the stripper; therefore, the stripper pressure should be fixed to provide the desired solute recovery efficiency.

If more than one organic material is to be absorbed, the analysis of the complete range of these organics should be separated into groups having atmospheric boiling points no different than 35°F. A characteristic material should be chosen for each group. The vapor pressure of each typical material at various low concentrations in the solvent to be used should be measured for at least three temperatures. This data is required to determine the equilibrium values for the absorber as well as for the stripper needed to regenerate the lean solvent.

ODOR CONTROL

Some contaminants in a gas stream are neither chemical pollutants nor objectionable particulates. They are malodorous materials that are considered a nuisance if vented into the atmosphere. The maximum desired atmospheric level of a malodorous substance is defined as that concentration just below the threshold of detection by 50% of an odor panel. Table 5-7 gives this detection limit for many common malodorous substances [10]. Note that many substances can be sensed by the olfactory nerves at levels below one part per billion. For instance, hydrogen sulfide can be detected to one fifth of one ppb, while butyric acid (the principal odor from rancid butter) can be detected to one half of one ppb.

Countercurrently operated packed scrubbers are one method for controlling malodorous emissions. A wet scrubber absorbs the malodorous material into the liquid phase; however, many of these substances have limited solubility in water. If the scrubber operates with a once-through water flow, the effluent liquid may be a source of water pollu-

Table 5-7

Odor Threshold for Common Materials

Chemical Compound	50% Threshold (ppb by vol)
Acetaldehyde	210
Acetic Acid	210
Acrolein	100
Benzyl Chloride	10
Butyric Acid	0.5
Carbon Disulfide	100
p-Cresol	0.5
Dimethyl Amine	21
Dimethyl Sulfide	1
Ethyl Acrylate	0.1
Ethyl Mercaptan	0.5
Formaldehyde	1000
Hydrogen Sulfide	0.2
Methyl Mercaptan	1
Monochlorbenzene	210
Nitrobenzene	4.7
Phenol	21
Phosgene	470
Pyridine	10
Styrene	47
Sulfur Dioxide	470
Toluene Diisocyanate	210
Trimethyl Amine	0.2

tion as the malodorous substance in the effluent liquid is desorbed into the surrounding atmosphere. If the scrubbing liquid is recirculated over the scrubber packing, the exit gas stream is limited to a contaminant concentration in equilibrium with this entering liquid.

For effective odor control, normally there is a chemically reactive compound added to the scrubbing liquid that converts the absorbed contaminant into a less objectionable substance. Hydrogen sulfide, for instance, can be absorbed by a solution of sodium hydroxide in which it is quite soluble. This is due to a chemical reaction with the absorbed solute that forms a stable sulfide. There are only a few inorganic odorous substances such as sulfur dioxide, hydrogen chloride, nitric oxide, hydrogen sulfide, hydrogen cyanide, ozone, chlorine, and ammonia. Removing such contaminants by absorption has been practiced for some time; however, it is becoming increasingly difficult to dispose of the spent scrubbing liquid. For economical reasons in large-capacity systems, the reactive absorbent may be regenerated. Thus, H_2S absorbed into an alkaline solution can be oxidized to elemental sulfur. Then the sulfur can be recovered and the scrubbing liquid recycled.

Removal of organic odors is a much more complex problem. Wet scrubbing using a combination of absorbent and oxidant has successfully reduced such odors [11]. The malodorous substance first is absorbed into the liquid phase; then the oxidant converts the absorbed contaminant to a less odorous substance. This sequence eliminates the normal Henry's Law vapor pressure that would be exhibited if the malodorous material simply were absorbed into water.

The four most popular oxidants used in the liquid phase are potassium permanganate, sodium hypochlorite, hydrogen peroxide, and chlorine dioxide. These oxidants represent an operating expense; thus, it is important to minimize their consumption. Many gas streams to be treated contain large amounts of organic particulates in addition to the malodorous constituents. Pretreatment of such gas streams to remove the non-odorous material is recommended in order to avoid excessive oxidant requirements. The operation of odor control systems requires careful control of the oxidant concentration as well as the solution pH. Degradation products also must be purged from the solution to prevent their build-up.

Table 5-8 gives some successful applications of this technique as applied to a variety of industrial odors. Such scrubber designs normally use a plastic packing, such as #1 or #2 Super Intalox packing. This type of packing presents a large surface area for malodorous material absorption and provides a high liquid residence time for oxidation of the absorbed contaminant. Typically, the tower diameter is selected to produce a superficial air velocity from 4.8 to 6.6 ft/s. The liquid circulation rate usually will be 11 to 19 gpm per 1,000 cfm of air flow. Packed-bed depth normally varies from 8 ft to 11 ft. An effective entrainment elim-

Table 5-8

Typical Odor Control Applications

Industry	Contaminant	Absorbent	Oxidant
Brass Foundry	phenolic resin	Na_2CO_3	$KMnO_4$
Varnish Plant	alkyd resin	NaOH	$KMnO_4$
Iron Foundry	amines	$NaHSO_4$	$KMnO_4$
Silver Plating	cyanides	NaOH	NaOCl
Food Processing	vegetable oil	$Na_2B_4O_7$	$KMnO_4$
Pulp Mill	organic sulfides	H_2SO_4	ClO_2
Hardboard Mfg.	linseed oil	NaOH	$KMnO_4$
Rendering	ham fat	NaOH	NaOCl

inator should be installed in the top of the scrubber to prevent the loss
of costly chemical solution in the outlet gas stream.

EXAMPLE PROBLEM—GAS SCRUBBING

An industrial wastewater treatment unit is ventilated at an air flow of
25,800 cfm at atmospheric pressure and a temperature of 65°F. The inlet
air stream contains 50 ppm by vol HCHO that is to be absorbed into water.
The exhaust air is to contain a time-weighted average of 2 ppm by vol maximum HCHO concentration. A scrubber design is needed that does not
require more than 4-in. H_2O total pressure drop.

For such a large size scrubber, a liquid irrigation rate of 6 gpm/ft² has
been selected. To keep the scrubber shell height reasonable, a 1½-in. size
plastic Pall ring packing will be used. From Table 5-3, the base K_Ga
value for this absorption system is 4.4 lb-mol/h · ft³ atm. This K_Ga value
must be adjusted for the higher liquid circulation rate based on the factor from Table 5-6.

$$K_Ga = \frac{1.13}{1.00}(4.4) = 5.0\,lb - mol/h \cdot ft^3 \cdot atm \qquad (5\text{-}A)$$

Because this is a liquid-film-controlled system, the small gas rate effect
is not significant in these graphical calculations. Using Figure 5-2, the
packed depth required for 96% HCHO removal at a gas rate of 5.0 ft/s
is 30.2 ft for #2 plastic Super Intalox packing. For the 1½-in. plastic Pall
rings, the bed depth can be corrected by factors taken from Table 5-5.

$$Z = \frac{1.00}{1.19}(30.2) = 25.4\,ft \qquad (5\text{-}B)$$

At 5.0 ft/s gas rate, the scrubber cross-sectional area required is 86.0
ft², so a 10-ft 6-in. ID tower will be specified. At 6 gpm/ft² liquid irrigation rate, the water feed flow is 520 gpm.

Next the pressure drop through the packed bed selected will be
checked. Gas density is 0.0757 lb/ft³ and the liquid density is 62.3 lb/ft³.
The flow parameter is:

$$X = \frac{259,800}{117,200}\left[\frac{0.0757}{62.3}\right]^{0.5} = 0.0773 \qquad (5\text{-}C)$$

The gas mass velocity in a 10-ft 6-in. ID tower gives a C_s value of 0.173
ft/s. The ordinate value for Figure 1-16 is 1.10. From this figure the pressure drop is 0.34 in. H_2O/ft for 1½-in. plastic Pall rings. The pressure drop
through the 25.4 ft packed depth is 8.6 in. H_2O total.

This pressure drop exceeds the allowable value; therefore, the gas rate
will be lowered to 3.5 ft/s. Referring to Figure 5-1, the packed depth

required is 21.2 ft of #2 plastic Super Intalox packing for 96% HCHO removal. A 17.8-ft depth of 1½-in. plastic Pall rings will be used based on the adjustment of packed depth from Table 5-5.

The air flow still will be 117,200 lb/h, but the liquid circulation rate increases to 740 gpm. This maintains the 6.0 gpm/ft² irrigation rate for a column diameter that has now been increased to 12-ft 6-in. ID. The new flow parameter is:

$$X = \frac{369,800}{117,200}\left[\frac{0.0757}{62.3}\right]^{0.5} = 0.110 \qquad (5\text{-}D)$$

The gas mass velocity has now been reduced giving a C_s of 0.122 ft/s. The ordinate value for Figure 1-16 is 0.77, which gives a pressure drop of 0.16 in. H_2O/ft. The pressure drop through a 17.8 ft bed of 1½-in. plastic Pall rings would be only 2.8 in. H_2O total.

Because the pressure drop is lower than necessary, the column diameter can be reduced slightly. The final design for this scrubber specifies a 12-ft 0-in. ID tower with a 19-ft 4-in. deep bed of 1½-in. plastic Pall rings. The liquid circulation rate is 680 gpm, and the pressure drop through the packing is only 3.6 in. H_2O total. This means that the tower internals can have a pressure drop of 0.4 in. H_2O, and the scrubber still will meet the original specifications.

WATER PURIFICATION

Since the early 1950s there has been concern regarding the effects of industrial liquid wastes discharged into rivers and lakes. In these earlier days most attention was focused on discharges of inorganic chemicals from metal-working processes such as steel mill pickling liquor and metal plating solutions. Such wastes were not treatable by, and reduced the efficiency of, conventional activated sludge sewage treatment plants.

Compounding the liquid waste problem was the fact that many municipal waste treatment plants were severely overloaded. As a result, raw sewage was bypassed, or only partially treated, in quite a few metropolitan areas. Further, industrial wastes with high BOD characteristics were discharged into city sewers by processors of food products (i.e., dairies, meat packers, and breweries) and oil refineries, causing overloading of existing facilities. Several European countries began to regulate liquid waste discharges before the United States. However, by the mid 1970s, the Environmental Protection Agency had become active in the control of such discharges.

POTABLE WATER STRIPPING

Chlorinated hydrocarbons frequently have been found in ground and surface drinking water supplies across the United States. In 1979 the EPA proposed maximum concentration limits for trihalomethanes in drinking water. Table 5-9 lists some of the chlorinated hydrocarbons commonly found in well water, as well as typical concentrations present. The Henry's Law constant for these compounds in water at 68°F also is given in this table [12].

Table 5-9

Chlorinated Solvent Well Water Contaminants

Compound	Concentration (µg/l)	H @ 68°F (atm/mol fraction)
Carbon Tetrachloride	20	1,290
Chloroform	180	170
1, 1 Dichloroethane	50	250
cis 1,2 Dichloroethylene	270	360
1,4 Dichlorobenzene		190
Methyl Chloride	120	480
Perchloroethylene	110	1,100
1,1,1 Trichloroethane	190	400
Trichloroethylene	60	550
Vinyl Chloride		355,000

Because of their low solubility in water (high value of Henry's Law constant), chlorinated hydrocarbons can be stripped from water using atmospheric air. Studies were carried out on air stripping by the EPA using packed columns [13, 14]. Much of this early data was developed using 1-in. size plastic saddle-type packings. As a result of such studies, large scale installations were designed. It soon became apparent that the 1-in. size packing was not economical for use in such large systems. Not only were the column diameters quite sizable due to the low capacity of such size packings, but the pressure drop from a packing factor of 40 produced a high fan horsepower requirement.

Because a large market was envisioned for tower packings in such applications, new packing shapes, such as Norton's Intalox Snowflake packing, were developed. This packing (shown in Figure 5-8) has a packing factor of only 13; thus, pressure drop is lower than that which would be produced by #3 plastic Super Intalox packing or 3½-in. plastic Pall ring packing. However, the mass transfer efficiency of Intalox Snowflake packing is similar to that of the 1½-in. size plastic Pall ring; thus, its use will allow practical bed depths. (See Table 3-4.)

Figure 5-8. Intalox® Snowflake® tower packing (plastic). (Courtesy of Norton Chemical Process Products Corporation.)

POTABLE WATER STRIPPER DESIGN

Air-stripping of water is a liquid-film-controlled mass transfer operation. First, it is necessary to select the air-to-water ratio so that the stripping factor can be calculated. Usually 350 to 750 SCFM of air is used per 100 gpm of water feed. The stripping factor is given by Equation 5-19 using the molar flows of air and water.

$$S^* = \frac{mG_m}{L_m} \qquad (5\text{-}19)$$

The Henry's Law constant can be used to express the equilibrium relationship between the gas and liquid phases because the pressure of both phases is the same, and the air leaving will be at almost the same temperature as the water entering the stripper [15].

$$m = \frac{H}{P} \qquad (5\text{-}20)$$

The number of transfer units required can be determined from Equation 5-21 using the inlet and outlet solute concentrations.

$$N_{OL} = \frac{S*}{S* - 1} \ln\left[\frac{(S* - 1)(x_i/x_o) + 1}{S*}\right]$$
(5-21)

Because of variations in the Henry's Law constant, and the VOC concentrations, the number of transfer units required should be determined for each solute present. The largest number of transfer units so calculated should be specified, because tests show that there is no effect of other organics being present [16]. Equation 5-21 assumes that the stripping gas contains no solute vapor.

For example, if we wish to strip trichlorethylene out of water at 68°F from an inlet concentration of 100 ppm by wt. to an outlet concentration of 10 ppb by wt. with H = 550 atm/mol fraction, the required N_{OL} is 9.9 transfer units using 400 SCFM of air per 100 gpm of water. If the solute is changed to perchlorethylene, with H twice as great (1100 atm/mol fraction), N_{OL} needed is reduced to 9.5 transfer units with the same air/water ratio and concentration range. If the air rate for TCE stripping is increased to 600 SCFM per 100 gpm of water, N_{OL} is lowered from 9.9 to 9.6 transfer units. However, if the air rate is reduced to 270 SCFM per 100 gpm of water, N_{OL} is increased to 10.2 transfer units for the same concentration range. The number of transfer units required has changed only slightly with the variation of gas-to-liquid ratio of 2.2 times for TCE stripping. Thus, the addition of one more transfer unit of packed depth can significantly reduce the air required for stripping through the same concentration range.

Again using Equation 5-21, if TCE is stripped using 400 SCFM of air per 100 gpm of water from an inlet concentration of 100 ppm by wt. to an outlet concentration of 25 ppb by wt., N_{OL} needed is only 8.9 transfer units. If the outlet concentration is to be reduced to 4 ppb by wt., N_{OL} increases to 10.9 transfer units with all other factors the same. From the above calculations it is apparent that specifying the proper concentration range for stripping should be done prudently, due to its significant effect on the total depth of tower packing needed.

Because of the relatively small air flow, the column diameter normally will be selected to provide a liquid irrigation rate between 15 and 40 gpm/ft². Next, the height of a transfer unit must be determined for the tower packing chosen. It has been found that the mass transfer coefficients for stripping trichlorethylene, perchlorethylene, chloroform, and carbon tetrachloride are the same [17]. The H_{OL} for #1 and #2 plastic Super Intalox packing is 3.2-ft and 4.7-ft, respectively, at a liquid rate of 30 gpm/ft². Tests conducted by the EPA in 1984 (stripping aromatics from water) and in 1987 (stripping TCE and PCE from water) indicate that H_{OL} varies as the liquid irrigation rate to the 0.24 power. This variation of H_{OL} with liquid rate is the same as for water deaeration and decarbonation (see Chapter 4).

Considering the number of transfer units normally required, a low value of H_{OL} is desirable. However, small size packings that provide low H_{OL} values have high packing factors that give rise to high pressure drops. Therefore, tests were performed at the University of Texas to evaluate Intalox Snowflake packing for air stripping TCE from water. This newer type of packing gave an H_{OL} value of only 3.0 ft at a liquid rate of 30 gpm/ft². A part of this increase in stripping efficiency for the University of Texas data may be due to the lack of attention given the liquid distribution systems in the previous EPA tests. (See Chapter 10 for a discussion of this effect.) Thus, in the first illustration of TCE stripping, the 9.9 transfer units could be supplied by use of a 30-ft-deep bed of Intalox Snowflake packing.

Because VOC stripping is highly liquid-film controlled, the value of H_{OL} will increase about 6% if the feed water temperature is lowered from 68° to 50°F. However, the impact of temperature is much more pronounced on the Henry's Law constant. Its value would be reduced by 40% on average for the compounds given in Table 5-9 at 50°F water temperature.

WASTEWATER STRIPPING

Volatile organic compounds are present in varying amounts in most water discharges. Thibodeaux proposed that volatile organics could be removed effectively from industrial wastewater by air stripping in a packed column [18]. Of course, steam stripping or adsorption on activated carbon also can be used to remove organic solvents from aqueous discharges. However, if the organic compound is only slightly soluble in water and has a reasonable vapor pressure (atmospheric boiling point less than 330°F), air stripping may provide the least expensive method for removing it from water discharges.

Because benzene is a known carcinogen, contamination of water by aromatic compounds is a major concern. As shown in Table 5-10, the Henry's Law constants for aromatic solvents are high enough to suggest that they can be removed from water by air stripping [19]. When considering air stripping of waste water, it is suggested that a test be run on the liquid to be treated using the method developed by Thibodeaux to determine whether there exists some concentration below which the compound may be unstrippable.

The theoretical minimum air requirement at equilibrium to strip aromatic-contaminated water can be calculated from the Henry's Law constant. Thus, at 68°F benzene stripping requires 69 SCFM of air, toluene

Table 5-10

Henry's Law Constant for Aromatic Compounds

Compound	H @ 68°F (atm/mol fraction)
Benzene	240
Ethyl Benzene	350
Styrene	115
Toluene	280
1,2,4 Trimethyl Benzene	260
m-xylene	290
o-xylene	200
p-xylene	260

stripping requires 60 SCFM of air, while ethyl benzene stripping requires only 48 SCFM of air for 100 gpm of liquid. Of course, many times, the theoretical minimum air requirement normally is specified. Dispersal of aromatic-containing air into the atmosphere may not be permitted under air quality regulations. If such is the case, the exit air will require treatment to destroy the organic compounds. This air discharge could be sent to a boiler, an incinerator, or a catalytic oxidizer. Under these conditions, the stripping column should be designed to minimize the air usage.

WASTEWATER STRIPPER DESIGN

As with potable water stripping, the air-to-water ratio must be selected so that the stripping factor can be determined, using Equations 5-19 and 5-20. Next, the inlet and outlet concentrations of solute must be specified so that the number of transfer units required may be calculated from Equation 5-21. Again, the number of transfer units needed should be calculated separately for each solute present and the largest value of N_{OL} used for column sizing.

Tests conducted by the EPA in 1984 (stripping aromatics from gasoline-contaminated water) gave the same H_{OL} values for 1-in. size plastic saddle-type packings as the tests conducted in 1987 (stripping TCE and PCE from ground water). Further, the variation of H_{OL} with liquid irrigation rates was practically the same for both tests. Thus, the H_{OL} value used for fixing the packed depth needed for aromatics stripping can be the same as given in the discussion of potable water stripper design.

As an illustration, consider stripping 90 gpm of aqueous effluent containing 140 ppm by wt. ethyl benzene to effect 99.9% removal. This liquid steam is at a temperature of 140°F, so that the Henry's Law constant for ethyl benzene will be increased above the value given in Table 5-10.

Because the inlet air is only at a temperature of 64°F, the liquid will be cooled during this stripping operation.

We will select 21 SCFM of air to strip each 1 gpm of water; therefore, the air flow to the column will be 1,890 SCFM. Based on the inlet air having 80% relative humidity and the exit air leaving saturated with water vapor at 140°F maximum temperature, the liquid effluent temperature will be 108°F by heat balance. The Henry's Law constants are 1,740 atm/mol fraction for the feed liquid and 840 atm/mol fraction for the effluent liquid. The stripping factors from Equation 5-19 at atmospheric pressure are 113 at the column bottom and 278 at the column top. To produce a 0.14 ppm by wt. ethyl benzene effluent will require an average of 6.95 transfer units.

Because the bed depth will not be excessive, #2 plastic Super Intalox packing has been selected for this stripping column. Because of the large amount of water evaporated from the 140°F feed liquid, the vapor rate at the top of the column is greater than at the bottom. A 36-in. ID tower is needed to restrict the pressure drop to a maximum of 0.40 in. H_2O/ft. At the operating liquid rate of 12.5 gpm/ft^2, we should obtain a 3.81 ft H_{OL} value; thus, a 26.5 ft depth of packing is required. As the exit air contains almost 20% water vapor, if this gas stream is to be incinerated, a gas cooler/condenser may be desired to reduce the water content of the gas.

EXAMPLE PROBLEM—VOC STRIPPING

It is desired to strip chlorinated hydrocarbons from 2,700 gpm of water that is at a temperature of 50°F. The principal contaminant is 890 ppb by wt. trichloroethylene, which must be reduced to 8 ppb by wt. The stripping air is at a temperature of 55°F and 65% relative humidity; therefore, little change in water temperature will occur during stripping. In order to minimize fan horsepower requirement, which will provide a low operating cost, Intalox Snowflake packing will be used.

Because tests have been run on Intalox Snowflake packing in TCE stripping at liquid rates as high as 42.2 gpm/ft^2, we will consider a minimum 9-ft 0-in. ID column size. At 50°F, the Henry's Law constant for TCE will be 330 atm/mol fraction. First, we will evaluate stripping using 400 SCFM of air per 100 gpm water, which gives a gas velocity of 3.0 ft/s in a 9-ft 0-in. ID tower. As an alternate, we will consider a 9-ft 6-in. ID column using 600 SCFM of air per 100 gpm of water, which gives a gas velocity of 4.0 ft/s. From Equations 5-19 and 5-20, the stripping factors will be 7.94 for the 9-ft 0-in. ID tower, and 11.91 for the 9-ft 6-in. ID tower. Using Equation 5-21, the number of transfer units required is 5.24 for the 9-ft 0-in. ID tower and 5.05 for the 9-ft 6-in. ID tower. Thus, increasing the air-to-water ratio by 50% only reduces the number of transfer units required by 3.6%.

The 9-ft 0-in. ID tower at a liquid irrigation rate of 42.4 gpm/ft^2 will produce a H_{OL} value of 3.26 ft for Intalox Snowflake packing. The 9-ft 6-in. ID tower operating at a lower liquid rate of 38.1 gpm ft^2 will give an H_{OL} value of 3.18 ft. Thus, the 9-ft 0-in. ID column needs a 17.1 ft deep packed bed, while the 9-ft 6-in. ID column requires only a 16.1 ft deep bed. Using a packing factor of 13, the Generalized Pressure Drop Correlation (see Chapter 1) shows a pressure drop of 0.068 in. H$_2$O/ft for the 9-ft 0-in. ID tower, and 0.114 in. H$_2$O/ft for the 9-ft 6-in. ID tower. The overall pressure drop for the 9-ft 0-in. ID tower will be only 1.8 in. H$_2$O, while the overall pressure drop for the 9-ft 6-in. ID tower will be 2.5 in. H$_2$O—after allowing for the inlet and outlet losses and the pressure drops due to tower internals. Because we have used the H_{OL} value from the University of Texas test data, a good quality liquid distributor is needed; otherwise, the packed depth will need to be increased about 20%.

The 9-ft 0-in. ID column design clearly is preferred. Not only does it have a slightly lower capital cost, but its fan power requirement is much lower than the 9-ft 6-in. ID column. Because the 9-ft 6- in. ID tower used 16,200 SCFM of air at 2.5 in. H$_2$O pressure, and the 9-ft 0-in. ID tower uses only 10,800 SCFM of air at 1.8 in. H$_2$O pressure, the smaller-diameter column requires less than one-half the fan horsepower.

NOTATION

A	Column cross-sectional area (ft^2)
a	Interfacial area (ft^2/ft^3)
BOD	Biological oxygen demand
E	Efficiency (%)
g	Gravitational constant (ft/s^2)
G_m	Gas phase flow (lb-mol/h)
H	Henry's Law constant (atm/mol fraction)
H_{OL}	Overall height of a liquid phase transfer unit (ft)
KE	Kinetic energy (ft-lb)
$K_G a$	Overall gas-phase mass transfer coefficient (lb-mol/h · ft^3 · atm)
$K_L a$	Overall liquid-phase mass transfer coefficient (lb-mol/h · ft^3 · mol/mol)
L_m	Liquid phase flow (lb-mol/h)
m	Slope of equilibrium curve
N	Solute transferred (lb-mol/h)
N_{OL}	Number of liquid phase transfer units
P	Total system pressure (atm)
p	Partial pressure in gas phase (atm)
p*	Vapor pressure of solute (atm)

148   Packed Tower Design and Applications

S*	Stripping factor
V	Superficial gas velocity (ft/s)
VOC	Volatile organic compound
w	Mass (lb)
x	Mol fraction solute in liquid phase
x*	Equilibrium mol fraction in liquid phase
x_i	Mol fraction solute in inlet liquid
x_o	Mol fraction solute in outlet liquid
y	Mol fraction solute in gas phase
y*	Equilibrium mol fraction in gas phase
y_i	Mol fraction solute in inlet gas
y_o	Mol fraction solute in outlet gas
Z	Packed depth (ft)
Δp_B	Partial pressure driving force at bottom (atm)
Δp_{LM}	ln mean pressure driving force (atm)
Δp_T	Partial pressure driving force at top (atm)

REFERENCES

1. Thibodeaux, L. J. *et al.*, *Industrial and Engineering Chemistry, Process and Design Development,* Vol. 16, November 3, 1977, p. 325.
2. *1983 Equipment Volume Industrial Gas Cleaning and Air Pollution Control,* Chapter 11, American Society of Heating, Refrigeration, and Air-Conditioning Engineers, p. 11.13.
3. Eckert, J. S. and Strigle, R. F., *Journal of the Air Pollution Control Association,* Vol. 24, No. 10, 1974, p. 961.
4. Foote, E. H., Norton Company Chamberlain Laboratories Internal Report, 1978.
5. *1988 ASHRAE Equipment Handbook, Chapter 11, Industrial Gas Cleaning and Air Pollution Control,* American Society of Heating, Refrigerating and Air-Conditioning Engineers, p. 13–21.
6. *Modern Pollution Control Technology,* Vol. 1, Research and Education Association, 1978, p. 21–36.
7. Tomany, J. P., *Pollution Engineering,* Vol. 2, No.1, 1970, p. 28.
8. Lim, C. *et al.*, "Recent Developments in Norton's Practical Flue Gas Treatment Systems," Institution of Chemical Engineers, The Problems of Acid Emissions Conference, Birmingham (UK), September, 1986.
9. McInnes, R. *et al.*, *Chemical Engineering,* Vol. 97, No. 9, 1990, p. 108.
10. "Odor Threshold for 53 Commercial Chemicals," Part 1, Manufacturing Chemists' Association, 1968.

11. Prokop, W. H., "Wet Scrubbing of Inedible Rendering Plant Odors," Air Pollution Control Association, Western Pennsylvania Section Meeting, March, 1974.
12. Kavanaugh, M. C. and Trussell, R. R., *Journal of American Water Works Association*, Vol. 72, No. 12, 1980, p. 684.
13. Cummins, M. D. and Westrick, J. J., "Packed Column Air Stripping for Removal of Volatile Compounds," National Conference on Environmental Engineering, A.S.C.E., Minneapolis, 1982.
14. Cummins, M. D. and Westrick, J. J., "Trichlorethylene Removal by Packed Column Air Stripping," National Conference on Environmental Engineering, A.S.C.E., Boulder, CO, 1983.
15. Carroll, J. J., *Chemical Engineering Progress*, Vol. 87, No. 9, 1991, p. 48.
16. Munz, C. and Roberts, P. V., *Journal of American Water Works Association*, Vol. 79, No. 5, 1987, p. 62.
17. Reijnen, G. K. *et al.*, *Water Supply*, Vol. 3, Pergamon Press, 1985, p. 219.
18. Thibodeaux, L. J., "Air Stripping of Organics from Wastewater," Second National Conference on Complete Water Reuse, Chicago, 1975.
19. Yaws, C. *et al.*, *Chemical Engineering*, Vol. 98, No. 11, 1991, p. 179.

6

HEAT TRANSFER

This chapter discusses the very complex phenomenon of combined heat and mass transfer. In some cases, these two transfer operations may take place in opposite directions across the interface between phases. At times, the mass transfer may involve more than one component. Methods for design of such columns will be developed despite the absence of rigorous theory for many of these engineering applications. This chapter deals with these complicated situations through empirical adjustments to heat transfer coefficients, based upon extensive practical experience.

There are many situations where a tubular heat exchanger is not efficient or desirable. The packed tower as a heat transfer device presents some very important advantages when heat is transferred between a gas or vapor phase and a liquid phase, which are mutually insoluble. While most other equipment offered for this service imposes some sort of surface between two fluids exchanging heat, in the packed tower, heat is transferred by intimate contact between the fluids. Thus, there is no reduction in the heat transfer rate because of fouling or scaling. Conventional tubular heat exchangers may have corrosion of the metal tube, or deposits may form on the tube surface. Both of these factors lower the heat transfer rate. Therefore, higher heat transfer coefficients are obtained in packed columns, leading to closer temperature approaches between the two fluids and considerably reduced initial equipment cost. In addition, the high pressure drop through the tubular equipment, which may be detrimental to the process, is avoided.

Although heat transfer is the primary purpose in such direct contact operations, in most cases, exchange of mass between fluids occurs simultaneously. However, heat transfer can occur without appreciable mass transfer, as when a hot gas stream is cooled by a very high-boiling liquid. Nevertheless, the design of many direct-contact heat transfer columns requires consideration of the variables affecting both mass and heat flow. It had been proposed that the ratio of the heat transfer rate to the mass transfer rate would equal the gas-phase humid heat capacity. The ratio of heat transfer coefficient to the product of mass transfer coefficient and gas-phase humid heat capacity then should be unity. While this relationship seems to hold for an air/water system, it does not apply to many organic vapors. Walker *et al.* show this ratio to vary between 1.22 and 1.92 for many organic solvent vapors in air [1].

Consider an evaporative cooling operation in which a hot gas stream is cooled by vaporization of a lower temperature liquid. Heat transfer from gas phase to liquid phase takes place by convection. The mass transfer coefficient is based on diffusion of the liquid vapor through a non-diffusing gas film and the rate of heat transfer through the gas phase, as well as heat conduction through the films. This occurs because at high liquid and gas rates, the ratio of the heat transfer rate to the mass transfer rate is constant. This occurs because at high flow rates (liquid rates of 4 gpm/ft^2 or greater) the heat transfer area is the same as the mass transfer area. At low flow rates (a liquid rate of 0.5 gpm/ft^2 or lower), mass transfer can be the limiting phenomenon, because the heat transfer area approaches twice the mass transfer area.

WATER COOLING THEORY

In heat transfer applications, either the liquid stream or the gas stream can be cooled. The most common application, in which the liquid stream is cooled, is a water cooling tower. Although there is sensible heat transfer between the warmer water and the cooler air, in this device the warm water primarily is cooled by evaporation of some of the water into the air stream. Both the heat and mass are transferred in the same direction, from the water to the air stream. Exit air from the water cooling tower may be assumed to be saturated with water vapor. Kern reports tests showing the exit air is 95% to 99% saturated [2]. Exit air enthalpy can be obtained from a psychrometric table. The inlet air condition usually is defined by the dry-bulb and wet-bulb temperatures. For practical design purposes the inlet air is assumed to be saturated with water at the wet-bulb temperature, because the enthalpy of this air is sufficiently close to the theoretically accurate adiabatic saturation temperature.

Inlet water temperature is known, and the desired exit water temperature is specified. The difference between these temperatures is called the *range*. Normally, the exit water temperature is at least 6°F warmer than the inlet air wet-bulb temperature. This temperature difference is called the *approach*.

The heat transferred into the air stream is:

$$Q = G_d (H_o - H_i) \qquad\qquad (6\text{-}1)$$

The outlet water flow is the inlet flow less the water evaporated into the air stream. This evaporation is:

$$W = G_d (h_o - h_i) \tag{6-2}$$

The heat transferred out of the water is:

$$Q = L_w \, Cpt_i - Cpt_o \, [L_w - G_d \, (h_o - h_i)] \tag{6-3}$$

which can be written as:

$$Q = L_w \, Cpt_i - L_w Cpt_o + G_d \, Cpt_o \, (h_o - h_i) \tag{6-4}$$

This equation can be simplified to:

$$Q = L_w \, Cp \, (t_i - t_o) + G_d \, Cpt_o \, (h_o - h_i) \tag{6-5}$$

The second term on the right side of Equation 6-5 is small in comparison to the first term at moderate temperatures, and can be neglected. Thus, by a combination of Equation 6-5 with Equation 6-1:

$$G_d \, (H_o - H_i) \cong L_w \, Cp \, (t_i - t_o) \tag{6-6}$$

Equation 6-6 can be rearranged to that of a straight line while eliminating the Cp for water, which equals 1 Btu/lb · °F:

$$H_o = \frac{L_w}{G_d} (t_i - t_o) + H_i \tag{6-7}$$

The exact solution of the equations that describe both the heat and mass transfer processes is rather complicated, although both must be considered as just described. However, for the most common case of an air/water system the ratio of the heat transfer coefficient to the product of the mass transfer coefficient and gas-phase humid heat capacity is unity. In this case, humidity and temperature potentials are combined into enthalpy driving forces that control the rate of transfer [3]. Equation 6-7 represents the operating line of a countercurrent flow water cooling tower. The equilibrium curve is a plot of the enthalpy of saturated air (in Btu/lb BDG) against the temperature of water in thermal equilibrium with the air.

The driving force in this application is the enthalpy difference, not the temperature difference. In the normal range of cooling tower operation from 85° to 125°F, the water vapor represents 70% to 83% of the total air enthalpy. This system is gas-film-controlled because the diffusing water vapor is of the same composition as the main-body liquid phase, and the heat transfer rate through the liquid phase is so high that the interface and bulk liquid phase are substantially at the same temperature.

The resistance to sensible heat transfer in the water film is so small that it may be neglected. The number of transfer units required can be obtained by integrating the area between the operating line and equilibrium curve with respect to the average driving force:

$$N_{OG} = \int_{H_i}^{H_o} \frac{dH_v}{H_v{}^* - H_v} \tag{6-8}$$

In Figure 6-1, AB is the equilibrium curve and CD is the operating line of the water cooling tower. Point C represents the temperature of the entering water (t_i) and the enthalpy of the saturated air leaving (H_o). Point D represents the desired temperature of the water leaving (t_o) and the enthalpy of the entering air (H_i) at wet-bulb temperature.

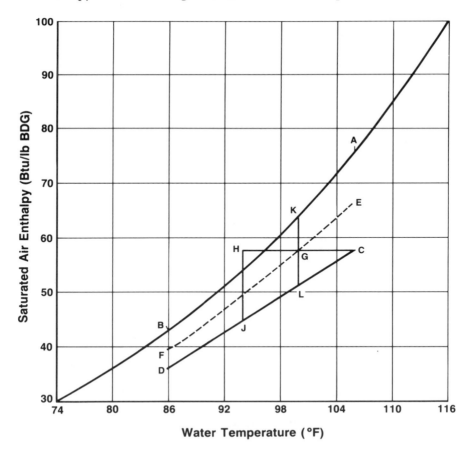

Figure 6-1. Water cooling operation.

The air flow rate must be sufficient so that the slope of the operating line L_w/G_d is low enough to avoid pinching off against the equilibrium curve. This can occur because the equilibrium curve AB has a convex curvature toward the operating line CD. Typically, L_w/G_d varies from 0.74 to 1.4 for normal water cooling ranges of 10° to 30°F.

For this gas-film-controlled system, the rate of mass transfer is proportional to gas rate to approximately the 0.8 power. This is similar to data on the isothermal evaporation of pure liquids from a pipe wall into a turbulent air stream. There, Gilliland and Sherwood showed that the mass transfer rate is proportional to the gas mass velocity to the 0.83 power [4]. For systems evaporating water into an air stream, the effect of the liquid rate is similar to that for absorption. Because a large percentage of the heat is transferred by the vaporization of water, it is reasonable to find that the effect of gas and liquid rates is similar to that for other gas-film-controlled mass transfer operations.

COOLING TOWER DESIGN

The number of transfer units (N_{OG}) can be determined by graphical integration. Line EF in Figure 6-1 is constructed as the locus of points equal to 0.5 $[H_v^* + H_v]$. Horizontal line CH intersects line EF at point G so that CG = GH. Vertical line HJ intersects line CD at point J. Vertical line KL through point G intersects curve AB at point K and line CD at point L. By the theory of similar triangles, HJ = KL. Because KL represents the average enthalpy driving force for water temperatures from point C to point J, HJ represents a change of air enthalpy equal to the average driving force. Therefore, CHJ represents one transfer unit. This process is repeated until a one transfer unit step gives a lower value of water temperature than represented by point D. The last step then is considered a fractional transfer unit.

In practice, the movement of the air stream through the tower can be a substantial operating cost. Cooling towers use either natural draft or a propeller-type fan to move the air stream. The total pressure drop through a forced-draft column, therefore, is limited to about 0.33 in. of water. The use of a random dumped tower packing is not customary in water cooling towers. Because of the pressure drop available, the maximum packed depth for large size plastic dumped packings is under 6 ft.

While very short packed depths of conventional mass transfer tower packings will provide a sufficient number of transfer units to cool the water as specified, such a short column may produce another problem. A short water cooling tower would discharge the humid air only 15 ft to 18 ft above the air intake. During periods of atmospheric inversion, the humid air may be recirculated back into the cooling tower air inlet. This occurrence would prevent the tower from cooling the water to the desired temperature. To avoid this problem, a short cooling tower needs a tall discharge stack for the humid air.

Table 6-1 gives the height of a gas-phase transfer unit for common dumped tower packings in water cooling applications. These heights were determined with packed depths providing at least three transfer units. In the design of columns with fewer transfer units, 9 in. to 12 in. of additional height over that calculated is recommended to allow for completion of liquid and gas distribution.

Table 6-1

Height of a Gas-Phase Transfer Unit (in.) for Water Cooling

Packing	\multicolumn{4}{c}{Size (in.)}
	1	1½	2	3 or 3½
Ceramic Intalox® Saddles	16	20	24	34
Plastic Super Intalox® Saddles	16	—	23	34
Plastic Pall Rings	17	20	22	34
Metal Pall Rings	14	17	21	31
Metal Hy-Pak® Packing	15	18	22	29
Intalox® Metal Tower Packing	14	16	19	26

In addition, these depths apply to packed beds with uniform liquid and gas distribution similar to that used in distillation columns. In many designs of commercial cooling towers, distribution is of a substantially lower quality. Thus, the packed depth specified must make allowance for these less efficient distributor designs. For large size dumped tower packings, the value of H_{OG} may be 25% to 40% greater than that from Table 6-1 when commercial liquid distributors are used.

COOLING TOWER FILL

Initially, industrial water cooling towers were equipped with a fill that was much less efficient than random dumped tower packing with respect to mass transfer. For example, splash grids of wood or plastic construction were arranged so that the falling liquid must contact alternate rows of grids. All the grids in a row ran in the same direction, although alternate rows could be transversely oriented. Such a fill commonly would be 25 ft to 30 ft in depth. Therefore, the grids were arranged to provide a high open area for gas flow to minimize pressure drop. Some newer plastic grids are contoured to encourage more streamlined air flow with reduced pressure drop.

Because of their low pressure-drop characteristics, structured packings of plastic have been used extensively in water cooling towers. Generally, such packings are of designs especially developed for water cooling, rather than the types typically used in other mass transfer operations. Such newer fill material for mechanical draft towers consists of vacuum-formed plastic sheets installed as vertical modules to minimize pressure drop. Arranging the sheets close together provides a relatively large surface area for mass transfer. Such a fill provides a pressure drop per transfer unit of height similar to that of random dumped packings, although the transfer unit height for such a fill may be twice that developed by the more efficient random dumped tower packing. While structured plastic cooling tower "fill" may be five times as efficient as wooden splash bars, uniform distribution of water is a prime requirement for maximum performance [5]. Also, careful attention must be given to water quality when using such "fill." The circulating water must be treated to prevent build-up of bacterial growth or slime. Also, makeup water added to replace evaporated water must be treated to avoid solid deposits.

Some cooling towers operate with natural draft. This is possible because the warmer, humid air inside the tower is less dense than the colder, drier outside air. Many such towers are hyperbolic and may require an overall height of 220 ft. The fill used in such a column must be quite open to avoid any significant pressure drop. Such fill can have a tee- or vee-shaped cross section molded from perforated plastic sheets. Corrugated sheets made of asbestos and cement are popular in large natural draft towers. A ceramic cellular block that is stacked into the tower also is used. These fills, however, provide a small interfacial area per cubic foot so mass transfer is rather low per foot of packed depth.

GAS QUENCH TOWERS

When the gas stream is cooled, one of three different types of operation usually will take place:

1. Gas cooling with liquid vaporization
2. Gas cooling with total condensation
3. Gas cooling with partial condensation

An example of Type 1 operation is a hot gas quench tower using water as the liquid coolant. In this application sensible heat is transferred from a hot gas stream to the cooler water. As the liquid temperature increases, water is vaporized into the gas stream, which raises its humidity. Thus, mass transfer is in the opposite direction to heat transfer.

The exit gas from the quench tower is assumed to be saturated with water vapor. The desired exit gas temperature usually is specified, and the inlet water temperature is known. Normally, the exit gas temperature is at least 3°F higher than the inlet water temperature. The inlet gas enthalpy must be calculated from gas temperature, heat capacity, and humidity. The heat capacity of common dry gases at atmospheric pressure and temperatures from 100° to 800°F is given in Table 6-2. The inlet gas stream temperature should be converted to its adiabatic temperature (that saturated gas stream temperature having the same enthalpy as the inlet gas). The entering hot gas stream is saturated quickly with water vapor and cools to its adiabatic saturation temperature. However, if the hot gas has a dew point temperature close to the exit water temperature, most of the heat transfer will be sensible, because only a small amount of mass transfer can occur.

Table 6-2

Heat Capacity of Common Gases

Gas	Heat Capacity (BTU/lb mol − °F)	
	@ 100°F	@ 800°F
Ammonia	8.66	11.11
Carbon Dioxide	9.17	11.86
Carbon Monoxide	6.97	7.44
Chlorine	8.45	8.67
Hydrogen	6.87	7.19
Hydrogen Chloride	6.96	7.29
Hydrogen Sulfide	8.32	9.72
Nitrogen	6.81	7.20
Oxygen	6.41	8.07
Sulfur Dioxide	9.27	11.00

Source: Perry's Chemical Engineer's Handbook [6]

If the exit water temperature is more than 20°F cooler than the inlet adiabatic gas temperature, a fog may be produced. This occurs because the inlet gas is cooled at a faster rate by sensible heat transfer than it is dehumidified by mass transfer. As a result, the gas is chilled below its dew point temperature. The resultant fog is of such small particle size that it is carried out of the quench tower with the exit gas stream. To prevent this occurrence, water flow to the quench tower should be reduced to raise the exit liquid temperature.

QUENCH TOWER DESIGN

Figure 6-2 illustrates the operation of a hot gas quenching column with water as the coolant. Line OP is the operating line of the quench column. If the amount of water evaporated is negligible, compared to the total water flow, the equation of this line is:

$$G_d (H_i - H_o) = L_w Cp (t_o - t_i) \qquad (6\text{-}9)$$

Equation 6-9 can be rearranged to that of a straight line while eliminating the Cp for water, which equals 1 Btu/lb · °F:

$$H_o = H_i - \frac{L_w}{G_d}(t_o - t_i) \tag{6-10}$$

The equilibrium curve MN is obtained in the same manner as for Figure 6-1. Point P represents the inlet gas enthalpy (H_i) and the outlet water temperature (t_o), while point O represents the enthalpy of the saturated outlet gas (H_o) and the temperature of the inlet water (t_i). Line RV is the locus of points equal to 0.5 [H_v* + H_v]. OS is a horizontal line intersecting line RV at U so that OU = SU. As in Figure 6-1, TS is an enthalpy change equal to the average driving force from a water temperature at point O to point T. Therefore, OST represents one transfer unit.

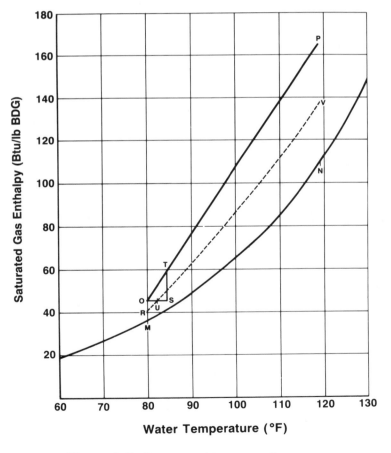

Figure 6-2. Gas quenching operation.

The cooling water rate must be large enough so the operating line slope L_w/G_d is sufficient to avoid intersection of the operating line with the equilibrium curve before the inlet gas enthalpy is reached. For gas cooling, the equilibrium curve has a concave curvature away from the operating line. For quenching flue gas from the combustion of natural gas at atmospheric pressure L_w/G_d varies from 2 to 7.

Using a logarithmic mean enthalpy driving force, based on terminal column conditions, is not recommended when calculating gas-quenching operations. Such a procedure usually produces a substantial column overdesign because the true enthalpy driving force is greater than the average of the terminal driving forces. This is due to the concave equilibrium curve.

TOTAL CONDENSER THEORY

In a Type 2 operation, the gas phase is a totally condensible vapor. In this case the mass transfer and heat transfer occur in the same direction—from the gas phase to the liquid phase. Usually the coolant liquid is of the same composition as the condensate. Thus, from a mass balance standpoint:

$$L_o' = L_i' + G_i' \qquad (6\text{-}11)$$

The heat transferred into the liquid phase is:

$$Q = L_o' \, Cpt_o - L_i'Cpt_i \qquad (6\text{-}12)$$

therefore, combining Equations 6-11 and 6-12:

$$Q = L_i' \, Cpt_o + G_i' \, Cpt_o - L_i' \, Cpt_i \qquad (6\text{-}13)$$

Equation 6-13 is simplified to:

$$Q = L_i' \, Cp \, (t_o - t_i) + G_i' \, Cpt_o \qquad (6\text{-}14)$$

The heat transferred from the vapor phase is:

$$Q = G_i' \, \Delta H + G_i' \, Cpv \, (T_i - t_o) \qquad (6\text{-}15)$$

or the heat load is:

$$Q = G_i' \, [\Delta H + Cpv \, (T_i - t_o)] \qquad (6\text{-}16)$$

There are no concentration differences across either the gas film or the liquid film for a single component vapor. The main resistance to condensation is the thermal gradient across the liquid film. Thus, the heat transfer coefficient primarily is a function of the thermal conductivity of the liquid, similar to the performance of vertical condenser tubes as described by Nusselt [7]. The thermal conductivity of most liquids decreases as the temperature increases; however, some liquids exhibit a maximum value of thermal conductivity at a particular temperature [8].

These total condensers are designed on a heat transfer basis using the relationship:

$$Q = U_v \, AZ \, \Delta T_{LM} \tag{6-17}$$

Because this type of operation essentially involves the Nusselt theory with enhanced liquid flow, a heat transfer coefficient approach is used for calculative purposes, rather than transfer units. Temperature differences are calculated as if a surface condenser were being used. If a single-component vapor is condensing at a constant pressure, the temperature difference at the liquid coolant inlet is $T_i - t_i$. Similarly, the temperature difference at the liquid coolant outlet is $T_i - t_o$. This is true because the vapor temperature remains constant from the first drop of condensate to the last drop. Thus, the logarithmic mean temperature driving force is:

$$\Delta T_{LM} = \frac{(T_i - t_i) - (T_i - t_o)}{\ln\left[\dfrac{(T_i - t_i)}{(T_i - t_o)}\right]} \tag{6-18}$$

This can be simplified to:

$$\Delta T_{LM} = \frac{t_o - t_i}{\ln\left[\dfrac{(T_i - t_i)}{(T_i - t_o)}\right]} \tag{6-19}$$

The volume of tower packing required from Equation 6-17 is:

$$AZ = \frac{Q}{U_v \, \Delta T_{LM}} \tag{6-20}$$

A volumetric heat transfer coefficient (U_v) is used in Equation 6-20. Normally, heat transfer coefficients are used with the rate of heat flow expressed per unit temperature difference per unit area. However, in direct-contact heat transfer, the conventional heat transfer coefficient must be multiplied by the interfacial area between gas and liquid to obtain a volumetric coefficient. The interfacial area is not always the geometric surface area of the tower packing. To simplify the calculation this interfacial area term is combined with the conventional heat transfer coefficient. This produces a volumetric coefficient for heat transfer in a manner analogous to the use of a mass transfer coefficient in absorption.

TOTAL CONDENSER DESIGN

The volumetric heat transfer coefficient primarily is a function of the liquid-phase properties. In particular, this coefficient depends on the volumetric liquid irrigation rate and the liquid viscosity. The heat transfer coefficient varies as:

$$U_v \propto \left[\frac{L_i'}{\rho_L u' A}\right]^{0.33} \qquad (6\text{-}21)$$

This variation with liquid rate is similar to the effect on the mass transfer coefficient in absorption operations.

The volumetric heat transfer coefficients are very high for Type 2 operations because there is little or no gas-film resistance, due to the absence of an inert gas phase. Values from 500 to 1,400 Btu/h · ft^3 · °F have been obtained for #50 IMTP packing with organic liquids having a thermal conductivity of 0.08 Btu-ft/h · ft^2·°F.

Packed beds find applications as total condensers at the top of distillation columns. In such services, the tower packing produces a low pressure drop that especially is desirable in high vacuum services. The arrangement of the packed condenser system consists of a liquid collector plate at the bottom to permit removal of the liquid from the column. Above this collector is a support plate and the packed bed that is irrigated by a liquid distributor using a portion of the condensate that is recycled after being cooled in an external heat exchanger. The organic vapor losses approach a limit corresponding to the vapor pressure above the cooled irrigating liquid.

Some liquids become extremely viscous when cooled. In such cases, the heat transfer coefficient should be calculated separately for the top and bottom of the packed bed. If the cool liquid at the top of the bed has a viscosity of 35 cps, and the warm liquid at the bottom of the bed has a viscosity of only 1.3 cps, the heat transfer coefficient at the top of the bed is only one-third that at the bottom of the bed—before allowing for variations in liquid flow rate and thermal conductivity. In such cases it may be desirable to use a primary lower condenser packed bed operating at a higher liquid inlet temperature and, therefore, a lower liquid viscosity and a higher heat transfer coefficient. Above this bed would be a secondary condenser packed bed, operating at a lower liquid inlet temperature to minimize vent loss of organic vapor. With this arrangement the primary condenser could handle over 80% of the total heat load and the secondary condenser the small balance of the condensing duty. Such an arrangement could require 15% less total packed depth to condense the same amount of inlet vapor as a single bed.

PARTIAL CONDENSER THEORY

By far the most important heat transfer applications for packed columns involve partial condensation of some vapor from a hot gas stream, which are Type 3 operations. In such cases, both the heat and the mass transfer occur in the same direction, from the vapor phase to the liquid phase. In this type operation, a part of the inlet gas stream is condensed, and the balance of the gas stream merely is reduced in temperature.

Such an operation is complicated from a theoretical standpoint. The driving force for heat transfer is the difference in the temperatures between the vapor and liquid phases. The driving force for mass transfer is the difference between the partial pressure of a component in the vapor phase and the vapor pressure of that component above the liquid phase. While in some previous operations, the designer could use the enthalpy difference as a driving force, which takes into account both heat and mass transfer, in this operation we will consider the design of columns in which the use of an enthalpy driving force is not practical. Therefore, the usual design approach is the use of a temperature difference driving force and a heat transfer coefficient. A further simplification is to calculate a logarithmic mean temperature difference, even though such may not be justified mathematically. The designer uses an overall heat transfer coefficient derived empirically from experience with the log mean temperature driving force. Thus, such heat transfer coefficients are specific for the particular system.

CHLORINE GAS COOLING

First, applications will be considered where a condensible vapor is present in an inert, noncondensible gas. An example of this situation is cooling a chlorine cell gas with water to condense the majority of the gas stream water vapor content. The simplified design method described here is based on a large bank of practical experience with the particular system discussed. Thus, an empirical adjustment of the heat transfer coefficients provides a suitable design basis to overcome the lack of precise theory.

The total enthalpy of the inlet gas as Btu/lb-mol BDG can be calculated from the water vapor content and the heat capacity of the inert gas. Because water vapor is being condensed throughout the packed bed, the exit gas is saturated with the water. Because the condensate is of the same composition as the irrigating liquid, specifying the inlet liquid temperature usually fixes the exit gas temperature within a narrow range. Thus, the exit gas enthalpy can also be calculated.

The total heat transferred is:

$$Q = G_d \, (H_i - H_o) \qquad (6\text{-}22)$$

Using Equation 6-20 to calculate the necessary packing volume requires a corrected heat transfer coefficient (U_v). The temperature differences then can be used as driving forces as with sensible heat transfer. If such an adjustment is not made, the amount of packed depth required will be overestimated. Equation 6-23 gives a method for calculating the adjusted heat transfer coefficient for several packings. This equation applies to dehumidification of an inert gas by direct contact with water at atmospheric pressure. The equation is based on data by Eckert *et al.* for a saturated inlet gas at temperatures from 110° to 150°F [9].

$$U_v = bH_M^{0.57} \qquad (6\text{-}23)$$

Values of coefficient b are given in Table 6-3. The heat transfer coefficient at the bottom of the bed should be calculated separately from the coefficient at the top of the packed bed. The logarithmic average coefficient then can be used to calculate the packed volume required. Equation 6-23 allows for the mass transfer of vapor because the gas phase enthalpy is, in large part, determined by the water vapor content of the gas stream. This empirical equation provides an easy method for a cooling column design.

Table 6-3

Dehumidification of Inert Gases Coefficient b for Heat Transfer Equation 6-23

Packing	Coefficient b
2 in. Plastic Pall Rings	13.8
3½ in. Plastic Pall Rings	11.8
2 in. Ceramic Intalox® Saddles	11.6
3 in. Ceramic Intalox® Saddles	10.0
#50 Intalox® Metal Tower Packing	13.1
#70 Intalox® Metal Tower Packing	11.1

The heat transfer coefficient is a function of vapor and liquid flow rates. The volumetric heat transfer coefficient value from Equation 6-23 is based on a vapor capacity factor (F_s) of 1.27 $lb^{0.5}/ft^{0.5} \cdot s$ and a water rate of 3,000 $lb/ft^2 \cdot h$. Even though theory suggests that the heat transfer coefficient varies as the 0.83 power of the gas rate, Nemunaitis and Eckert report that the coefficient varies as the first power of F_s for the dehumidification of air [10]. The same authors also state that the coefficient varies as the 0.68 power of the liquid rate. Thus, if the liquid-to-gas ratio is held constant, the heat transfer coefficient increases much faster than the hydraulic loading.

Later work by Strigle and Foote indicated that the heat transfer coefficient varied as the 0.74 power of the vapor capacity factor [11]. This same work also showed that the heat transfer coefficient was a function of the 0.40 power of the liquid flow rate. The effect of liquid rate subsequently has been verified in industrial operations. These exponents for the effects of gas and liquid rates are similar to those for gas-film-controlled mass transfer operations. This is not surprising since 76% to 83% of the total enthalpy of the saturated air tested was represented by the enthalpy of the water vapor in the air. These later tests were conducted using 2-in. metal Pall rings, 2-in. plastic Pall rings, and #2 Hy-Pak packing. In this same series of tests 3-in. or 3½-in. packing of the same type gave a heat transfer coefficient 12% to 15% lower than the 2-in. size.

The heat transfer coefficients have been determined by the cited investigators at atmospheric pressure. Industrial experience indicates that this coefficient increases at higher operating pressures to a greater extent than merely due to the effect of gas density on the vapor capacity factor (F_s). At pressures above 1 atm, it is suggested that the heat transfer coefficient be increased by the 0.30 power of the operating pressure expressed in atmospheres.

The average temperature driving force for making this calculation is:

$$\Delta T_{LM} = \frac{(T_i - t_o) - (T_o - t_i)}{\ln\left[\frac{(T_i - t_o)}{(T_o - t_i)}\right]} \tag{6-24}$$

The inlet gas temperature (T_i) for use in Equation 6-24 is the adiabatic saturation temperature of this gas stream. The logarithmic average temperature driving force and the logarithmic average heat transfer coefficient, adjusted for hydraulic flow rates, permit calculation of the packed depth required from Equation 6-20.

Because the heat transfer coefficient (U_v) is a function of the vapor and liquid mass flow rates, it depends on column cross-sectional area. In this type of operation, the maximum vapor and liquid loadings occur at the bottom of the column. The diameter of the tower thus is fixed so that the pressure drop at the bottom of the packed bed does not exceed 0.40 in. H_2O/ft of packed depth when a 2-in. or smaller size random dumped packing is used.

VACUUM CRUDE STILLS

The second Type 3 application involves the condensation of a portion of the vapor stream by progressive cooling with condensate. An example of this situation occurs in a vacuum crude tower in petroleum refining (see Figure 6-3). In this operation crude oil, from which lower-boiling components have been distilled at atmospheric pressure, is heated, then flashed under vacuum. The ascending vapor in the column is cooled by means of a pumparound of externally cooled condensate. This cooled liquid preferentially condenses the higher-boiling components from the vapor stream. Thus, the vapor ascends the column at its hydrocarbon dew point. Steam can be added to the furnace heating the reduced crude feed to decrease residence time and prevent coking. Steam also can be added to the bottom of the column to strip any remaining volatile components from the residue. A small quantity of inert gases, plus any added steam, leaves the column top saturated with lower boiling hydrocarbons at the exit vapor temperature.

Columns typically have at least two pumparound condensing sections. In addition, there is a wash bed located above the flash zone that is irrigated with a small amount of condensate from the lower pumparound section. Tower packings now are being used in these columns because of the low pressure drop and high rates of heat transfer they provide. The traditional flash zone pressure of 60 to 90 mm Hg produced in a trayed column has been reduced to 20 to 35 mm Hg by the use of modern tower packings. The requirement for added steam to lower the hydrocarbon partial pressure needed for flashing the feed is greatly reduced. Thus, the cost of the added steam is much less, and the steam required to operate the vacuum jets is reduced because the quantity of inerts is smaller [12]. Also, the load on the water pollution control system is lower because there are fewer mols of hydrocarbon vapor leaving the column top to the barometric condensers.

Heat is recovered from each pumparound liquid stream to preheat the crude feed to the atmospheric still. Therefore, the temperature of the liquid return to the vacuum tower is fixed. As a result, the amount of heat removed in a pumparound bed is a function of the liquid circulation rate and the temperature of the liquid draw. This temperature is determined by the heat transfer coefficient developed by the tower packing used and depth of packing installed. The heat load for the packed bed is the difference in the total heat contents of the inlet and outlet vapor streams

Figure 6-3. Vacuum crude still. This 40-ft ID tower was revamped from trays to random packing.

to the section. Although two pumparound sections normally are used to maximize heat recovery, the vacuum gas oil products usually are combined and serve as feed for catalytic cracking. Additional packed sections have been installed when there is another use for the vacuum gas oil.

The outlet vapor stream has much less mass than the inlet stream, due to a large percentage of vapor condensation in the section. The heat load on the packed bed is greater than the heat removed by external pumparound coolers because the vacuum gas oil condensate normally is discharged from the system at the same temperature it is withdrawn from the column. The logarithmic mean temperature difference driving force for each packed bed is determined from Equation 6-24.

Pumparound sections usually contain from 4 ft to 9 ft of packed depth. The traditional method for calculating bed depth is by use of Equation 6-20. This equation is a simplified representation of a complex group of heat and mass transfer processes. A considerable amount of industrial experience has led to the development of satisfactory empirical equations for the calculation of overall heat transfer coefficients.

Because there are a great many organic compounds in crude oil, it is not possible to precisely characterize this system. Design procedures for such systems, therefore, have been developed empirically by packing manufacturers from operating data. Typically, an overall volumetric heat transfer coefficient is calculated from an equation such as:

$$U_v = d \left[\frac{G_i'}{1000\,A\rho_G} \right]^{0.74} \left[\frac{L_i'}{1000\,A} \right]^{0.40} \tag{6-25}$$

The exponents for the effects of vapor and liquid flow rates are similar to those determined by Strigle and Foote. In Equation 6-25 the inlet gas flow (G_i') is the vapor rate to the bottom of the pumparound section, and the inlet liquid flow (L_i') is the pumparound return to the top of the bed. This equation applies where G_i'/A is greater than 400 lb/ft$^2 \cdot$ h and L_i'/A is not less than 600 lb/ft$^2 \cdot$ h. The constant d is a function of the packing type and size, as well as the mean average boiling point of the condensate. In a typical heavy vacuum gas oil pumparound section, the value of d for #70 IMTP packing is 21.9, as shown in Table 6-4. For 2-in. slotted ring packings, the value of d is 24.1; however, such packings have twice the pressure drop per foot of depth as #70 IMTP packing. The 1½-in. slotted ring packings have a value for d of 25.8, but they likewise produce a greater pressure drop than 2-in. slotted ring packings.

The volumetric heat transfer coefficient for the light vacuum gas oil pumparound section is 20% to 25% greater than for the heavy vacuum gas oil pumparound. This is due to the influence of the higher condensate

Table 6-4

Vacuum Crude Stills Coefficient d for Heat Transfer Equation 6-25

Equivalent Packing Size (in.)	Slotted Ring Packings	IMTP® Packings
1½	25.8	27.7
2	24.1	25.8
3	20.6	21.9

molecular weight in the lower pumparound section on the vapor density and the liquid-phase properties.

The volumetric heat transfer coefficients for #70 IMTP packing are about 70% greater than those for grid structures that previously have been used to provide low pressure drop in some of these columns. The #40 size of IMTP packing can provide over twice the volumetric heat transfer coefficient of grids under the same vapor and liquid flow rates. Normally, packings smaller than 1½-in. size are not used in heavy hydrocarbon service.

Unfortunately, the heat transfer coefficient is not completely independent of the packed depth. This occurs because the spray-type liquid distributor typically used in these towers also provides some amount of heat transfer. This results in proportionally better performance from short packed beds than from deeper beds. By correlating operating data from such towers, Graf reports that vapor-to-liquid temperature differences of 50°F are typical [13]. A deep packed bed is required to obtain a 20°F temperature difference between vapor and liquid streams. Figure 6-4 shows the effective packed depth as compared to an actual packed depth if each foot of bed depth greater than 4 ft were equally efficient.

Because of the high heat transfer rates available with packed beds, the packed depth calculated from Equation 6-20 can be quite short. Only a 6 in. to 9 in. design safety factor is applied above the calculated packed depth, after adjustment for the actual to effective depth is made, as shown in Figure 6-4. Because these vacuum towers normally are large in diameter, it is customary to install beds of not less than 16 packing diameters, or a 42-in. high minimum depth, in the heat transfer sections to ensure proper vapor and liquid contact.

Many times the design of the vacuum crude tower involves only determining the packed depth in each section because the column already exists. In the case of a new installation, the column diameter must be fixed based on the pressure drop. Generally, the total pressure drop from column top to feed flash zone will be 10 to 15 mm Hg. The pressure drop will decrease significantly from the bottom to the top of each heat trans-

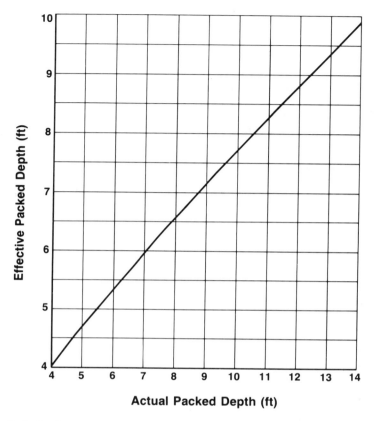

Figure 6-4. Performance of pumparound sections with spray distribution.

fer section. The pressure drop actually may be somewhat higher at the top of the wash bed than at the bottom, due to evaporation of part of the wash liquid.

As stated, Equation 6-25 has been developed empirically. It therefore should be applied only to columns operating under vacuum. Equations for calculating heat transfer coefficients at atmospheric or higher pressures indicate a greater effect of vapor loading. However, the actual heat transfer coefficient value may be considerably higher than for vacuum service at the same vapor capacity factor (F_s) and temperature driving force (ΔT_{LM}).

ATMOSPHERIC CRUDE STILLS

In the refining of petroleum, the first distillation process is carried out at a pressure of 1.2 to 1.6 atmospheric absolute in a column containing 30 to 50 actual trays [14]. The energy input to this still is provided by heating the crude feed in a direct-fired heater to a sufficient temperature (normally 650° to 725°F) to vaporize all the lower boiling products, plus about 20% of the bottoms. The overhead vapor is cooled to condense light straight-run gasoline, part of which is used as reflux, while the uncondensed gases are sent for recovery of LPG values. Additional liquid sidestreams are taken off to provide heavy naphtha, light distillate (kerosene), heavy distillate (diesel), and atmospheric gas oil. The bottoms usually serve as feed to the vacuum crude still. Most atmospheric crude stills use a series of pumparounds that remove some of the heat load and provide cooled liquid reflux. Normally three actual trays are used in the pumparound sections to reheat the cooled liquid return from about 150°F below column temperature [15]. For fractionation between product streams, five to eight actual trays usually are required.

Recently tower packings have been used to increase the capacity of these stills. Because of the limited height available between sidedraws with the usual 24-in. tray spacing, random-dumped packings have been used in the pumparound sections for heat transfer and structured packings to replace the fractionating trays. Again, Equation 6-20 can be used to calculate the depth of packing required in the pumparound sections. The heat load (Q) is determined from the pumparound liquid rate and the inlet and outlet liquid temperatures. The temperature driving force is calculated by Equation 6-24. The heat transfer coefficient (U_v) can be determined from the following equation:

$$U_v = rC_{si}^{1.38} \left[\frac{L_i'}{8 \, A\rho_L} \right]^{0.41} \tag{6-26}$$

where

$$C_{si} = \frac{G_i'}{3600 \, A[\rho_G (\rho_L - \rho_G)]^{0.5}} \tag{6-27}$$

In Equations 6-26 and 6-27, G_i' is the vapor flow to the bottom of the bed and L_i' is the liquid flow to the top of the bed. The exponents for the effects of vapor and liquid flow rates on the heat transfer coefficient are based on work by Huang and Fair [16]. The coefficient r is shown in Table 6-5 and applies to values of G_i'/A greater than 420 lb/ft$^2 \cdot$ h and values of L_i'/A of 1,000 lb/ft$^2 \cdot$ h minimum.

Table 6-5

Atmospheric Crude Stills Coefficient r for Heat Transfer Equation 6-26

Equivalent Packing Size (in.)	Slotted Ring Packings	IMTP® Packings
1½	1310	1410
2	1220	1320
3	1050	1120

OLEFIN PRIMARY FRACTIONATOR

The cracked gas from an olefin furnace is cooled to between 360° and 420°F by heat exchangers, followed by a direct oil quench, before entering the primary fractionator. The function of this column is to cool the cracked gas by direct contact with quench oil and reflux. Simulation of this column is complex and uses at least 22 characteristic components, ranging from hydrogen to gas oil in boiling points. In addition to cooling the cracked gas, only C-8 and lighter compounds are of value in the overhead naphtha product, which requires some rectification of the vapor stream.

In a typical design, this tower will contain at least four open-type trays in the lower section and a minimum of seven fractionating trays in the upper section. The function of the lower section is to cool the incoming gas by sensible heat transfer with a pumparound of cooled quench oil (bottoms). This quench oil will leave the column at 350° to 400°F, and the pumparound will be cooled to between 270° and 330°F before being returned to irrigate the lower section trays. At least 90% of the components in the cracked gas feed that are heavier than C-10s will be condensed by these angle trays, baffle trays, or splash decks. A small slip-stream of bottoms is sent to a stripper to remove the C-8 and lighter components, because the stripped bottoms have only fuel value.

The reflux to the top of this column is aromatic naphtha, which has been condensed and decanted in the water quench tower. The valve trays or sieve trays in the upper section of this column will cool the cracked gas from 320° to 350°F to between 210° and 250°F. This cooling is accomplished by evaporation of reflux so that the vapor flow increases from bottom to top of this upper section. The reflux flow is controlled to limit the outlet gas temperature to not less than 20°F above the water dew point, so that all the water in the cracked gas passes through this column.

This upper section is designed on the basis of theoretical heat transfer trays—one from which the vapor and liquid leave at the same temperature. The HETP value in this service is 20% to 30% greater than for simple fractionation, as given in Chapter 7. Strigle and Hiramatsu show the results of replacing 9 valve trays in the upper section of a 17.4 ft ID

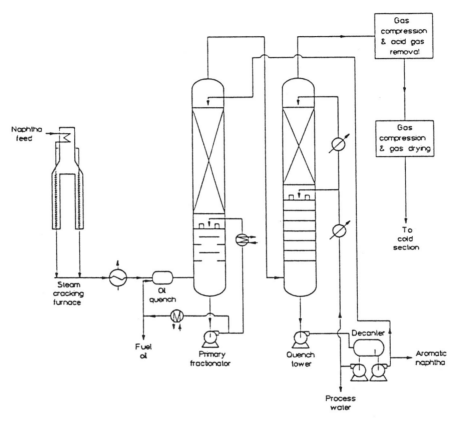

Figure 6-5. Olefin plant hot section. Source: *Oil and Gas Journal* [18].

Table 6-6

Product Distribution From Steam Cracking Various Feedstocks
(lb product per 1000 lb feed)

Feed	Ethylene	Propylene	Butadiene	BTX
Ethane/Propane	600–630	100–120	20–30	15–30
LPG	440–460	160–180	30–40	30–45
Full Range Naphtha	320–350	130–160	40–50	110–150
Atmospheric Gas Oil	255–300	115–135	45–55	95–135

Source: Petrochemical Handbook [17]

primary fractionator with a bed of #50 IMTP packing [18]. Their data on the column temperature profile is shown in Table 6-7.

The primary incentive for replacement of the trays in the upper section of this tower was pressure drop reduction. The overall column pressure drop with trays was 47.4 in. H_2O before revamp and only 10.0

Table 6-7

Primary Fractionator Temperature Profile (°F)

Stream	Trayed Column	Packed Column
Vapor to Oil Quench	727	714
Vapor to Column	367	365
Quench Oil Bottoms	361	360
Oil to Quench	340	342
Quench Oil to Column	282	275
Reflux to Column	183	180
Vapor from Column	239	232

in. H_2O after revamp, even though the lower four trays were not changed. Such pressure drop reduction will increase the suction pressure on the compressors, thus reducing the compression energy required.

As the capacity of olefin plants is increased, tray spacings of 30 in. are being used to avoid excessively large tower diameters. Such columns, with 10 or more trays in the upper section, can be modified to permit additional heat recovery by the use of modern packings. Because rectification of the cracked gas will be accomplished with IMTP packing by replacing only 70% to 75% of the trays, there is adequate height available to install a packed pumparound bed below the rectifying bed. Condensate can be withdrawn from the bottom of this pumparound at a temperature of 290° to 310°F, then cooled by 50° to 60°F before return to the top of this bed. Thus, heat can be recovered at substantially higher temperatures than would be available if this amount of heat was recovered from the water quench tower.

If the entire height available by replacing trays on 30-in. spacing is used for rectification with IMTP packing, the number of theoretical stages will be substantially increased. While 50% additional stages may reduce the exit vapor temperature only about 2°F, the C-10 plus components in this vapor can be reduced by over 90%.

OLEFIN WATER QUENCH TOWER

Another Type 3 application involves condensing of a portion of the vapor stream by progressively cooling it with water. An example is the water quench tower in a naphtha-fed olefins plant. The primary function of this column is to condense the dilution steam added in the cracking furnace. In this operation, the exit vapor from the primary fractionator, which is at the hydrocarbon dew point temperature, is cooled further with recirculated water streams to reduce compression energy requirements. In addition to condensing water vapor, the recycled water streams condense the higher hydrocarbons in the vapor. The inlet vapor typically has a water dew point of 180° to 195°F; however, the inlet vapor temperature usually is 30° to 50°F above the water dew point. This gas stream contains, as major components, hydrogen plus a complete range of hydrocarbons from methane through C-9 aromatics. Normally, the C-4 and lighter hydrocarbons pass through this tower uncondensed. Thus, the vapor stream ascends the column at the hydrocarbon dew point.

The entering vapor quickly is cooled to the adiabatic saturation temperature with respect to water. Thus, the vapor superheat, plus the heat of vaporization of the higher-boiling hydrocarbons, is converted to heat of vaporization of water. The vapor then progresses up the column at the water dew point as well as the hydrocarbon dew point. The vapor leaving the quench tower normally is at a temperature about 8° to 14°F above the water feed temperature to the column top when trays are used.

The effluent liquid from the quench column flows to a decanter where the smaller hydrocarbon phase is separated from the larger water phase. Most of the hydrocarbon phase is returned to the primary fractionator as reflux. The balance of this hydrocarbon liquid is stripped to remove C-4 and lighter compounds. The water phase, after removal of the amount of water condensed from the vapor stream, is recycled through heat recovery systems for reboiling light hydrocarbon fractionators (such as the C-3 splitter) before being returned to the quench column. The majority of this water is returned to the center of the column at a temperature of 125° to 140°F; however, 30% to 40% of the recirculated water is cooled further and fed to the top of this column at 80° to 95°F. The heat load on the packed bed is greater than the heat load on the pumparound water coolers because both the hydrocarbon condensate and the water condensate are discharged from the system at the liquid effluent temperature.

Normally, the column upper section uses 5 to 9 valve or sieve trays, which develop a pressure drop of 0.10 to 0.16 psi per actual tray [19]. These trays can be replaced with #50 IMTP packing to obtain the desired heat transfer using an 8-ft to 14-ft deep bed. This packed depth will cool the vapor stream to a temperature within 3° to 5°F of the top water feed temperature. The vapor entering the upper section of the quench column normally is 10° to 20°F higher in temperature than the liquid leaving this section.

The heat transfer coefficients in this upper section are high—U_v for #50 IMTP packing is 35% greater than for valve trays on 24-in. spacing.

Figure 6-6. This primary fractionator and water quench tower were revamped with IMTP® packing.

The principal reason to install packing in this section is to reduce the pressure drop by 85% to 90%, as compared with valve or sieve trays in the same section. This results in an overall pressure drop reduction of 70% to 75% for the quench column, even when the angle trays are left in the bottom section. Thus, the resulting higher suction pressure reduces the compression ratio, and therefore the power requirement, on the first compression stage.

The lower sections of water quench towers typically employ baffle trays, splash decks, or angle trays. These devices have a very low efficiency, so that 6 to 12 actual trays are installed, which develop a pressure drop of only 0.02 psi per actual tray. If the effluent liquid from this lower section of the tower could be heated an additional 5°F, the useful heat available for cold section reboilers would increase from 77% to 82% of the total heat load on the water quench column. When this section is equipped with high capacity packing, the exit liquid temperature can be raised to within about 5°F of the inlet vapor adiabatic saturation temperature. This can be done without increasing the pressure drop compared to the trays. Normally a 10-ft to 14-ft depth of #70 IMTP packing is specified for the lower section. Such a packed depth provides a 70% to 100% increase in theoretical stages compared to the trays that are replaced.

The volumetric heat transfer coefficients (U_v) in this section are very high. They can be up to 90% greater than those applicable to the upper section for the same tower packing—if there is a large mass of condensed hydrocarbon. Usually such a column will condense practically all of the hydrocarbons with a molecular weight greater than 90. Thus, such an increase can be expected when a full-range naphtha is cracked. However, the increase in U_v for the lower section as compared to the upper section will not be as great when the inlet vapor contains only light hydrocarbons, such as produced by cracking a NGL feedstock.

In revamping the water quench tower's upper and lower sections, the column performance depends on the temperature approach between vapor and liquid at each end of the column. This is because the liquid from the upper section normally flows into the lower section of the tower, in addition to the mid-pumparound liquid return. It is desirable to minimize the top pumparound return liquid flow to recover the greatest amount of the available heat. However, the top water flow must be sufficient to keep the operating line for this column section from pinching against the equilibrium curve and rapidly increasing the required number of theoretical stages. Otherwise, an attempt to raise the effluent liquid temperature to a maximum value for heat recovery purposes by reducing top water return flow may cause increased outlet vapor temperature from the column with the same top liquid feed temperature. Operating data for a water quench column in which the six angle trays in the lower section and the five valve trays in the upper section were replaced with IMTP packing are given in Table 6-8 [20].

Table 6-8

Water Quench Tower Operating Profile

Stream	Trayed Column	Packed Column
Vapor to Column	221°F	221°F
Liquid from Column	176°F	188°F
Center Water Flow	1224 T/h	1213 T/h
Center Water Feed	138°F	138°F
Top Water Flow	772 T/h	507 T/h
Top Water Feed	91.4°F	91.6°F
Vapor from Column	96.4°F	96.3°F
Column Pressure Drop	30.6 in. H_2O	7.9 in. H_2O

EXAMPLE PROBLEM

The gas stream leaves a first-stage compressor in an olefin plant at a pressure of 48 psia and a temperature of 196°F. The gas flow rate is 295,000 lb/h consisting of 240 lb-mol/h of water vapor and 10,000 lb-mol/h of hydrocarbon. The exit gas must be cooled to 97°F. Water to cool this gas steam is available at 90°F for use in a direct-contact gas cooler. The heated water effluent from this column should be at a temperature of about 130°F so that it can be returned to the center of the water quench tower. What will be the size of a packed interstage cooler, and how much can it reduce the gas-side pressure drop of 4.0 psi through the present tube-and-shell heat exchangers?

The inlet gas stream contains 2.34 mol % water vapor and has a heat capacity of the hydrocarbon vapor of 0.434 Btu/lb · °F. The enthalpy of the inlet gas stream is 88.36 Btu/lb dry gas. Likewise, the enthalpy of the outlet gas stream at 97°F is 40.78 Btu/lb dry gas.

The inlet gas stream contains 0.0149 lb H_2O vapor/lb dry gas, while the outlet gas stream contains 0.0114 lb H_2O vapor/lb dry gas.

Water vapor content of gas in = 0.0149(290,675) = 4,331 lb/h

Water vapor content of gas out = 0.0114(290,595) = 3,313 lb/h

Water vapor condensed = 4,331 − 3,313 = 1,018 lb/h

In addition, 80 lb/h of hydrocarbon will be condensed, slightly reducing the dry gas flow leaving the column as just indicated.

The heat balance for the cooler is:

Heat content of gas in = 88.36(290,675) = 25.684 × 10^6 Btu/h

Heat content of gas out = 40.78(290,595) = 11.850 × 10^6 Btu/h

Cooling load = 25.684 × 10^6 − 11.850 × 10^6 = 13.834 × 10^6 Btu/h

For a 40°F temperature rise in the cooling water, the inlet water feed rate is 345,700 lb/h.

The bottom of the column has a gas flow of 295,000 lb/h with a density of 0.196 lb/ft^3 and a liquid flow of 346,798 lb/h with a density of 61.5 lb/ft^3. The flow parameter for Figure 1-16 gives a value of 0.0664 at this point. A 9-ft 6-in. ID column is selected that produces a C_s of 0.334 ft/s at the bottom of the column. The ordinate on Figure 1-16 is 1.12, which gives a pressure drop of 0.34 in. H$_2$O/ft for #70 IMTP packing. At the top of the column, the gas flow rate is 293,902 lb/h with a density of 0.232 lb/ft^3 and the liquid flow is 345,700 lb/h with a density of 62.1 lb/ft^3. The flow parameter is 0.0719 and the C_s is 0.304 ft/s, giving a pressure drop of 0.28 in. H$_2$O/ft for #70 IMTP packing at the top of the column. The average pressure drop through the #70 IMTP packing is 0.31 in. H$_2$O/ft for a nonfoaming system.

Because only 0.03 wt% of the hydrocarbon entering the column condenses, the system can be treated as an inert gas dehumidification by use of Equation 6-23. For #70 IMTP packing, the value of the coefficient is 11.1 at atmospheric pressure, as shown in Table 6-3. Correcting this coefficient to the 0.3 power of the pressure, at 48 psia this coefficient will increase to 15.9. The base heat transfer coefficient at the bottom of the bed will be 1,396 Btu/h · ft^3 · °F, while at the top of the bed it will be 899 Btu/h · ft^3 · °F. The heat transfer coefficient must be adjusted for the effects of gas and liquid flow rates. This adjustment is made by taking U_v as a function of the vapor capacity factor (F_s) to the 0.74 power and the liquid mass flow rate to the 0.40 power. The adjusted logarithmic average volumetric heat transfer co-efficient is 2,270 Btu/h · ft^3 · °F.

The inlet gas stream has a water dew point temperature of 105.5°F. However, because this gas is superheated, the adiabatic saturation temperature should be used to calculate the temperature driving force at the bottom of the column. The gas leaving the column is at the hydrocarbon and water dew point; therefore, its temperature can be used to calculate the driving force at the top of the column. The temperature difference driving forces next are determined:

At top $\Delta T = 97 - 90 = 7.0°F$ (6-A)

At bottom $\Delta T = 138.3 - 130 = 8.3°F$ (6-B)

The ln mean temperature driving force for this column is, therefore, 7.63°F.

$$Z = \frac{13,834,000}{2270\,(70.88)\,(7.63)} = 11.3 \text{ ft.} \qquad (6\text{-C})$$

Due to the empirical nature of the heat transfer coefficients, a 15% safety factor will be applied to the calculated packed depth. To carry the 13.834 × 10^6 Btu/h heat load, we will specify a packed depth of 13 ft in a 9-ft 6-in. ID column. This system is assumed to be slightly foaming because some insoluble hydrocarbon condenses into the water phase. After making allowance for an increase in pressure drop due to foaming, plus the pressure drop through the column internals, the overall column pressure drop is expected to be only 0.23 psi. This is a substantial reduction of the pressure drop compared to the conventional tube-and-shell interstage cooler. Even considering the pressure losses through the piping and the separator drum, the compression ratio required for the second-stage compressor is reduced by 8%.

NOTATION

A	Column cross-sectional area (ft^2)
BDG	Bone dry gas
Cp	Heat capacity of liquid (Btu/lb · °F)
Cpv	Heat capacity of gas (Btu/lb · °F)
C_s	Capacity factor (ft/s)
F_s	Vapor capacity factor (lb$^{0.5}$/ft$^{0.5}$ · s)
G_d	Bone dry gas flow (lb/h)
G_i'	Inlet gas flow (lb/h)
G_o'	Outlet gas flow (lb/h)
H_i	Inlet gas enthalpy (Btu/lb BDG)
H_o	Outlet gas enthalpy (Btu/lb BDG)
H_M	Molar gas enthalpy (Btu/lb-mol BDG)
H_{OG}	Overall height of a gas transfer unit (ft)
H_v	Gas enthalpy (Btu/lb BDG)
H_v*	Equilibrium gas enthalpy (Btu/lb BDG)
h_i	Inlet gas humidity (lb H$_2$O/lb BDG)
h_o	Outlet gas humidity (lb H$_2$O/lb BDG)
L_i'	Inlet liquid flow (lb/h)
L_o'	Outlet liquid flow (lb/h)
L_w	Inlet water flow (lb/h)
N_{OG}	Number of overall gas transfer units
Q	Heat transferred (Btu/h)
T_i	Inlet gas temperature (°F)
T_o	Outlet gas temperature (°F)
t_i	Inlet liquid temperature (°F)
t_o	Outlet liquid temperature (°F)
U_v	Volumetric heat transfer coefficient (Btu/h · ft^3 · °F)
u'	Viscosity (lb/ft · h)
W	Water evaporated (lb/h)
Z	Packed depth (ft)
ΔH	Heat of vaporization (Btu/lb)

ΔT_{LM} In mean temperature driving force (°F)
ρ_G Gas density (lb/ft³)
ρ_L Liquid density (lb/ft³)

REFERENCES

1. Walker, W. H. *et al., Principles of Chemical Engineering,* McGraw-Hill, 1937, p. 593.
2. Kern, D. Q., *Process Heat Transfer,* McGraw-Hill, 1950, p. 594.
3. McAdams, W. H., *Heat Transmission,* 3rd ed., McGraw-Hill, 1954, p. 325.
4. Gilliland, E. R. and Sherwood, T. K., *Industrial Engineering Chemistry,* Vol. 26, 1934, p. 516.
5. Burger, R., *Hydrocarbon Processing,* Vol. 70, No. 3, 1991, p. 59.
6. Perry, J. H. *et al., Chemical Engineers' Handbook,* 4th ed., McGraw-Hill, 1963, p. 3–116.
7. Nusselt, W. Z., *Ver deut Ingeneurung,* Vol. 60, 1916, p. 541.
8. Perry, R. H. and Chilton, C. H., *Chemical Engineers' Handbook,* 5th ed., McGraw-Hill, 1973, p. 3–214.
9. Eckert, J. S. *et al.,* "Technical Data Related to Tower Packing," Norton Company, 1968, GR-290 A, B, and C.
10. Nemunaitis, R. R. and Eckert, J. S., *Chemical Engineering Progress,* Vol. 71, No. 8, 1975, p. 60.
11. Strigle, R. F. and Foote, E. H., "Technical Data Related to Tower Packing," Norton Company, 1975, GR-303, 305, and 306.
12. Hainbach, J. J. and Rubero, P. A., *Oil and Gas Journal,* Vol. 76, No. 12, 1978, p. 72.
13. Graf, K., *Oil and Gas Journal,* Vol. 83, No. 20, 1985, p. 60.
14. Gary, J. H. and Handwerk, G. E., *Petroleum Refining,* Marcel Dekker, 1975, p. 39.
15. Watkins, R. N., *Petroleum Refinery Distillation,* 2nd ed., Gulf Publishing, 1979, p. 46.
16. Huang, C. C. and Fair, J. R., "Direct-Contact Gas-Liquid Heat Transfer in a Packed Column," University of Texas, 1988.
17. *Petrochemical Handbook, Hydrocarbon Processing,* Vol. 48, No. 11, 1969, p. 176.
18. Strigle, R. F. and Hiramatsu, K., *Oil and Gas Journal,* Vol. 81, No. 39, 1983, p. 63.
19. Sauter, J. R. and Younts, W. E., *Oil and Gas Journal,* Vol. 84, No. 35, 1986, p. 45.
20. Strigle, R. F. and Nakano, T., *Plant/Operations Progress,* Vol. 6, No. 4, 1987, p. 208.

7

ATMOSPHERIC DISTILLATION

Distillation is the most widely used method for separating mixtures of liquids in the chemical and hydrocarbon processing industries. Separation takes place because the vapor phase is of a different composition than the liquid phase.

Distillation operations are classified on the basis of column operating pressure. Atmospheric distillations are considered to be those separations carried out at column pressures between 0.4 and 5.5 atmospheres absolute. Vacuum distillations are those operating at pressures below atmospheric, usually not greater than 300 mm Hg top column pressure. The pressure drop through such a column usually is an important design criterion. Vacuum column design is discussed in Chapter 8. Pressure distillations normally use a top column pressure of 80 psia or greater. The design of such columns is discussed in detail in Chapter 9. Because atmospheric pressure distillations are widely used in the separation of liquid mixtures, this chapter is devoted to a discussion of the fundamental principles of distillation as applied to operations carried out at pressures close to atmospheric. First, we will review the fundamental equilibrium relationships, and the determination of the number of theoretical stages required to effect the desired separation. Then, we will examine methods for establishing column capacity, followed by a discussion of factors affecting separation efficiency. Generally, the same factors that complicate the column design also reduce the economic viability of columns equipped with trays. Although packed columns for atmospheric pressure distillations are not as widely used, their design will be discussed first. This design is relatively less complicated and provides an appropriate basis for the chapters on vacuum and pressure distillations. These same principles also apply to distillations at low pressures or at high pressures, which are reviewed in detail in these later chapters.

IDEAL VAPOR/LIQUID EQUILIBRIUM SYSTEMS

According to Raoult's law, the equilibrium partial pressure of a component in the vapor phase is equal to the mol fraction of that component in the liquid phase multiplied by the vapor pressure of the pure component at the operating temperature. This law applies to an ideal system; one that has no interaction between components:

$$p = xp^* \qquad (7\text{-}1)$$

Dalton's law states that the partial pressure of a component in the vapor phase equals the mol fraction of that component in the vapor times the system pressure:

$$p = yP \qquad (7\text{-}2)$$

Combining these two equations gives an equilibrium relationship between the vapor-phase composition and liquid-phase composition for an ideal system:

$$\frac{y}{x} = \frac{p^*}{P} \qquad (7\text{-}3)$$

Distillation separates two components because of the difference in the equilibrium relationships between the various components. The ratio of the equilibrium relationships between components A and C is termed the relative volatility of A to C:

$$\alpha_{AC} = \frac{y_A x_C}{x_A y_C} \qquad (7\text{-}4)$$

Relative volatility is a measure of the ease of separation of two components. The greater the value of α_{AC}, the more readily component A can be separated from component C. Thus, an α value of 2 or greater indicates that the separation is not difficult, while an α value of less than 1.4 indicates that a large number of theoretical stages will be needed to effect the separation. From Equation 7-3, for an ideal system, the relative volatility is the ratio of the vapor pressures of the pure components A and C at the temperature of distillation:

$$\alpha_{AC} = \frac{p^*_A}{p^*_C} \qquad (7\text{-}5)$$

Boiling temperature is fixed by the column operating pressure, as well as by the liquid-phase composition. The vapor pressure for each component varies with the temperature at constant latent heat of vaporization in accordance with the Clapeyron equation:

$$\log p^* = b - \frac{j}{T} \qquad (7\text{-}6)$$

where b and j are constants. The use of Antoine's equation somewhat improves the accuracy of predicting vapor pressure:

$$\log p^* = b - \frac{j}{T + i} \qquad (7\text{-}7)$$

where i is an additional constant. The constants for Equation 7-6 or Equation 7-7 are determined experimentally for a particular component. An extensive table of Antoine constants is presented by Reid *et al.* [1].

Because these constants differ for various compounds, the vapor pressures for different components usually do not change at the same rate with temperature variations. For an ideal system, the relative volatility between the two components, as expressed by Equation 7-6, varies with the boiling temperature. As an example, consider the separation of a system of toluene and ethyl benzene. Assume that the separation produces substantially pure toluene as distillate and equally pure ethyl benzene as bottoms. If the distillation column is operated at atmospheric pressure, the relative volatility between these two components is 2.1. If the distillation pressure is raised to 5 atmospheres absolute, the relative volatility is reduced to 1.8. However, if the pressure of distillation is lowered to 200 mm Hg absolute, the relative volatility increases to 2.3. Thus, separation becomes easier as the column pressure is reduced.

The equilibrium ratio often is used in the calculation of hydrocarbon separations. It is the ratio of the vapor composition to the liquid composition with which it is in equilibrium:

$$K = \frac{y}{x} \qquad (7\text{-}8)$$

From Equation 7-3, for an ideal system:

$$K = \frac{p^*}{P} \qquad (7\text{-}9)$$

There is an equilibrium ratio representing each component in the system. For light hydrocarbons, the equilibrium ratio for any one component increases at higher temperatures and decreases at higher pressures. In addition, the value of K is altered by the other components present in the system, as well as the concentration of the specified component in the liquid phase. The value of the equilibrium ratio usually decreases as the molecular weight increases for a homologous series of compounds. This is because the vapor pressure at any fixed temperature decreases as molecular weight increases. However, the variation of α with temperature is less than the variation of K with temperature, which adds to the convenience of calculative methods using the relative volatility.

As previously stated, the relative volatility of one component compared to another indicates the ease of separation of these components by distillation. The relative volatility of component A compared to component C also is expressed as a ratio of the equilibrium ratio for component A to the equilibrium ratio for component C:

$$\alpha_{AC} = \frac{K_A}{K_C} \qquad (7\text{-}10)$$

The value of the relative volatility generally decreases as the pressure increases, as just illustrated for the system toluene and ethyl benzene. Thus, separation for this particular system is greater per theoretical stage for a vacuum distillation than for a high-pressure distillation of the same mixture.

NONIDEAL VAPOR/LIQUID EQUILIBRIUM SYSTEMS

At atmospheric pressure, the vapor phase essentially follows the ideal gas law, so that deviations from idealism are due to liquid phase behavior. When the liquid phase is not ideal, the equilibrium ratio is modified by the activity coefficient (γ):

$$K = \gamma K' \qquad (7\text{-}11)$$

where K' is the equilibrium ratio calculated from Equations 7-3 and 7-9. The liquid phase normally is ideal when all components are similar, such as a series of saturated aliphatic hydrocarbons. Nonideal liquids usually are mixtures of molecularly dissimilar components that associate in the liquid phase, such as methanol and benzene or acetone and chloroform. Hydrogen bonding often is a significant factor in nonideal liquid mixtures. Such systems can deviate substantially from Raoult's law (Equation 7-1). In all separations carried out by distillation only a few systems are totally ideal. Many show a variation in relative volatility with liquid-phase composition other than that anticipated due to the change of boiling temperature with composition. One such system is propylene and propane at 17 atm pressure. In this system, the relative volatility changes from 1.08 in the propylene-rich top of the column to 1.14 in the propane-rich bottom of the column.

The activity coefficient (γ) is a function of the temperature and composition of the liquid phase. If the volatilities of all components are increased, the deviation from idealism is considered positive (γ greater than 1.0). If the volatilities of all components are reduced, the deviation from idealism is considered negative (γ less than 1.0). Van Laar developed a method to calculate the effect of liquid composition on liquid-phase activity coefficients for nonpolar, binary systems at a given temperature [2]. The constants for these equations are determined from experimental VLE data. This method applies to systems that show either positive or negative deviation from Raoult's law, but it will not predict curves exhibiting maximum or minimum values of γ. This method has been used on multicomponent mixtures by assuming a pseudobinary system of key components.

A better method of calculation for multicomponent mixtures has been developed by Wilson [3]. The binary parameters still must be determined from experimental VLE data. This method applies to mixtures of polar and nonpolar molecules (such as n-hexane and ethanol) that are strongly nonideal. Also, this method has the ability to model nonideal systems, even in dilute regions. However, this method does not predict curves exhibiting maximum or minimum values of γ, nor will it predict immiscibility.

The UNIFAC model predicts liquid-phase activity coefficients for nonideal mixtures when no VLE data are available [4]. This model uses a group contribution method with about 50 identified functional groups. The liquid-phase activity coefficients are calculated from an equation by use of molecular configuration. The parameters calculated are independent of temperature. This method is restricted to systems in which all components are condensable. It is as accurate as the Wilson method, but has a more theoretical basis. However, despite the theoretical basis of UNIFAC, the constants for each functional group are essentially empirical.

At pressures below 5.5 atm, the vapor phase normally may be considered ideal. In such a situation, Equations 7-2 and 7-8 apply. Certain systems, such as acetic acid and water, form dimers in the vapor phase. In these cases, the degree of dimerization determines not only the VLE, but the average molecular weight of the vapor. This, in turn, controls the gas density used in the hydraulic capacity calculations.

VAPOR/LIQUID EQUILIBRIUM RELATIONSHIPS

As previously stated, atmospheric distillations in this chapter are considered to be those distillations operating at column pressures above 0.4 atm and less than 5.5 atm absolute. In this pressure range, the column pressure drop usually is small compared to the system pressure. Also the liquid surface tension usually is high enough to avoid capacity restrictions, which will be discussed in Chapter 9.

The feed composition and flow rate are known, as is the specification for the top distillate and column bottoms. Normally the concentration of one heavy component, known as the heavy key, is specified in the distillate. Likewise, the concentration of one light component, known as the light key, is specified for the bottoms. Sometimes the percentage recovery of one of the feed components is the specification for either the distillate or the bottoms.

To calculate the vapor composition, it is necessary to develop an equilibrium relationship. For the distillation of an ideal binary system of components A and C, the equilibrium relationship is given by:

$$y_A = \frac{\alpha_{AC} x_A}{1 + (\alpha_{AC} - 1)x_A} \tag{7-12}$$

This relationship is derived from the definition of relative volatility, as given in Equations 7-4 and 7-10.

Using Equation 7-12, a curve can be established that shows the relationship between the liquid composition and the equilibrium vapor composition at a constant relative volatility. Figure 7-1 shows curves at α values of 1.4, 2.0, and 4.0, which represent separations of increasing ease. The equilibrium relationships between vapor and liquid compositions for some nonideal binary systems are shown in Figure 7-2. Curve I is a methanol/water system, and Curve II is a water/acetic acid system. Note that these curves no longer are symmetrical like those in Figure 7-1.

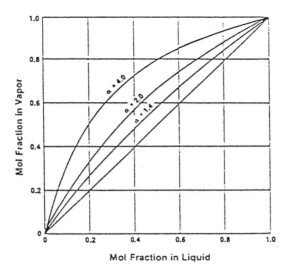

Figure 7-1. Vapor/liquid equilibrium relationship ideal system.

Care must be taken in the selection of experimental vapor/liquid equilibrium data used in the calculations. These data should cover the range of compositions proposed for the column being designed. Extrapolation of VLE data, especially into high purity areas, can be a source of significant errors.

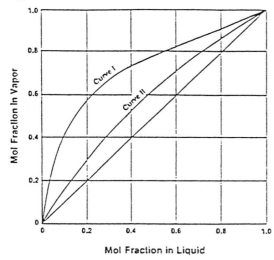

Figure 7-2. Vapor/liquid equilibrium relationship non-ideal system.

DETERMINATION OF THEORETICAL STAGES

The number of theoretical stages required for a given separation is calculated by one of the conventional methods. In many binary distillations, the molar flow rates of vapor and liquid are substantially constant. For systems in which the molar heats of vaporization and liquid heat capacities are almost the same and heat losses are negligible, McCabe and Thiele have developed a graphical method for determining the number of theoretical stages required [5]. Under these conditions, the operating line of the distillation column can be represented by a material balance equation. For a column with a total condenser, the overhead vapor and distillate are of the same composition. The operating line for the rectifying section must pass through the distillate composition. If a partial condenser is used, the reflux composition will be a liquid in equilibrium with the condenser outlet vapor composition. A partial condenser usually provides one additional theoretical stage. In this case, the condenser outlet vapor constitutes at least some of the distillate product.

Usually the reboiler is considered as one theoretical stage, so that the vapor to the bottom of the column is in equilibrium with the liquid bottoms product. The operating line for the stripping section must pass through the bottoms composition. In a binary distillation, the feed should be introduced into the column at the equilibrium stage repre-sented by the intersection of the two operating lines. The required the-oretical stages are determined using a stepwise procedure between the operating lines and the equilibrium curve. Figure 7-3 demonstrates this graphical procedure for a separation requiring three theoretical stages rectifying and four theoretical stages stripping.

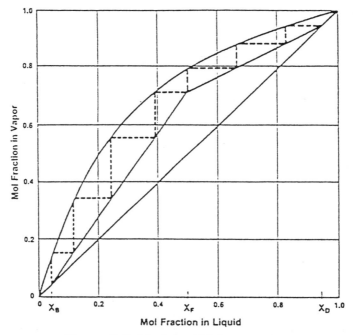

Figure 7-3. McCabe-Thiele procedure.

One of the more widely used methods for calculating the number of theoretical stages in multicomponent systems was developed by Lewis and Matheson [6]. Again, the molar flow rates of vapor and liquid in each section are assumed to be constant. On each equilibrium stage, the summation of the concentrations of all vapor components must equal unity. The same is true for the summation of the concentrations of all liquid components. Further, the vapor and liquid compositions of each component are related by the K value for that component.

Generally this method requires considerable trial-and-error, as a tem-perature first must be assumed, then the K values for each component must be calculated. This procedure is repeated until a matched compositional profile is obtained for each stage.

The starting points for the calculations are the distillate and bottoms compositions, if the concentrations of all components are known. When only a single high-boiling impurity concentration (heavy key) is specified in the distillate, and only a single low-boiling impurity concentration (light key) is specified in the bottoms, a different starting point is needed. In this latter case, the calculations may be started from the feed point, because the feed composition is known for all components. When there are a number of low-boiling components similar to the light key and/or a number of high-boiling components similar to the heavy key, a method developed by Thiele and Geddes can be used to calculate the distribution of such components [7]. This method assumes the number of theoretical stages in each section and the temperature of each stage. The split of each component between overhead and bottoms then can be calculated.

Again a trial-and-error calculation is required by adjusting the temperature profile of the column until the assumed number of theoretical stages equals that required to obtain the specified separation. This method especially is useful in evaluating the performance of an existing column.

It is possible to specify a minor light component to control bottoms product purity, or a minor heavy component to control distillate purity. The number of theoretical stages of separation required then must be calculated by a rigorous method, rather than by a pseudobinary procedure.

Computers have greatly reduced the effort and increased the calculation speed. They easily produce the necessary repetitive evaluations required to satisfy simultaneously the material and heat balances and equilibrium relationships. In computerized calculations, the selection of the equation of state influences the number of calculated theoretical stages required. Each equation of state was developed primarily from a specific data bank that usually was confined to a certain type of compound. As an example, the Benedict-Webb-Rubin equation of state was developed from experimental data on methane through n-heptane [8]. This equation is preferred to generate K values for these light hydrocarbons. The equation of state specified for the calculations should be the one based on data for compounds most closely resembling those being separated.

The Braun K-10 Correlation was developed to generate K values for light hydrocarbons at pressures below 100 psia and at temperatures above 100°F [9]. This correlation has proved useful in the calculation of refinery columns, including those processing heavy fractions. Also, it can be used for aromatic distillations, so long as nonideal compounds are not present.

The Soave-Redlich-Kwong equation is a modification of the original Redlich-Kwong equation for predicting K values [10]. The Soave modification produces a significant improvement in the prediction of VLE data for mixtures, as well as pure substances. This method probably is the most widely used prediction for a large variety of hydrocarbon systems from cryogenic conditions to high-pressure operations.

The Peng-Robinson equation was developed to overcome some of the shortcomings of the SRK equation [11]. This equation has been used to regress experimental data on C-2 and C-3 splitters. Generally, the Peng-Robinson equation gives a better simulation of actual column performance than the SRK equation, which predicts more conservative results.

Computer programs usually calculate the properties of compounds present in the column feed from a set of equations rather than from a library of experimental data. Calculated physical properties should be checked against experimentally determined values to verify these properties during final design.

CONDITION OF FEED

For a system with constant molal heats of vaporization, q equals the mol fraction of liquid in the feed. The q-line for the feed passes through x_F on the 45° line and has a slope of $\dfrac{q}{q-1}$ on a McCabe-Thiele diagram.

For a liquid feed at the bubble point, the q-line is vertical. For a vapor feed at the dew point, the q-line is horizontal.

The minimum reflux ratio needed for a specific separation requires an infinite number of theoretical stages. On a McCabe-Thiele diagram, this is represented by an operating line, which intersects the q-line for the feed at the equilibrium curve. For easy separations (i.e., an α greater than 1.8), an operating reflux ratio 25% greater than minimum usually is specified. For separations where an air-cooled condenser can be used, and exhaust steam is the energy source, an operating reflux ratio as high as 1.35 times the minimum may be specified. For difficult separations (i.e., an α less than 1.4), the operating reflux ratio should be at least 12% greater than the minimum required, unless the vapor/liquid equilibrium is known with a high degree of precision.

In determining the number of theoretical stages required, the calculations usually should start at both the reboiler and the condenser and proceed toward the feed point. The bottoms product and distillate compositions are known or specified, and the bottoms and distillate product rates are known or can be calculated by material balance from the feed rate and composition. Such a procedure minimizes calculative errors while meeting the specified product compositions.

MAXIMUM OPERATIONAL CAPACITY

After the operating reflux ratio has been selected, the hydraulic vapor and liquid loadings are calculated for each column section. Unless flow rates change significantly within the column, the hydraulic loadings need be determined only at the top and bottom of the tower, as well as above and below the feed point.

A packed column diameter historically was selected to produce a pressure drop of 0.40 in. to 0.60 in. H_2O/ft of packed depth at the point of maximum hydraulic loading [12]. This rule was applied as long as the liquid specific gravity was at least 0.80. This design basis was selected from experience with 1½-in. and 2-in. ceramic Intalox saddle and metal Pall ring packings in columns that operated in the packing loading region. Such a sizing procedure neglected any effect of flow rates on separation efficiency.

In the experimental work that led to the development of a modern, high void fraction random dumped packing (Intalox Metal Tower Packing), it was found that vapor velocities could be increased to such a high rate that significant liquid entrainment was produced without incurring correspondingly high pressure drops. Further, because the entrained liquid was carried up the column, separation efficiency eventually dropped at vapor velocities that still were below the packing's maximum hydraulic capacity (flooding point).

Figure 7-4 is a plot of the separation efficiency (HETP) of a random dumped tower packing as a function of vapor velocity for an atmospheric distillation. Vapor velocity is expressed as a capacity factor to account for the effect of vapor and liquid densities:

$$C_s = \frac{G*}{[\rho_G(\rho_L - \rho_G)]^{0.5}} \tag{7-13}$$

In Figure 7-4, the liquid rate at constant reflux ratio increases in direct proportion to the vapor rate. On this curve, the region from point B to point C exhibits a constant separation efficiency typical for the packing. As C_s increases further, the vapor rate becomes great enough to begin to interact with the liquid phase. This generates increased interfacial area beyond point C, due to liquid holdup increasing with vapor rate. In previous publications, this point has been referred to as the "loading point" of the packing [13]. At rates just greater than this point, the separation efficiency increases (HETP becomes lower). With further vapor rate increase, liquid entrainment finally is initiated. Because this liquid recycle reduces the concentration gradient, the effective HETP increases. This results in a maximum efficiency (minimum HETP value) at the rate represented by point D.

The column actually can be operated at a vapor rate as high as that represented by point F without exceeding the HETP value typical for the packing. Therefore, the C_s at point F has been designated as the maximum operational capacity of the packing [14]. This rate provides perfectly stable operation because it has been determined from separation efficiency. This approach to packed column capacity has been verified by the work of Kunesh *et al.* [15]. This definition of maximum operational capacity has been accepted by the American Institute of Chemical Engineers [16]. The maximum hydraulic capacity of the packing is up to 20% higher than the rate at point F for atmospheric distillations.

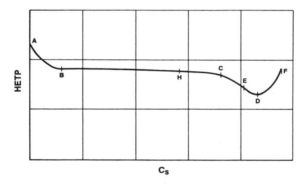

Figure 7-4. Typical packing performance. (From Strigle [14]. Reproduced by permission of the American Institute of Chemical Engineers.)

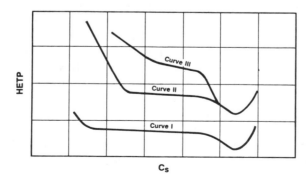

Figure 7-5. Effect of liquid distribution on packing efficiency.

MINIMUM OPERATING RATE

Similarly, the rate represented by point B in Figure 7-4 is the minimum flow at which the typical HETP value can be realized. Usually this rate represents a limitation of liquid distribution techniques rather than the minimum wetting rate of the tower packing [17]. In atmospheric distillations, liquid rates normally are not less than 1.5 gpm/ft^2.

Figure 7-5 illustrates the effect of liquid distribution on separation efficiency. Curve III shows the operation of a poorly designed liquid distributor where the natural internal distribution characteristics of the packing and the vapor flow actually are responsible for the majority of the liquid distribution. This poor liquid distribution severely curtails the operational flexibility of the packing because the separation obtained varies with the vapor rate. Curves I and II show significant improvements in column performance in that constant efficiency is maintained over a wider range of vapor flow rates. Curve II represents the performance of standard liquid distributors typical of those commercially available during the 1970s. The minimum operating capacity for Curve II is much greater than that for Curve I because of poorer liquid distribution at lower rates. Curve I illustrates the operation of high-performance liquid distributors (see Chapter 10). Curve I shows a lower HETP value, as well as a wider flow range at constant HETP, than Curve II because uniform liquid distribution is maintained.

Vapor maldistribution theoretically could lead to the same lack of performance, as illustrated in Figure 7-5. There is, however, a much better radial mixing of the vapor phase in the packed bed because it almost always is in the turbulent flow regime. Vapor distribution normally is not a problem as long as the pressure drop through the packed bed is at least 0.10 in. H$_2$O/ft of packed depth, and the inlet vapor nozzles are operating at F$_s$ vapor rates not greater than 22 lb$^{0.5}$/ft$^{0.5}$ · s. For columns in which the packed depth is less than the column diameter, vapor maldistribution can be a problem.

Pressure drop usually is not critical in atmospheric distillations, therefore, the design C$_s$ normally is selected above the loading point (point C in Figure 7-4) and below the maximum efficiency rate (point D). Typically, the flow rate at point C is 70% to 75% of that at maximum operational capacity (point F). The design C$_s$ (point E) should be chosen to permit at least a 15% increase in flow rates before reaching the maximum operational capacity of the packing. This will allow for normal feed and heat input variations. The design C$_s$ should not be less than 80% of the maximum operational C$_s$, if the greatest possible turndown ratio is desired. Although the separation efficiency from point C to point F is greater than that typical of the packing, this advantage normally is not used for design purposes.

COLUMN DIAMETER SELECTION

It may be desirable to change column diameter if the hydraulic loading varies greatly from top to bottom of the column or from one packed bed to another. The cost of a column diameter change may be excessive for small diameter columns or where the diameter change is less than 12 in. However, there may be a problem of mechanical stability, if the bottom of the column is of a smaller diameter than the top. Another option is to change packing size at constant column diameter to accommodate variations in hydraulic loading.

By experimentation with systems such as those listed in Table 7-1, the maximum operational capacity for Intalox Metal Tower Packing was determined. This capacity was expressed as a function of the flow parameter and system properties by Dolan and Strigle [18]. The flow parameter is a ratio of the square roots of the liquid kinetic energy to the vapor kinetic energy:

$$X = \frac{L}{G}\left[\frac{\rho_G}{\rho_L}\right]^{0.5} \tag{7-14}$$

Flow parameter values from 0.04 to 0.17 are normal for atmospheric distillations.

Figure 7-6 is a plot of the maximum operational capacity as a function of the flow parameter for IMTP packing. These curves indicate that the maximum capacity of this packing is reduced by approximately 0.2 times the log of the flow parameter as the liquid rate or operating pressure is

Table 7-1

Experimental Systems

System	Pressure (absolute)
Acetone and Water	740 mm Hg
Cyclohexane and n-heptane	260 mm Hg
Cyclohexane and n-heptane	740 mm Hg
Cyclohexane and n-heptane	24 psia
Cyclohexanone and Cyclohexanol	70 mm Hg
Ethylbenzene and Styrene	50 mm Hg
Ethylene and Ethane	300 psia
Ethylene glycol and diethylene glycol	45 mm Hg
Ethylene glycol and water	230 mm Hg
Iso-octane and toluene	100 mm Hg
Iso-octane and toluene	740 mm Hg
Propylene and Propane	280 psia
Propylene and Propane	330 psia
Propylene and Propane	430 psia

increased. C_o is the maximum capacity factor for each size of packing reduced to a standard condition. Test data indicate that the maximum capacity of the packing varies as the 0.20 power of the surface tension of the liquid phase for distillation operations. This variation is similar to that reported by Fair for the capacity of sieve trays with respect to jet flooding [19]. If data on non-boiling systems are included with distillation data, the maximum operational C_s varies as the surface tension to the 0.16 power; therefore, this exponent has been assigned for use with Figure 7-6. Thus, where the liquid phase has a surface tension of 15 dyne/cm, the maximum operational C_s will be 3% lower than with an 18 dyne/cm liquid surface tension. The data do not justify an increase of more than 8% for the maximum operational C_s as surface tension is increased above 20 dyne/cm.

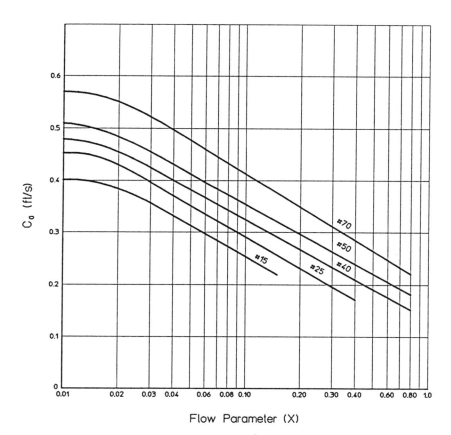

Flow Parameter (X)

Figure 7-6. Capacity correlation: Intalox® Metal Tower Packing. (From Strigle with permission of The American Institute of Chemical Engineers, 1993, AIChE. All rights reserved [43].)

In addition, the experimental data indicate that the maximum C_s value at constant flow parameter varies as the liquid viscosity to the -0.10 to -0.13 power. For liquid viscosities between 0.07 and 1.1 cps, an average of the -0.11 power of liquid viscosity can be used. Therefore, an ethanol/water distillation column would have a 3% lower maximum operational C_s in the ethanol-rich rectifying section where the liquid viscosity is 0.39 cps than in the water-rich stripping section with a liquid viscosity of only 0.30 cps. Likewise, the data do not support an increase of more than 9% for the maximum operational C_s, as liquid viscosity is decreased below 0.20 cps. Equation 7-15 is used to calculate the maximum operational capacity for a particular service.

$$C_s = C_o \left[\frac{\sigma}{20} \right]^{0.16} \left[\frac{\mu}{0.20} \right]^{-0.11} \tag{7-15}$$

Standard values of 20 dyne/cm for surface tension and 0.20 cps for liquid viscosity have been used to prepare Figure 7-6. This correlation was developed from data on liquids with surface tensions as low as 5 dyne/cm and viscosities as high as 1.1 cps.

The maximum operational capacity of structured packings can be correlated to the flow parameter in the same manner as illustrated for random dumped packings. Figure 7-7 is such a plot for five sizes of Intalox structured tower packing. This chart is based on data developed by three groups of investigators, as described in Chapter 2. These data, ranging from a pressure of 16mm Hg absolute for an ortho/para xylene system to 300 psi for an isobutane/n-butane system, were correlated by Hausch *et al.*, as shown in Figure 7-7 [20]. Again, the curves indicate that the maximum capacity is reduced by a factor times the log of the flow parameter. However, the value of this factor tends to increase as the surface area of the packing decreases.

Equation 7-15 also is used to calculate the maximum operational capacity of this structured packing. The values of C_o are taken from Figure 7-7 for the flow parameter involved. Limitations for physical properties are the same as for Figure 7-6.

EFFICIENCY CONSIDERATIONS

Distillation efficiency commonly is expressed as height equivalent to a theoretical stage (HETP). In a trayed column, the HETP value is the tray spacing divided by the fractional overall tray efficiency. A theoretical stage is a mass transfer stage from which the liquid and vapor streams leave in equilibrium. In a packed column, the liquid in the packed bed would be in equilibrium with the gas stream located one HETP value above it in the packed bed. Thus, the stepwise procedure McCabe and

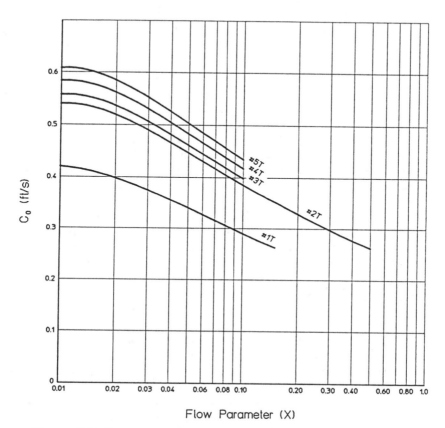

Figure 7-7. Capacity correlation: Intalox® Structured Packing.

Thiele developed to simulate the performance of a trayed column is somewhat difficult to envision for operation of a packed column.

Because a packed bed is a continuous contacting device, an equilibrium stage concept based on a transfer unit has been proposed. The
height of a transfer unit is defined as that depth of packing required to
produce a change in the composition equal to the mass transfer driving
force causing that change [21]. It can be shown that when the equilibrium curve and operating line are straight:

$$H_{OG} = H_G + \frac{mG_m}{L_m} H_L \qquad\qquad (7\text{-}16)$$

This equation is based on the two-film theory, which assumes that the vapor film is in equilibrium with the liquid film at the interface. The operating line slope for a distillation column is L_m/G_m. The ratio of the equilibrium curve slope to the operating line slope is called the lambda factor.

$$\lambda = \frac{mG_m}{L_m} \tag{7-17}$$

At total reflux, the λ factor equals m, because L_m equals G_m. The operating pressure has little effect on the values of H_G or H_L. However, the resultant higher temperatures encountered in high pressure distillations decrease the value of H_L, probably because of reduced liquid viscosity and the increased value of liquid diffusivity.

In practical cases, the equilibrium relationship seldom is linear. If the operating line and equilibrium curve were straight and parallel, then HETP would equal H_{OG}. If the operating line and equilibrium curve are linear, but not parallel, then:

$$\text{HETP} = \frac{\ln \lambda}{\lambda - 1} H_{OG} \tag{7-18}$$

At total reflux, the λ value in the stripping section must be greater than 1, and the λ value in the rectifying section must be less than 1. From Equation 7-18, a higher HETP value might be expected in the rectifying section than in the stripping section of a fractionator, if the value of H_{OG} is constant. However, in commercial applications, the HETP value varies less than the H_{OG} value. This was demonstrated by Eckert and Walter for 1-in. and 2-in. metal Pall ring packings [22]. Therefore, the efficiency of tower packings in distillation usually will be considered in terms of HETP values.

HETP PREDICTION

Despite the great amount of data available, no method yet exists for HETP prediction with a high degree of confidence. The prudent designer, therefore, resorts to commercial experience for the separation of similar compounds as a first choice for selection of the design HETP value. Vital *et al.* present an extensive list of HETP values for various tower packings in more than 40 different services [23]. Although not stated, these HETP values probably were obtained using commercial-quality liquid distributors. If industrial experience is not available, as may be the case with a new process, the designer uses pilot plant data to estimate the HETP value for design purposes.

However, there are a number of occasions where the designer is faced with developing a design HETP value without any actual experience. The designer then must rely on a calculated value obtained from some correlation. A model has been proposed by Onda *et al.* to calculate H_{OG} by means of Equation 7-16 [24]. This model evaluates H_G and H_L values from mass transfer coefficients:

$$H_G = \frac{G_m}{k_G aAP} \tag{7-19}$$

$$H_L = \frac{L_m}{k_L aA} \tag{7-20}$$

This model requires a calculation of the interfacial area. The equation used for this calculation is based on the geometric surface area of the packing and a critical surface tension that is, in turn, dependent on the packing material.

Because the Onda model showed an average deviation of about 40% for the calculated value compared to the experimental HETP value, Bolles and Fair proposed an improved model for predicting separation efficiency [25]. This model also calculates H_{OG} by means of Equation 7-16. The H_{OG} value then is converted to an HETP value by use of Equation 7-18. Unfortunately, this model makes a correction for the effect of the packed bed depth on both H_G and H_L; thus, the calculation becomes an iterative procedure. In addition, there is a proposed correction for tower diameter that is greater for ceramic Raschig ring packing than for ceramic Berl saddle packing. Therefore, this model has incorporated within it corrections for lack of proper packing performance, which really were specific to the actual testing device.

The improved Bolles and Fair model still had a standard deviation of almost 25% for the calculated values compared to the experimental data; therefore, Porter and Jenkins conducted an extensive review of the data bank from which that model was developed [26]. They eliminated the runs made at very high and very low vapor rates and confined the data base only to distillation runs. Porter and Jenkins then found that this improved model needed only about a 20% safety factor to give the calculated design HETP value a 95% confidence limit for prediction of the residual data base.

Based on this work, Porter has proposed that HETP at total reflux is a function of the flow parameter and the liquid viscosity:

$$HETP = \lambda H_s \left(vX^{0.5} + w\mu \right) \tag{7-21}$$

In this correlation, v and w are constants and H_s is the HETP value for the packing as determined experimentally for a standard distillation system.

Norton Chemical Process Products Corporation has developed a proprietary correlation for prediction of HETP values based upon a regression of their own data, plus that of Billet and Fractionation Research, Inc. [27]. This model indicates that the HETP value primarily is a function of surface tension and liquid viscosity. The flow parameter and vapor density also show minor influences. This correlation is applicable to systems with a liquid-phase surface tension above 4 dyne/cm and less than 33 dyne/cm and a liquid viscosity of at least 0.08 cps but not greater than 0.83 cps. It does not apply to aqueous systems, interacting compounds, or systems with a relative volatility of 3 or greater.

The Norton correlation for modern, random dumped packings used in distillations at pressures up to 200 psia, as initially developed by Dolan [28], is:

$$\ln \text{HETP} = n - 0.187 \ln \sigma + 0.213 \ln \mu \qquad (7\text{-}22)$$

The data of Strigle and Porter give the relative HETP values for IMTP packings, metal Pall ring packings, and ceramic Intalox saddle packings of three different sizes [29]. Using these data, Table 7-2 gives the values for n in Equation 7-22 for each of these packings.

As discussed in Chapter 2, the mass transfer coefficients for random dumped packings and sheet metal structured packings are nearly the same for sizes with similar surface areas. Thus, it is reasonable to extend Equation 7-22 to predict HETP values for such structured packings. Data on three sizes of Intalox structured packing is available from the manufacturer for an iso-octane/toluene distillation at atmospheric pressure. This data was obtained with the same equipment as reported by Strigle and Porter for the random packing evaluations. Table 7-3 gives values for n for use in Equation 7-22 for this structured packing.

These predicted HETP values are based upon the use of high-performance column internals (as discussed in Chapter 10). However, a correction for the lambda effect must be applied to this calculated value, if lambda has a value greater than 1.8 or less than 0.6.

The HETP value used for final specification of packed depth should be based on the same vapor/liquid equilibrium, equation of state, and physical properties as used in the calculation of the required number of theoretical stages. For easy separations (less than 10 theoretical stages), a 20% design safety factor can be applied to a typical HETP value without severe economic penalty. For separations requiring 15 to 25 theoretical stages, a 16% design safety factor commonly is applied to the HETP value. For more difficult separations, the design HETP value used must be as precise as possible.

Figure 7-8. Atmospheric fractionators. These packed columns are used for aromatics processing.

Table 7-2

**Constant n for HETP Correlation
(Equation 7-22)**

Tower Packing	Value of n
#25 IMTP® Packing	1.13080
#40 IMTP® Packing	1.37030
#50 IMTP® Packing	1.56860
1 in. Pall Ring	1.13080
1½ in. Pall Ring	1.39510
2 in. Pall Ring	1.65840
1 in. Intalox® Saddle	1.13080
1½ in. Intalox® Saddle	1.41570
2 in. Intalox® Saddle	1.72330

Table 7-3

**Constant n for HETP Correlation
Intalox® Structured Packing**

Packing Size	Value of n
1T	0.76830
2T	1.01280
3T	1.38680

TYPICAL DESIGN EFFICIENCY

Packed columns maintain a high separation efficiency in both liquid-film-controlled and gas-film-controlled systems. For many years, packed columns have been used for absorption systems that characteristically are liquid-film-controlled. As an example, the HETP value for a trayed column might be twice as great in an absorption operation as compared to a distillation operation. For the same systems, the HETP value for IMTP packing in the absorption operation typically would be only one-third greater than for the distillation operation.

In atmospheric distillations, the gas film many times offers a resistance to mass transfer similar to that of the liquid film. The vapor density is low, providing a high molecular diffusion rate in that phase. The diffusion coefficient in the vapor phase at atmospheric pressure may be several orders of magnitude times that in the liquid phase. However, the liquid-phase resistance becomes increasingly important as the liquid viscosity increases, which reduces the diffusion rate in that phase. Also, there is a tendency for the liquid-film resistance to increase as the liquid molecular weight increases.

Table 7-4

**Typical Separation Efficiency
Intalox® Metal Tower Packing**

Packing Size	HETP (ft)
#25	1.2 to 1.6
#40	1.5 to 2.0
#50	1.8 to 2.4

Table 7-4 gives the range of HETP values obtained with three sizes of IMTP packing in typical distillation systems [30]. HETP values for #15 IMTP packing are about 10% less than those for #25 IMTP packing; while the HETP values for #70 IMTP packing are 1.4 times those for #50 IMTP packing. These values apply to systems with liquid surface tensions of 13 dyne/cm or greater and liquid viscosities of 0.70 cps or less. For liquids with lower surface tension or higher viscosity, the HETP value increases. However, the efficiency loss at higher liquid viscosities is much less for tower packings than for trays. The values in Table 7-4 apply to paraffins, naphthenes, aromatics, alcohols, and ketones with molecular weights not greater than 100. HETP values for Intalox Structured packing 2T vary from 13 in. to 17 in. for similar systems. HETP values for size 1T are 20% lower and HETP values for size 3T are about 45% higher than for size 2T. These HETP values do not apply to systems with chemical reactions, chemical association, or high level ionization in the liquid phase. Values for such systems should be determined by commercial experience or from pilot plant data.

EFFICIENCY IN MULTICOMPONENT SYSTEMS

Tray efficiencies for 54 columns refining petroleum were reported by Drickamer and Bradford, which they correlated against feed viscosity [31]. This correlation contains data on systems having liquid viscosities from 0.07 cps to 0.50 cps. O'Connell produced a similar correlation that also included the effect of relative volatility [32]. From these correlations, the HETP for trays on 18-in. spacing increases by 50% to 75%, for a change from a liquid viscosity of 0.15 cps to a viscosity of 0.44 cps. For the same viscosity change, the HETP value for random dumped tower packing would be only 25% higher at the greater viscosity than at the lower viscosity.

If the sum of the mol fraction of light key plus the mol fraction of heavy key in the feed does not exceed the sum of the mol fractions of the two largest lighter-than-light key components plus the sum of the mol fractions of the two largest heavier-than-heavy key components, the designer

Table 7-5

Aromatic Feed Composition

Component	Mol Fraction	Atmospheric Boiling Temperature (°F)
n-hexane	0.007	155.7
benzene	0.199	176.2
n-heptane	0.012	209.2
toluene	0.184	231.1
n-octane	0.024	258.2
p-xylene	0.062	281.0
m-xylene	0.250	282.4
o-xylene	0.120	292.0
n-nonane	0.016	303.5
indene	0.126	358.9

should use caution in determining the design HETP value. As an example, consider separation of an aromatic feed in which toluene is the light key and m-xylene is the heavy key.

The sum of the mol fractions of toluene and m-xylene is 0.434. The sum of the mol fractions of benzene, n-heptane, o-xylene, and indene is 0.457. In this case, the physical properties of the phases may not be representative of a binary separation of the light key and heavy key that provided the basis for determining the number of theoretical stages required. Thus, the design HETP value obtained from physical properties of the system should be applied only to the number of theoretical stages determined by a rigorous method for multicomponent mixtures.

The concentration of components lighter than the light key in the distillate will be greater than the ratio of x_D/x_B for the light key. Likewise, the concentration of components heavier than the heavy key in the bottoms will be greater than the ratio of x_B/x_D for the heavy key. If the light key and the heavy key are not adjacent boiling compounds, the method developed by Geddes can be used to predict the distribution of intermediate boiling components at total reflux [33]. Hengstebeck provides a more exact method for determining the distributions of non-key components at finite reflux ratios [34].

EFFECT OF LAMBDA ON EFFICIENCY

The values for HETP shown in Table 7-4 apply to systems with relative volatilities not greater than 2. From Equation 7-12, the value of the equilibrium curve slope (m) at constant relative volatility varies from α at very low light-key concentrations (x approaches zero) to $1/\alpha$ at very high light-key concentrations (x approaches unity).

In a feed consisting of an equal molar binary mixture, the λ factor for components of differing relative volatilities can be examined. In each case, the distillate is assumed to be 90 mol % light component and the bottoms to contain 10 mol % light component. Table 7-6 gives the λ factor at total reflux for three different difficulties of separation. Note that the λ factor deviates further from unity as α is increased.

Table 7-6

Lambda Factors at Total Reflux

	$\alpha = 1.20$	$\alpha = 1.60$	$\alpha = 2.00$
Top of Rectifying Section	0.862	0.675	0.554
Bottom of Rectifying Section	0.992	0.947	0.889
Average for Rectifying Section	0.928	0.811	0.721
Top of Stripping Section	0.992	0.947	0.889
Bottom of Stripping Section	1.153	1.424	1.653
Average for Stripping Section	1.073	1.185	1.271

Because commercial columns do not operate at total reflux, the same column as illustrated in Table 7-6 now will be operated at an external reflux ratio of 9 to 1. This reflux ratio is high enough to permit operation of a system with a relative volatility as low as 1.20. Table 7-7 gives the λ factors for this column at the same relative volatilities as listed in Table 7-6.

Table 7-7

Lambda Factors at 9:1 Reflux Ratio

	$\alpha = 1.20$	$\alpha = 1.60$	$\alpha = 2.00$
Top of Rectifying Section	0.958	0.750	0.616
Bottom of Rectifying Section	1.102	1.052	0.988
Average for Rectifying Section	1.030	0.901	0.802
Top of Stripping Section	0.902	0.861	0.808
Bottom of Stripping Section	1.048	1.294	1.503
Average for Stripping Section	0.975	1.078	1.155

At a finite reflux ratio, the λ factor in the rectifying section increases compared to total reflux, because L_m/G_m for this section is less than unity. The value of λ in the stripping section is reduced, because L_m/G_m is greater than unity in this section.

At λ factors between 0.6 and 1.8, the HETP achieved is relatively insensitive to the λ factor value [35]. At greater deviations of λ from unity, the HETP value increases. The data of Koshy and Rukovena indicate that the effect of the λ factor on HETP varies as follows for λ factors greater than 1.0:

$$\frac{\text{Actual HETP}}{\text{Standard HETP}} = 1 + 0.278\,(\ln \lambda)^3 \qquad (7\text{-}23)$$

At λ factors less than 1.0, Equation 7-23 becomes:

$$\frac{\text{Actual HETP}}{\text{Standard HETP}} = 1 + 0.278\,(\ln \frac{1}{\lambda})^3 \qquad (7\text{-}24)$$

At high values of λ the HETP values can be almost twice those given in Table 7-4. Thus, the HETP for a methanol/water system at atmospheric pressure can increase from 1.33 ft in the rectifying section at a λ factor of about 1.5 to an HETP of 2.6 ft in the stripping section at a λ factor of 4.6.

For more difficult separations (α less than 1.4) the reflux ratio usually is high; therefore, the equilibrium curve slope (m) and the operating line slope L_m/G_m are of similar values. Because λ is close to unity, the normal HETP values may be used, and no correction is needed for the effect of λ to specify the required packed depth. However, for easy separations (α greater than 2.0), the designer normally should use low reflux ratios to keep λ close to unity (between 0.6 and 1.8), so that normal values of HETP are obtained. If high reflux ratios are used for such systems to obtain high purity products, the λ factor decreases in the rectifying section and increases in the stripping section. Under these conditions, the λ factor can be important in determining the design HETP value for the specification of packed depth. For large values of λ, the equilibrium curve slope (m) is high. This indicates that the liquid film resistance is large, resulting in greater HETP values.

HIGH PURITY PRODUCTS

In high purity distillate production, any vapor bypassing results in increased heavy-key concentration in the distillate. To avoid excessive vapor wall flow, the packing size should be selected in accordance with Table 7-8. In such operations, it is important that the reflux distributor wet the top of the packed bed all the way to the column wall. Special measures must be used to ensure that the support ring for the liquid distributor or bed limiter does not interfere with the liquid irrigation pattern imposed on the packed bed top surface.

Likewise, in the production of a high-purity bottoms product, any liquid flowing down the wall that is not stripped by the rising vapor causes an increase of light-key concentration in the bottoms. The importance of wall flow can be illustrated by calculating the maximum percentage

Table 7-8

Maximum Packing Size

Nominal Packing Size (in.)	Minimum Column ID (in.)
1	12
1½	18
2	24
3½	42

of feed liquid that can be tolerated in the bottoms product to meet specifications. If 0.5 wt % or less of the feed is acceptable, wall flow may be a problem. In such cases it may be advisable to install wall wipers in the column stripping section. These devices must be very carefully designed to avoid limiting column capacity. Where liquid wall flow is significant, individual packed bed depth should not exceed 10 column diameters. This rule only applies to small diameter columns (less than 42-in. ID).

Where high purity distillate (x_{LK} greater than 0.995) or high purity bottoms product (x_{LK} less than 0.005) is specified, the temperatures within the column cannot be used to control the column operation. Composition changes do not cause any significant boiling temperature variation at this low impurity level. The product composition should be measured by an on-line analyzer for control of reflux ratio or reboiler duty. This same control problem occurs in the separation of mixtures involving three or more close-boiling components.

FEED POINT LOCATION

Improper feed point location may require more theoretical stages than calculated. For a binary system, the feed point is located where the feed liquid composition matches the downflowing liquid composition in the column. With a multicomponent feed, the theoretical stage that matches the light-key concentration in the feed probably will not match the heavy-key concentration. In such a case, the feed stage should be selected so that the ratio of light key to heavy key in the liquid feed is the same as the ratio in the downflowing liquid within the column.

If the column feed is vapor, then the foregoing guidelines apply to the location of the feed point with respect to matching the upflowing vapor within the column. If the feed is a vapor-and-liquid mixture or a liquid that flashes on entering the column, special adaptors are added to the feed distributor to separate the vapor and liquid feed portions. In this case, the feed location should be selected based on the major molar flow (vapor or liquid) of the feed in the fully flashed condition.

In the revamp of existing trayed columns, the designer faces additional challenges because both column dimensions and locations of nozzles and manholes are fixed. In cases requiring a large number of theoretical stages, it often is possible to use one of the existing trayed column feed points, because a mislocation of feed by only 5% or less of the total number of stages is not likely to have a significantly adverse effect on separation performance.

The suitability of the feed location should be evaluated by the effect it produces on the separation curve. This curve is a plot of separation factor against theoretical stages. The separation factor is defined as:

$$S_F = \log \left[\frac{x_{LK}}{x_{HK}} \right] \qquad (7\text{-}25)$$

If the selected feed point location produces a region of little or no change in S_F, fewer theoretical stages may be required. If the S_F shows a reversal in the value near the feed stage, a new feed point location should be selected.

AZEOTROPIC DISTILLATION

Ordinary distillation cannot be used to separate azeotropes (constant boiling mixtures) and may not be practical for the separation of very close boiling components. Minimum boiling azeotropes have activity coefficients greater than unity, while maximum boiling azeotropes have activity coefficients less than unity. In azeotropic distillation, another component (entrainer) is added to the system. The entrainer must form a lower-boiling azeotrope with at least one of the feed components than the azeotrope formed by the components in the feed to be separated. The entrainer cannot be separated from the condensed overhead vapor by distillation; therefore, if possible, this azeotrope with the entrainer should form two liquid phases when the overhead vapor is condensed. In this way, the entrainer is separated easily from the distillate, so that it can be returned to the column as reflux. Alternately, if the distillate is a single liquid phase, the entrainer may be recovered by liquid extraction from the condensed overhead to permit its return to the azeotropic distillation column. The entrainer selected must be sufficiently volatile so that it can be stripped from the bottoms product to avoid its loss from the column and contamination of the bottoms liquid. The entrainer should not be too volatile, because it must be present in large concentrations in the liquid phase.

Ethanol and water cannot be separated by conventional distillation at atmospheric pressure due to the formation of a minimum boiling azeotrope at 172.7°F. However, benzene can be added to this system as an entrainer, which produces a ternary azeotrope boiling at 148.7°F. This ternary azeotrope is condensed and separated into a benzene-rich phase and a water-rich phase. The benzene phase is returned to the main column as reflux, while the aqueous phase is fed to another column to recover the ethanol and benzene. The main column bottoms product is pure ethanol.

Although the reflux usually is a single liquid phase, redistributors in the rectifying section may handle two liquid phases; therefore, special designs may be required for this service. Even in the distillation of some feed mixtures that do not form azeotropes, a low-boiling component can be vaporized in such quantity that it causes the remaining components to form two immiscible liquid phases. Such is the case when acetone is distilled from an aqueous feed that also contains cumene. Upon removal of the acetone, the cumene and water become immiscible. The use of #50 IMTP packing in such a two liquid-phase service is discussed by Fulmer and Graf [36].

Davies *et al.* demonstrated that when two liquid phases are formed in a distillation column, foaming occurs on those plates with a liquid composition near the two-phase transition [37]. This phenomenon may require a reduction in the normal design vapor flow rate to control the foaming action. Liquid redistributors, as well as the feed distributor, require special designs to maintain uniform liquid-phase composition when operating with two liquid phases in the column.

The presence of two liquid phases in a random packed bed does not necessarily reduce the separation efficiency because of failure of one phase to wet the packing surface. It has been demonstrated, using a distillation of ethanol and water, that the HETP values obtained were not significantly different for uncoated carbon steel IMTP packing than for the same packing coated with polytetrafluorethylene resins, so as to render it non-wetting [38]. Based on case histories, Harrison concludes that there is no reason to expect other than normal capacity or pressure drop in a three-phase system for random packings [39]. He suggests that efficiencies depend on the specific characteristics of the systems.

Unfortunately, there is little experience regarding the use of structured packings in three-phase service. Because sheet metal structured packing manufacturers have purposely modified the metal surface to promote wetting, there is a concern regarding preferential wetting with one liquid phase to the exclusion of the other.

EXTRACTIVE DISTILLATION

Another method for separating very close boiling components takes advantage of the chemical dissimilarity of the feed compounds. In extractive distillation, the other component (solvent) that is added to the column is a high-boiling liquid that alters the relative volatilities between feed components. While normally the lower boiling feed components

Figure 7-9. Acetone-cumene distillation column. (Courtesy of GE Plastics.)

would be present in the distillate in greater concentrations than in the feed, the solvent may reverse the relative volatility relationship between the key components in the feed mixture. For example, the separation of butenes from butanes can require multiple columns with a total of 280

Table 7-9

Atmospheric Boiling Temperatures of C-4 Hydrocarbons

Hydrocarbon	Atm Boiling Point (°F)
Iso-butane	10.9
1-butene	20.7
n-butane	31.1
Trans 2-butene	33.6
cis 2-butene	38.7

trays by conventional distillation [40]. The very close boiling points (as illustrated in Table 7-9) produce low relative volatilities, which require a high reflux ratio and a large number of theoretical stages.

The addition of a solvent to a mixture of C-4 hydrocarbons can greatly reduce the vapor pressures of the butenes while not affecting the vapor pressures of the butanes [41]. Thus, the distillate product from an extractive distillation employing such a solvent will be butanes, and the bottoms will contain butenes.

The solvent normally is added to the distillation column above the feed point, while above the solvent feed point is a wash bed to which some of the liquid distillate is returned as reflux. This arrangement prevents any solvent vapor being carried overhead from the column, which would represent a solvent loss from the system as well as contamination of the distillate product. The solvent feed distributor may require special design if the mixture of reflux and solvent feed either foams or flashes.

The solvent selected is distilled easily from the bottoms liquid because it normally has a boiling point 50° to 100°F higher than the feed components to be separated. This solvent should be miscible in all proportions with the feed components at distillation temperatures. It should have great selectivity for altering the relative volatility between feed components.

The reduction in normal vapor pressure for the associated feed component varies with the concentration of solvent used. The effect of the solvent is dependent on intermolecular attractive forces, with hydrogen bonding having the most significance [42]. Solvents usually are selected based on laboratory tests to determine their effect on the normal vapor pressure of a compound. Because the bottom column temperature increases due to the higher solvent boiling point, the reboiler duty should be evaluated in solvent selection.

The presence of the solvent in the liquid phase flowing down the column materially changes the liquid properties. The designer must take account of these altered properties, as well as the flow rates in hydraulic sizing calculations. Further, these altered properties may cause a reduction in separation efficiency (an increase in HETP) because of a liquid-phase resistance increase.

Extractive distillation usually is preferred over azeotropic distillation, if both methods can be used to separate the feed components. The bulk of the solvent in extractive distillation is not vaporized in each cycle, as compared to azeotropic distillation where the entrainer is recovered from the overhead vapor stream. The energy input necessary to effect separation usually is lower for extractive distillation than for azeotropic distillation. Also, an extractive distillation column can operate over a wider range of pressures than an azeotropic distillation column, because the azeotropic composition is a function of pressure. Finally, there usually is a wider choice of solvents than entrainers, thus enabling the designer to minimize added component cost.

EXAMPLE PROBLEM

A 6-ft 6-in. ID aromatics distillation column operates at a top pressure of 21.4 psia. The column feed consists of benzene through C-10 aromatics from a heavy naphtha reformer. It is desired to separate the toluene and lighter components from the xylenes and heavier aromatics.

The present column contains 60 actual valve trays on 20-in. spacing that develop 42 theoretical stages of separation. The feed to the column is 61,750 lb/h, which produces 18,580 lb/h of distillate containing 0.40 wt % total xylenes, and 43,170 lb/h of bottoms containing 0.25 wt% toluene. The feed is a superheated liquid that undergoes a 12 wt % flash on entering the column.

The reflux flow required with trays is 70,600 lb/h. Can this column be revamped with tower packing to increase its capacity? Will this tower packing provide a greater number of theoretical stages in order to reduce the reflux ratio and energy costs?

The analysis of the feed to the column is:

Component	Wt%
benzene	0.3
heptane	0.6
toluene	25.5
octane	4.2
p-xylene	9.9
m-xylene	26.7
o-xylene	19.2
nonane	1.3
indene	12.0
naphthalene	0.3

The mass transfer height available in the column is 102 ft from tray #1 to tray #60. A simulation of the present column operation indicates that the bottom of the rectifying section has a higher loading than the top of that section. Likewise, the bottom of the stripping section has a higher loading than the top of that section.

The use of #40 IMTP packing will be considered to revamp this column. At the present feed rate to the trayed column the flow parameter at the bottom of the rectifying section is:

$$X = \frac{72340}{90920}\left[\frac{0.235}{46.6}\right]^{0.5} = 0.0565 \qquad (7\text{-}A)$$

From Figure 7-6, the C_o value for #40 IMTP packing is 0.369 ft/s. After adjustment of the maximum capacity for system properties, the trayed column operating at a C_s of 0.231 ft/s is at only 65% of the maximum operational capacity of the #40 IMTP packing.

Likewise, at the present rate the flow parameter at the bottom of the stripping section is:

$$X = \frac{133360}{90190}\left[\frac{0.245}{46.2}\right]^{0.5} = 0.108 \qquad (7\text{-}B)$$

From Figure 7-6, the C_o value for #40 IMTP packing is 0.313 ft/s. Here the trayed column operating at a C_s of 0.225 ft/s is at 75% of the maximum operational capacity of #40 IMTP packing, after adjustment for system properties. Thus, a revamp with this packing can increase the trayed column capacity by 15%, even if the efficiency is no greater.

From Equation 7-22, the HETP values for #40 IMTP packing are expected to be 1.65 ft rectifying and 1.68 ft stripping. A design HETP of 1.91 ft will be used for the rectifying section to provide 24 theoretical stages with an appropriate safety factor. A design HETP of 1.95 ft for the stripping section will produce 23 theoretical stages in the available column height. With the increase to 47 theoretical stages possible with the #40 IMTP packing, the external reflux ratio can be lowered from 3.8 to 3.2 to produce the same separation.

Due to the lower reflux ratio, the vapor flows within the column are reduced substantially. The feed rate, after revamp with the #40 IMTP packing, can be increased by 30%. The design will be checked at these higher rates.

If the reflux flow now is increased to 77,290 lb/h from 70,600 lb/h, the flow parameter at the bottom of the rectifying section is:

$$X = \frac{79240}{103400}\left[\frac{0.235}{46.6}\right]^{0.5} = 0.0544 \qquad (7\text{-}C)$$

From Figure 7-6, the C_o value for #40 IMTP packing is 0.372 ft/s. After adjustment of the maximum capacity for system physical properties, the #40 IMTP packing will operate at 73% of its maximum operational capacity at the bottom of the rectifying section.

In the stripping section at the bottom, the flow parameter is:

$$X = \frac{157650}{101540} \left[\frac{0.245}{46.2} \right]^{0.5} = 0.113 \tag{7-D}$$

From Figure 7-6, the C_o value for #40 IMTP packing is 0.310 ft/s. The packed column will operate at 85% of the maximum operational capacity of #40 IMTP packing at the bottom of the stripping section, after adjustment for system properties.

Thus, a revamp of this column with #40 IMTP packing can increase the feed capacity by 30%, while still maintaining a sufficient excess capacity allowance for operating variations. Further, the packed column will have a lower condenser duty and a lower reboiler duty per ton of feed than the presently trayed column.

Alternatively, this column could be revamped using Intalox Structured packing 3T, because this packing has an efficiency similar to #40 IMTP packing. From Equation 7-22, the HETP values for this structured packing are expected to be 1.71 ft rectifying and 1.75 ft stripping. Using a design HETP of 1.98 ft, 23 theoretical stages can be realized in the rectifying section. Likewise, for a design HETP of 2.03 ft, 22 theoretical stages of packed depth can be installed in the stripping section. With 45 total theoretical stages available, the external reflux ratio needed is 3.4; therefore, the reflux flow will be 63,170 lb/h at the present feed rate for the trays. The flow parameter at the bottom of the rectifying section is:

$$X = \frac{64740}{83320} \left[\frac{0.235}{46.6} \right]^{0.5} = 0.0552 \tag{7-E}$$

From Figure 7-7, the C_o value for Intalox Structured packing 3T is 0.462 ft/s. After adjustment of this maximum capacity for physical properties, the present rate with trays represents only 52% of the maximum capacity of the structured packing at the bottom of the rectifying section.

Based on the previous calculations, the use of Intalox structured packing 3T will permit an increase of 45% in the feed rate for the present trayed column. With this packing, the column would operate at 75% of maximum operational capacity at the bottom of the rectifying section. The bottom of the stripping section would run at not more than 87% of maximum operational capacity in order to provide a 15% safety factor.

NOTATION

A	Column cross-sectional area (ft^2)
a	Interfacial area (ft^2/ft^3)
C_o	Standard maximum C_s (ft/s)
C_s	Capacity factor (ft/s)
G	Gas mass velocity $(lb/ft^2 \cdot h)$
G*	Gas mass velocity $(lb/ft^2 \cdot s)$
G_m	Gas-phase flow (lb-mol/h)
HETP	Height equivalent to a theoretical stage (ft)
H_G	Height of a gas-film transfer unit (ft)
H_L	Height of a liquid-film transfer unit (ft)
H_{OG}	Overall height of gas transfer unit (ft)
K	Equilibrium ratio
K′	Equilibrium ratio for ideal liquid
k_G	Gas-film mass transfer coefficient $(lb\text{-}mol/h \cdot ft^2 \cdot atm)$
k_L	Liquid-film mass transfer coefficient $(lb\text{-}mol/h \cdot ft^2 \cdot mol/mol)$
L	Liquid mass velocity $(lb/ft^2 \cdot h)$
L_m	Liquid-phase flow (lb-mol/h)
m	Slope of equilibrium curve
MOC	Maximum operational capacity (ft/s)
P	Total system pressure (atm)
p	Partial pressure in gas phase (atm)
p*	Vapor pressure of component (atm)
S_F	Separation factor
T	Absolute temperature (°K)
VLE	Vapor/liquid equilibrium
X	Flow parameter
x	Mol fraction in liquid phase
x_B	Mol fraction in bottoms liquid
x_D	Mol fraction in distillate liquid
x_F	Mol fraction in feed liquid
x_{HK}	Mol fraction heavy key in liquid
x_{LK}	Mol fraction light key in liquid
y	Mol fraction in gas phase
α	Relative volatility
γ	Activity coefficient for liquid phase
λ	Lambda factor
μ	Liquid viscosity (cps)
ρ_G	Gas density (lb/ft^3)
ρ_L	Liquid density (lb/ft^3)
σ	Surface tension (dyne/cm)

REFERENCES

1. Reid, R. C. *et al., The Properties of Gases and Liquids,* Appendix A, McGraw-Hill, 1977.
2. Van Laar, J. J., *Z. Phys Chemie,* Vol. 83, 1913, p. 599.
3. Wilson, G. M., *Journal of the American Chemical Society,* Vol. 86, 1964, p. 127.
4. Frendenslund, A. *et al., A.I.Ch.E. Journal,* Vol. 21, No. 6, 1975, p. 1086.
5. McCabe, W. L. and Thiele, E. W., *Industrial and Engineering Chemistry,* Vol. 17, 1925, p. 605.
6. Lewis, W. K. and Matheson, G. L., *Industrial and Engineering Chemistry,* Vol. 24, 1932, p. 494.
7. Thiele, E. W. and Geddes, R. L., *Industrial and Engineering Chemistry,* Vol. 25, 1933, p. 289.
8. Benedict, M. *et al., Chemical Engineering Progress,* Vol. 47, No. 9, 1951, p. 449.
9. Cajander, B. C. *et al., Journal of Chemical Engineering Data,* Vol. 5, 1960, p. 251.
10. Soave, G., *Chemical Engineering Science,* Vol. 27, No. 6, 1972, p. 1197.
11. Peng, D. Y. and Robinson, D. B., *Industrial and Engineering Chemistry Fundamentals,* Vol. 15, 1976, p. 59.
12. Strigle, R. F., *Chemical Engineering Progress,* Vol. 81, No. 4, 1985, p. 67.
13. Leva, M., *Tower Packing and Packed Tower Design,* 2nd ed., United States Stoneware, 1953, p. 35.
14. Strigle, R. F. and Rukovena, F., *Chemical Engineering Progress,* Vol. 75, No. 3, 1979, p. 86.
15. Kunesh, J. G. *et al.,* "Liquid Distribution Studies in Packed Beds," American Institute of Chemical Engineers Meeting, Chicago, November 1985.
16. *A.I.Ch.E. Equipment Testing Procedures, Packed Columns,* 2nd ed., 1990, p. 3.
17. Schmidt, R., *Institution of Chemical Engineers Symposium Series No. 56,* Vol. 2, 1979, p. 3.1/1.
18. Dolan, M. J. and Strigle, R. F., *Chemical Engineering Progress,* Vol. 76, No. 11, 1980, p. 78.
19. Fair, J. R., *Petroleum/Chemical Engineering,* Vol. 33, No. 10, 1961, p. 45.
20. Hausch, G. W. *et al.,* Norton Company Chamberlain Laboratories Internal Report, 1989.
21. Lydersen, A. L. *Mass Transfer in Engineering Practice,* John Wiley & Sons, 1983, p. 75.
22. Eckert, J. S. and Walter, L. F., *Hydrocarbon Processing,* Vol. 43, No. 2, 1964, p. 107.
23. Vital, T. J. *et al., Hydrocarbon Processing,* Vol. 63, No. 12, 1984, p. 75.

24. Onda, K. *et al.*, *Journal of Chemical Engineering, Japan*, Vol. 1, No. 1, 1968, p. 56.
25. Bolles, W. L. and Fair, J. R., *Institution of Chemical Engineers Symposium Series No. 56*, Vol. 2, 1979, p. 3.3/35.
26. Porter, K. E. and Jenkins, J. D., *Institution of Chemical Engineers Symposium Series No. 56*, Vol. 3, 1979, p. 75.
27. Billet, R., *Chemical Engineering Progress*, Vol. 63, No. 9, 1967, p. 53.
28. Dolan, M. J., Norton Company Engineering Department Internal Report, 1982.
29. Strigle, R. F. and Porter, K. E., *Institution of Chemical Engineers Symposium Series No. 56*, Vol. 2, 1979, p. 3.3/19.
30. Strigle, R. F. and Dolan, M. J., *Canadian Process Equipment and Control News*, October 1983, p. 82.
31. Drickamer, H. G. and Bradford, J. B., *Transactions of American Institute of Chemical Engineers*, Vol. 39, 1943, p. 319.
32. O'Connell, H. E., *Transactions of American Institute of Chemical Engineers*, Vol. 42, 1946, p. 741.
33. Geddes, R. L., *A.I.Ch.E. Journal*, Vol. 4, No. 4, 1958, p. 389.
34. Hengstebeck, R. J., *Distillation Principles and Design Procedures*, Reinhold Publishing, 1961, p. 187.
35. Koshy, T. D. and Rukovena, F., *Hydrocarbon Processing*, Vol. 65, No. 5, 1986, p. 64.
36. Fulmer, J. W. and Graf, K. C., *Hydrocarbon Processing*, Vol. 70, No. 10, 1991, p. 87.
37. Davies, B. *et al.*, *A.I.Ch.E. Journal*, Vol. 33, No. 1, 1987, p. 161.
38. Strigle, R. F., *Process Engineering*, March 1989, p. 49.
39. Harrison, M. E., *Chemical Engineering Progress*, Vol. 86, No. 11, 1990, p. 80.
40. Strigle, R. F. and Fukuyo, K., *Hydrocarbon Processing*, Vol. 65, No. 6, 1986, p. 47.
41. Emmrich, E., and Lackner, K., *Hydrocarbon Processing*, Vol. 68, No. 1, 1989, p. 71.
42. Yeh, A. and Berg, L., "Reversing the Relative Volatility by Extractive Distillation," A.I.Ch.E. Symposium Series, Vol. 82, No. 250, 1987, p. 169.
43. Strigle, R. F., *Chemical Engineering Progress*, Vol. 89, No. 8, 1993, p.79.

8

VACUUM DISTILLATION

Distillations carried out at pressures less than 0.4 atm (300 mm Hg absolute) normally are considered as vacuum distillations from an equipment design viewpoint. Distillation commonly is carried out under vacuum to reduce the boiling temperature for one of these reasons:

1. The relative volatility between components generally increases as the boiling temperature drops. This higher relative volatility improves the ease of separation, which lowers the number of theoretical stages needed for a given separation. If the number of theoretical stages is held constant, the reflux ratio required for the same separation can be reduced. In addition, if the number of theoretical stages and the reflux ratio are maintained constant, product purity will be increased.
2. Lower distillation temperatures are desirable when processing thermally sensitive products. Lower bottoms temperatures retard undesirable reactions such as product decomposition, polymerization, or discoloration.
3. Separations can be achieved for components with very low vapor pressures or compounds that degrade at temperatures near their atmospheric boiling point.
4. Lower reboiler temperatures permit the use of less costly energy sources such as low pressure steam or hot water.

In the past, steam distillation has been used to reduce the partial pressure required of the feed components. These low-volatility components then can be vaporized at temperatures below their atmospheric boiling points. This type of distillation no longer is widely used because of these associated detrimental features:

1. Steam required is costly because several mols of steam usually are needed for each mol of feed component vaporized.
2. Presence of steam in the column usually increases the corrosion rate on commonly used metals.

218

3. Steam condensate, after separation of the distillate product, usually requires waste treatment before it can be discharged to the environment.

MAXIMUM CAPACITY OF PACKING

As distillation pressure is reduced, for the equivalent vapor rate (same C_s value) the mass flow of vapor per sq ft of column cross-sectional area is less than at atmospheric pressure. Therefore, at the same reflux ratio, the mass flow of liquid per sq ft also is lower than for an atmospheric pressure distillation. Thus, liquid irrigation rates decrease as the operating pressure is lowered.

The capacity of the fractionating device is determined both by its ability to handle high vapor velocities and by the pressure drop developed. Columns equipped with fractionating trays inherently produce a higher pressure drop than tower packings. This is so because the vapor not only must flow through an orifice restriction in the tray deck, but also it must bubble through some depth of liquid on that tray. In a packed column, the vapor must only overcome the aerodynamic flow resistance generated by the packing elements. Because liquid irrigation rates are low, the liquid holdup is small, and the geometric void fraction of the dry packed bed is only slightly reduced.

By revamping a trayed vacuum column with IMTP random packing or Intalox structured packing, the pressure drop can be reduced by as much as 90% [1]. This lower pressure drop can be used to reduce bottom column pressure and, therefore, the bottoms liquid temperature. In this case, the temperature difference driving force for heat transfer in the reboiler increases compared to a trayed column. For a new installation using a fixed heat source, the reboiler size is reduced. Alternately, the lower pressure drop can be used to increase the top column pressure. This option may permit the use of an air-cooled condenser rather than a water-cooled unit, with resultant operating cost savings. In any event, a higher top column pressure reduces the installed and operating costs of the vacuum producing system.

The maximum operational C_s is the greatest vapor flow rate attained before loss of normal separation efficiency of the packing (see Chapter 7). In vacuum distillations, massive entrainment of liquid upward in the vapor phase throughout the packed bed will limit the maximum operational capacity (maximum C_s) because it reduces the separation efficiency. However, if liquid entrainment only occurs at the top of the bed, as long as the entrained liquid carried into the condenser is of the same composition as the reflux liquid, the separation is not impaired. Thus, some entrainment in the operation of the column is acceptable and simply constitutes a recycle of liquid in addition to the usual reflux.

The maximum operational capacity of IMTP packing can be obtained from Figure 7-6. Likewise, the maximum operational capacity of Intalox structured packing can be taken from Figure 7-7. In vacuum distillations, the flow parameter (abscissa value) normally will be less than 0.04. As the flow parameter is reduced to very low values, the maximum C_s value approaches a constant value (as illustrated in Figures 7-6 and 7-7). In high-vacuum operations, the flow parameter can have a value less than 0.01. To produce a conservative design in this case, the maximum C_s, applicable to an abscissa value of 0.01, should be used for column sizing. Maximum operational capacity increases as the surface tension of the liquid phase to the 0.16 power. Such capacity increase is limited to a value 8% greater than those from these charts as surface tension exceeds 32 dyne/cm. Maximum operational capacity is a function of the liquid viscosity to the -0.11 power. Thus, the capacity would be reduced by 13% at a liquid viscosity of 0.70 cps compared to the C_s value taken from Figure 7-6 or Figure 7-7 for a standard liquid viscosity of 0.20 cps. These correction factors are based on data for distillation with liquid viscosities not greater than 1.1 cps and not less than 0.07 cps. Reasonable extrapolations of this data field are not anticipated to produce major deviations.

COLUMN DIAMETER SELECTION

Usually the top column pressure is set by the selection of the vacuum-producing equipment. In special cases involving thermally sensitive products, the bottom column pressure may be fixed by the maximum allowable product temperature. A pressure drop from top to bottom of the column is assumed for design purposes, and this pressure gradient is presumed constant for each theoretical stage. When the column pressure drop is greater than the absolute top column pressure, the usual design procedures may require some modification.

Feed composition and flow rate normally are known. Feed condition (temperature and pressure) must be determined carefully, because a liquid feed may flash on entering a vacuum column. Feed enthalpy changes significantly with feed condition, and this in turn, affects the reboiler duty and the internal column vapor and liquid flow rates.

The distillate and bottoms specifications allow calculation of the required number of theoretical separation stages and the corresponding reflux ratios. (The procedures used are discussed in Chapter 7.) The assumed column pressure drop gives the design pressure gradient per theoretical stage allowable for any reflux ratio. The tower could be designed with a lower C_s vapor rate (larger diameter), thus permitting the use of a larger number of theoretical stages for the same allowable column pressure drop. This would allow the use of a lower reflux ratio. On the other hand, the tower diameter could be made smaller (giving a higher C_s vapor rate), which would permit the use of fewer theoretical stages for the same column pressure drop. In this case, a higher reflux ratio would be required to obtain the same product purity.

The minimum pressure gradient per theoretical stage for random dumped tower packings is about 0.4 mm Hg, which is provided by IMTP packing. Data published by Meier *et al.* indicates a pressure gradient of only 0.1 mm Hg per theoretical stage can be obtained with a typical structured packing [2]. This value gives the maximum number of theoretical stages that can be obtained with the specified column pressure drop, which fixes the lowest available operating reflux ratio. Normally, the C_s vapor rate at the top of the column is greater than at the bottom, due to the change in vapor density with absolute pressure. An average of the C_s values for the top and bottom vapor rates usually can be set at 60% of the maximum operational C_s for the tower packing selected. The column pressure drop at this vapor rate sets the minimum number of theoretical stages produced and fixes the highest usable operating reflux ratio.

After the operating reflux ratio is selected, the internal column flows can be calculated. Based on these flows, the column diameter is determined. The packed depth then is calculated from the number of theoretical stages required and the design HETP value for the packing to be used. Finally, the pressure drop for the entire column is calculated.

The generalized pressure drop correlation (Figure 1-15 or 1-16) gives the pressure drop for any flow parameter to a value as low as 0.005. Commercial experience with random packings has shown this correlation to be suitable for the design of columns operating at top pressures as low as 5mm Hg absolute. The generalized correlation provides a conservative design pressure gradient at column pressures less than 0.10 atm absolute.

The generalized method developed by Bravo *et al.* can be used to predict the pressure gradient of structured packings (see Chapter 2) [3]. Normally vacuum towers are not operated in the loading region of the packing, due to the column pressure drop restriction. This correlation is based on data with C_s values as low as 0.05 ft/s.

Because vapor density varies with absolute pressure, the pressure gradient through the tower packing should be calculated at several column locations. Because ΔP is proportional to C_s^2 at low liquid rates, the C_s at any location is a function of $\Delta P^{0.5}$ at that point. Average C_s can be determined from the pressure gradients calculated for the packing at the top and at the bottom of the bed. The overall pressure drop is the product of packed depth and pressure gradient for the average C_s value. The average pressure gradient through a packed bed is represented by:

$$\Delta P = [0.5\ \Delta P_T^{0.5} + 0.5\ \Delta P_B^{0.5}]^2 \tag{8-1}$$

The arithmetical average of the pressure gradient at the tower top and the pressure gradient at the tower bottom, rather than Equation 8-1, may be used to calculate the overall pressure drop. This method only slightly overstates the pressure drop as long as the pressure gradient at the top is less than 2.5 times the pressure gradient at the bottom.

Due to the change in vapor density with absolute pressure, the pressure drop should be calculated separately for each packed bed. Total column pressure drop is the summation of the pressure drops through the packed beds plus the pressure drops through the tower internals. Overall column pressure drop determined this way must be compared with the pressure drop originally assumed. This procedure should be repeated by varying column diameter or packing size until the assumed and calculated pressure drops agree.

To reduce the number of iterations needed, it is suggested that the C_s value be calculated for the required pressure gradient per theoretical stage at the average column pressure. The estimate of column diameter necessary for this C_s value usually is close to that generated by the final design solution.

As previously stated, in those cases where the column pressure drop exceeds the absolute top column pressure, special consideration must be given to the design. The pressure gradient per theoretical stage no longer will be constant, as the vapor density will be greatly different from top to bottom of the column. In such cases, it may be desirable to change column diameter to minimize the variation in pressure gradient. The top of the column, which has the greatest vapor velocity due to the lowest vapor density, can be of larger diameter than the bottom of the column. For example, in a vacuum distillation separating ethyl benzene from styrene monomer, the rectifying section usually has a diameter about 1.2 times that of the stripping section. However, it is not necessary to change the column diameter for each packed bed. Optimum column design may involve the use of a smaller packing size in the lower bed than is used in the upper bed of the same section. The smaller packing is more efficient and requires a lower height to produce the specified number of theoretical stages. Due to increased vapor density, the reduced C_s value in the lower bed permits use of the smaller packing size in the same column diameter. The pressure gradient per theoretical stage may be nearly the same for this bed as for the bed above using larger size packing.

CHOICE OF FRACTIONATING DEVICE

While bubble-up trays can be operated at the low liquid irrigation rates commonly encountered in vacuum distillation, their high pressure gradient of about 8 mm Hg per theoretical stage renders their use impractical for most vacuum operations. A well-designed sieve tray may exhibit a pressure gradient as low as 3 mm Hg per theoretical stage [1]. Thus, multiple columns operated in series are required with trays for many occasions where more than 25 theoretical stages are required in the separation of heat-sensitive materials.

IMTP packing can provide up to 70% greater capacity than trays when operated at the same pressure gradient per theoretical stage. Thus, modern random packings may offer the least expensive choice for vacuum distillations in which no more than 12 theoretical stages are required, even at top column pressures as low as 10 mm Hg absolute. Table 8-1 shows the performance of various random packings compared to 2-in. metal Pall rings at a pressure gradient of 0.5 in. H_2O (0.94 mm Hg) per theoretical stage [4].

Table 8-1

Comparison of Random Packings
0.94 mm Hg Pressure Gradient per Theoretical Stage

Packing	Relative Tower Diameter	Relative Packed Depth	Relative Packing Volume
2 in. Pall Rings	1.00	1.00	1.00
1½ in. Pall Rings	1.02	0.77	0.80
#50 IMTP® Packing	0.85	0.91	0.66
#40 IMTP® Packing	0.89	0.75	0.59
#25 IMTP® Packing	0.99	0.60	0.58
2 in. Intalox® Saddles	1.10	1.08	1.31
1½ in. Intalox® Saddles	1.15	0.81	1.07

As stated in Chapter 2, structured packings are especially suited for use in vacuum distillation. Their low pressure gradient (ΔP) combined with their high mass transfer efficiency (low HETP value) provide pressure gradients per theoretical stage that are only one-third those of modern random packings. Structured packings can provide a large number of theoretical stages while using only one reboiler and one condenser, even if columns are operated in series. They can operate at very low absolute pressures (less than 10 mm Hg) where liquid irrigation rates are quite low due to the enhanced wetting produced by special surface texturing.

At very low top column pressures, the vapor mass flow is small for a given velocity because of the low vapor density. Therefore, the mass flow of reflux liquid also is quite low. Although tower packings can be operated at very low liquid rates, especially in organic systems, the minimum liquid rate necessary to provide uniform irrigation of the packed bed top surface may be dictated by the liquid distribution system. Thus, maximum column diameter is established for such a vacuum still. It especially is important in difficult separations (relative volatility is less than 1.4) that the liquid distributor provide a geometrically consistent distribution pattern. In addition, uniform liquid flow must be provided from each distribution point to produce a constant irrigation rate per sq ft of column cross-sectional area. The typical standard liquid distributor can operate uniformly down to a liquid flow rate of about 90 gal/ft$^2 \cdot$ h. Specially designed distributors have been developed that produce uniform distribution at flow rates as low as 12 gal/ft$^2 \cdot$ h with liquids having a surface tension of 25 dyne/cm or less. Using high capacity packings should be considered as a way to reduce the column diameter—even at the expense of column height. This increases the irrigation rate and permits operation within the capabilities of the liquid distribution system.

At very low column pressures, the pressure drop through a typical tube-and-shell condenser may be great enough to require unreasonably expensive vacuum-producing equipment. In these cases, an internal pumparound condensing bed, installed in the top of the column, should be considered instead of the more conventional external tubular condenser. This packed bed can be designed to operate at a pressure drop as low as 0.7 mm Hg. (The design of such a packed bed is described in detail in Chapter 6.)

EFFICIENCY CONSIDERATIONS

As discussed in the preceding chapter, the relative volatility between components usually varies with the distillation temperature. Only a few systems, such as toluene and n-octane, exhibit a nearly constant relative volatility regardless of the distillation temperatures. Normally, the relative volatility increases as distillation pressure is lowered due to the accompanying reduction in boiling temperatures. For example, the relative volatility of a 17.6 mol% acetone/82.4 mol% water system increases from 19 at atmospheric pressure to 24 at 200 mm Hg absolute pressure [5]. Likewise, the relative volatility of a 72.4 mol% methanol/27.6 mol% water system increases from 2.8 at atmospheric pressure to 3.7 at 200 mm Hg absolute pressure.

In atmospheric distillations, the pressure drop through the column is such a small percentage of the pressure at the top of the column that it produces a negligible effect on the vapor/liquid equilibrium. In vacuum distillations requiring a large number of theoretical stages, the pressure at the column bottom can be significantly greater than at the top. For example, in a separation of cyclohexanone and cyclohexanol the relative volatility between components can vary from 2.1 at the column top at 45 mm Hg absolute pressure down to a value of 1.5 at the bottom of a trayed column at 250 mm Hg absolute pressure. The resultant change in vapor/liquid equilibrium due to the increase in liquid temperature at the high pressure at the bottom of the column must be accounted for when calculating the required number of theoretical stages. If this is not done, and the VLE applicable to the pressure at the top of the column is used for a calculation of the entire column, the number of theoretical stages required for the specific separation can be seriously underestimated. While such a modification of the VLE is a very arduous undertaking for manual calculations, it can be accomplished readily by a computer, especially for ideal systems where the vapor pressure of the components can be expressed by simple equations. This separation is discussed in detail later in this chapter.

The tower packing efficiency in vacuum distillation need not be less than in distillation at atmospheric pressure. Typical values of HETP for IMTP packing in atmospheric pressure distillations are given in Table 7-4 (see Chapter 7). Diffusion in the vapor phase is quite rapid, as long as this phase consists of the same components as the liquid phase. Due to the reduced column pressure, the boiling temperature of the liquid phase is lower than at atmospheric pressure. This may change the liquid physical properties significantly. In vacuum distillation, therefore, the liquid phase usually offers a substantial resistance to mass transfer.

In particular, the liquid viscosity of many high-boiling organic materials tends to increase sharply at lower temperatures. This especially is likely to occur if the liquid phase is approaching the solid transition temperature of one or more of the components. If the viscosity of the liquid phase increases from 0.22 cps (common of many organic liquids at their atmospheric boiling point) to 0.75 cps, the HETP value can increase by 30%. If the viscosity of the liquid increases to 1.5 cps (as occurs in some vacuum distillations), the HETP will increase by 50% above the value typical for atmospheric distillation. Table 8-2 shows the effect of liquid viscosity on typical HETP values in distillations.

Table 8-2

Effect of Liquid Viscosity on Packing Efficiency

Liquid Viscosity (cps)	Relative HETP (%)
0.22	100
0.35	110
0.75	130
1.5	150
3.0	175

In the past, steam sometimes was added to the vapor phase for the purpose of reducing the partial pressure of the organic material necessary to cause its vaporization. However, because the steam represents a noncondensable inert vapor, it tends to increase the vapor phase resistance to mass transfer. Thus, the HETP may be higher for steam distillations than for distillations at lower absolute pressures. Further, adding steam requires a capacity increase from the system producing the vacuum. The distillate also must be separated from the condensed water and dried. With modern high capacity, low pressure drop packings, the design trend is toward elimination of steam distillation and the use of a lower absolute column pressure.

Condensers for vacuum towers often are operated at temperatures substantially below the dew point of the overhead vapor from the column. This is done to reduce the vapor pressure above the liquid distillate and minimize loss of distillate product in the noncondensable inerts that must be vented. The condenser must be operated above the solidification temperature of any components present in the entering vapor, which may require the use of tempered cooling water. If highly subcooled reflux is returned to the column, one additional theoretical stage should be added to the rectifying section to allow for reheating of the reflux liquid to its boiling temperature.

EFFECT OF PRESSURE ON AZEOTROPIC DISTILLATION

As stated in Chapter 7, the composition of an azeotrope varies with the distillation pressure. Thus, the azeotrope between ethanol and water contains 89.4 mol% ethanol at atmospheric pressure, 90.2 mol% ethanol at 380 mm Hg, and 92.0 mol% ethanol at 190 mm Hg absolute pressure [6]. Similarly, the azeotrope between methyl ethyl ketone and water contains 65.4 mol% MEK at atmospheric pressure, 70.0 mol% MEK at 350 mm Hg, and 72.2 mol% MEK at 200 mm Hg absolute pressure. Because MEK and water form two immiscible liquid phases upon condensation of the overhead, these two compounds can be separated by distilling each of these two phases separately. Because the azeotrope of ethanol and water is a single-phase liquid, separation of these two components can be achieved by distillation in two columns operating at different pressures in order to shift the azeotropic composition.

In some cases, the azeotrope no longer will exist if the pressure is changed. Thus, acetone and methanol form an azeotrope containing 80.0 mol% acetone when distilled at atmospheric pressure. However, if the pressure is lowered to 100 mm Hg absolute, these compounds can be separated by simple distillation, because no azeotrope is formed at this reduced pressure [7].

PASTEURIZATION

In the distillation of products from naturally occurring raw materials, the feed may contain a small percentage of very low-boiling compounds that are not desired in the distillate product. A separate column could be used to stabilize the feed by removal of these very low boilers before distillation in the main column. This stabilizer would require additional energy to operate the reboiler and condenser. However, it may be possible to install a pasteurization section at the top of the main column to remove these very low boilers.

As an example, consider a mixture of components ranging from C-12 to C-22 alcohols. (An analysis of the feed is given in Table 8-3.) The distillation is to recover at least 95% of the C-16 alcohol in the feed mixture; however, the product is to contain a minimum of 65 wt % C-16 alcohol and a maximum of 1.0 wt % C-12 alcohol. A distillation at reduced pressure is selected in order to minimize the temperature to which the product is exposed.

Table 8-3

High-Molecular-Weight Alcohol Distillation

Alcohol	Feed (wt %)	Product (wt %)	Bottoms (wt %)
C-12	2.3	0.8	—
C-14	21.0	28.6	—
C-16	46.7	65.4	5.3
C-18	17.2	5.2	48.8
C-20	7.8	—	28.0
C-22	5.0	—	17.9

The feed enters such a column between the rectifying and stripping sections as a liquid. If 10,000 lb/h of feed were subjected to simple vacuum fractionation, the distillate product would contain all 230 lb of C-12 alcohol present in the feed. In a simple fractionation, therefore, the distillate contains 3.2 wt% C-12 alcohol, which does not meet the product specifications. The bottoms containing 5.3 wt% C-16 alcohol represents only a 3.2% loss of the C-16 alcohol in the feed.

However, another packed bed can be installed above the rectifying section as a pasteurization section to separate C-12 alcohol from C-16 alcohol. Because less than 4% of the feed is removed as distillate at the column top, the reflux liquid returned to the column is about 24 times this distillate flow. At this high reflux ratio in the pasteurizing bed, only a few theoretical stages are needed to make the desired separation.

Below the pasteurization section, the product is removed as a liquid sidedraw. This product contains only 0.8 wt% C-12 alcohol and represents 95.5% recovery of the C-16 alcohol present in the feed. The total energy input for the operation of this column is less than that required for a more conventional arrangement of two columns operated in series.

STYRENE PURIFICATION

Perhaps the largest-scale application of vacuum distillation is the separation of ethyl benzene from styrene monomer. Such a column typically operates at a top pressure of 50 mm Hg absolute, or higher, so that the distillate may be condensed in an air cooler. The distillate primarily consists of ethyl benzene but also contains any water, benzene, and toluene present in the feed. This distillate also contains up to 5% styrene. The bottoms product is styrene monomer, purified to a specification of 400 to 1,000 ppm ethyl benzene content. The bottoms product also contains some tars formed in the reactors and polymer that is present in the feed or formed in the distillation column. The bottoms product specification is fixed by market requirements; however, the styrene present in the distillate merely recycles through the dehydrogenation reactor.

The feed styrene is a reactive monomer that tends to polymerize in the stripping section of this column. Any styrene polymer formed in this recycle column is removed in the subsequent finishing column, thereby representing a loss of product that otherwise would be available for sale. This loss can be as high as 24 lb of styrene monomer per ton of styrene in the feed. The rate of polymerization is a function of time, temperature, and styrene concentration [8]. The concentration of styrene in the liquid phase of the column stripping section is fixed by the feed composition and the bottoms product specification. The liquid temperature in the column stripping section is a function of the pressure in that section. Trayed columns usually are designed to restrict the styrene monomer bottoms product temperature to a maximum of 223°F to minimize polymer formation. By the use of IMTP packing, the pressure drop can be reduced by 65% to 70% compared to that customary for trays. At this lower bottom column pressure of only 104 mm Hg absolute, the temperature is about 182°F. Thus, the average liquid temperature in the stripping section is reduced from 198°F with sieve trays to only 168°F with IMTP packing.

One of the properties of IMTP packing is its very low liquid holdup characteristic. This feature provides about a 70% reduction in liquid retention time in the column stripping section with IMTP packing as compared to a column equipped with trays. The lower stripping section temperatures and reduced liquid retention time prevent around 85% of the styrene polymerization that normally occurs in a trayed column. In addition, the free draining ability of IMTP packing avoids any polymer buildup in the packed bed.

A typical trayed column design has a rectifying section that provides about 45% greater cross-sectional area than the stripping section. Because this column is designed to a pressure drop limitation, and IMTP packing provides a very low pressure drop, a small packing size can be used to revamp a trayed column if no additional capacity is desired. Such a revamp increases the number of theoretical stages developed by almost 20%, as compared to the trays. This permits a reduction in the operating reflux ratio that reduces the heat input required per ton of styrene product by 15% [9]. In addition, the bottoms liquid temperature of only 182°F does not require the use of high pressure steam as an energy source for the reboiler. The reduced product temperature allows the use of low pressure steam, generated by cooling the reactor effluent vapor, as a source of energy for the distillation column.

Obviously, a larger size of random tower packing or a structured packing will provide even a greater feed capacity when operated at the same reflux ratio as the trayed column. Further, the use of a structured packing will produce an even lower pressure drop and product temperature. In addition, a structured packing with similar capacity to a random packing will develop a lower HETP value, which can provide up to 35% more theoretical stages of separation with the same packed depth.

McMullan *et al.* describe the modification of a large diameter tower from sieve trays to IMTP packing [10]. Due to the very low liquid flow rates, only three to four distribution points were used per sq ft in the liquid distributor in order to avoid plugging, which could occur with smaller orifices. Experience has demonstrated that uniform liquid and vapor distribution is required to obtain the large number of theoretical stages needed for this separation. This column now is providing a total of 63 theoretical stages in four packed beds.

Carbon steel random packings have been used successfully in styrene recycle columns. However, it is essential that the column be kept free of water, because water-wetted rust produces large agglomerates in this system. For this reason, as well as operating experience, only stainless steel normally is used as a material of construction for structured packings in recycle columns.

CAPROLACTAM MANUFACTURE

The manufacture of Nylon 6 (trademark of E.I. duPont deNemours and Company) involves another large vacuum distillation application: the separation of cyclohexanone from cyclohexanol in the production of caprolactam. Such a column normally operates at a top pressure of

Figure 8-1. Styrene plant. (Courtesy of Westlake Styrene.)

45 to 70 mm Hg absolute and usually is equipped with 70 to 80 actual trays. The distillate is cyclohexanone, containing about 1,000 ppm cyclohexanol impurity, while the bottoms contains up to 4% cyclohexanone. Such a trayed column typically uses a high external reflux ratio of about 7.2 [11]. The distillate specification is fixed; however, the cyclohexanone present in the bottoms is recycled back through the reaction system. The feed contains some high molecular weight reaction products, which are separated from the bottoms liquid in a subsequent vacuum still before recycling the cyclohexanol.

A typical trayed column develops a pressure drop of 190 to 250 mm Hg. This system changes relative volatility significantly with temperature. At the column top, with a pressure of 45 mm Hg absolute, the relative volatility between cyclohexanone and cyclohexanol is 2.1. At the bottom of the trayed column, with a pressure of 295 mm Hg absolute, the relative volatility is reduced to about 1.4. It is apparent that the difficulty of separation increases rapidly at higher temperatures. Therefore, the higher the operating pressure, the larger the number of theoretical stages required at any fixed reflux ratio. Additional trays in the column become less and less effective due to the reduction in relative volatility, because the resultant increased column pressure raises the boiling temperature.

Strigle *et al.* have published the results of a pilot plant test on this system that indicates #25 IMTP packing provides an HETP value of 21 in. throughout its operating range [12]. The pressure drop through the packing varies with the vapor rate, which is influenced by the reflux ratio. In turn, the required reflux ratio for a fixed number of theoretical stages is controlled by the relative volatility. To study the effect of revamping such a sieve tray column with #25 IMTP packing, a computer model was used. This study showed that when the column is revamped with IMTP packing, the pressure drop at the same feed rate is only 20% of that produced by 76 sieve trays. The absolute pressure at the bottom of the packed column is 115 mm Hg, compared to 298 mm Hg at the bottom of the trayed column. The relative volatility at the bottom of the packed column has increased to almost 1.7 from a value of only 1.4 with trays.

The increase in average relative volatility permits a 40% reduction in reflux flow. This means a 35% reduction in condenser load through the use of IMTP packing, as compared to the trayed column. With the available vertical height provided by the 76 trays, this column could be modified with #40 IMTP packing. In this case, the feed rate could be increased by 15%, compared to the #25 IMTP packing, while retaining the same bottom column pressure and number of theoretical stages of separation.

The development of structured packings further enlarged the application of packed columns in this separation. In the past, trayed columns often used three progressively smaller diameters from top to bottom, due to the change in vapor density with pressure. The inherently higher capacity and lower HETP values provided by structured packings, as compared to trays, have made it possible to equip only the two lower sections of such a tower with structured packings, while achieving the same product specifications at greater capacity.

Fringe benefits from the use of a packed column include a lower temperature at the bottom of the column. This reduces the formation of polymeric material that must be separated from the cyclohexanol. The loss of raw material and subsequent tar disposal problems, therefore, are minimized.

DIMETHYL TEREPHTHALATE PURIFICATION

DMT is produced by oxidation of p-xylene followed by esterification with excess methanol. In some processes, the oxidation and esterification are carried out stepwise with p-toluic acid and methyl p-toluate as intermediate products. The DMT must be purified to polymer grade by a combination of distillation and crystallization. The most difficult separation involves a vacuum distillation of the dimethyl terephthalate from the monomethyl terephthalate. Under consideration is a typical DMT distillation column operating at a top column pressure of 40 mm Hg absolute and containing 30 actual trays that each develop a pressure drop of 4 mm Hg. This column operates at a bottom pressure of 160 mm Hg absolute and a temperature of 457°F. The reboiler is heated by 600 psig saturated steam that has a temperature of 489°F. Overhead vapor, at a temperature of 352°F, goes through an air-cooled condenser. The reflux liquid returns to the column subcooled by almost 50°F.

This column could be revamped using #40 IMTP packing, which would reduce the pressure drop at the same capacity by 70% (as compared to the 30 trays) while producing identical products. However, the very low pressure drop of this packing can be used to reduce the plant energy consumption, because the system relative volatility is constant throughout a pressure range of 40 to 160 mm Hg. Rather than lower the pressure at the bottom of the column, the pressure at the top of the column could be increased to 120 mm Hg absolute. The result would be an increase in the temperature at the top of the column to 414°F. Such an arrangement permits installation of a steam generator to act as a condenser for the overhead vapor. Thus, 100 psig saturated steam at 338°F can be generated by the column. Such steam can be used for general purpose, low grade process applications, or it can be reduced in pressure for space heating purposes.

GLYCOL SEPARATION

In the manufacture of ethylene glycol, product separation is accomplished by vacuum distillations. The glycol mixture first is dehydrated, then the MEG is recovered from the higher glycols. The dehydration normally is performed at a top column pressure between 180 and 230 mm Hg absolute to permit use of an air-cooled condenser. Because of the great difference in boiling points between water and MEG, the relative volatility of this system is about 50. Although only seven to nine total theoretical stages may be required to achieve the desired purities of the products, the HETP value obtained will be very high because of the large lambda effect (see Chapter 7). Tests in a pilot plant column operated at 230 mm Hg top pressure gave an average HETP value of 51 in. for #50 IMTP packing in this separation.

Because of the lambda effect, this system is operated at a reflux to distillate ratio of only 0.20 to 0.25. Although a slightly greater number of theoretical stages may be required at such a low reflux ratio, the HETP value realized will be lower [13]. With such a low reflux ratio, the liquid irrigation rate at the top of the column may be in the order of only 20 gal/ft^2 · h. A special design of liquid distributor is required to produce a high quality of liquid irrigation to the packed bed, otherwise separation efficiency will be adversely affected (see Chapter 10).

In commercial practice, the monoethylene glycol separation from higher glycols has been carried out in two trayed columns operated in series. The pressure at the bottom of each column is limited to 165 mm Hg absolute by the boiling temperature necessary to avoid product degradation. Each column typically operates at a top pressure of 50 mm Hg absolute and contains 33 actual trays. Each of these trayed columns has a reboiler and a condenser that consume significant amounts of energy.

Tests run in a pilot plant column separating MEG and DEG at top pressures of 45 to 95 mm Hg absolute gave an average HETP value of 39 in. for #40 IMTP packing. Thus, #50 IMTP packing would be expected to produce a 48-in. HETP value in this same vacuum separation. The low pressure gradient available with #50 IMTP packing reduces the pressure drop to only 34 mm Hg per column at the same flow rates as the trayed columns. Such a tower revamp permits the use of two columns in series with only one reboiler and one condenser. This reduces the overall energy consumption by 50%.

Further, the vertical height available in these towers, if revamped with #40 IMTP packing, provides almost a 30% increase in the number of theoretical stages available as compared to the trays. Even with this smaller size packing, total pressure drop through both columns in series is only 90 mm Hg. However, this increase in theoretical stages also can reduce the required reflux flow by almost 15%. Thus, a significant reduction in the energy requirement is possible for this distillation.

The low pressure drop with IMTP packing, as compared to trays, provides a capital cost savings, as well as an operating cost savings. A capital cost savings can be realized by using only one column shell for the complete separation. Such a design permits the column to operate at a top pressure of 85 mm Hg absolute and still have a bottom pressure of only 153 mm Hg absolute. Not only is the one column and one foundation less costly than two towers and two foundations, but the additional pumps, piping, and controls are eliminated. In addition, the overhead vapor temperature is more than 20°F hotter, due to the higher pressure at the top of the column, while the bottom column temperature is reduced slightly because the pressure has been lowered from 165 mm Hg. Therefore, both the condenser heat exchange surface and the vacuum-producing equipment can be smaller and less costly, as compared to that required for the trayed columns previously used.

REFINERY VACUUM TOWERS

In the refining of petroleum, operation under vacuum normally is carried out only in the processing of very high-boiling fractions. The bottoms liquid from the atmospheric crude still contains fractions with true boiling points above 750°F. The atmospheric bottoms may represent as much as 30% by volume of the crude charge; thus, economics dictate the recovery of any volatile fractions from the bottoms [14]. This liquid is heated in a furnace and fed to the vacuum crude still, if the vacuum gas oil products from this tower are used only for catalytic cracking feed. The design of such a column can be carried out by treating it as a series of partial condensing sections as described in Chapter 6.

However, if the light vacuum gas oil is to be sold, then contamination with heavy vacuum gas oil may give a high end-point temperature. In such a case, a fractionating bed must be installed between the heavy gas oil pumparound and the light gas oil pumparound. This fractionating bed will be irrigated with light vacuum gas oil. Only a small amount of reflux is used to prevent reducing the temperatures of liquid sidedraws. Because of the need to minimize pressure drop, as well as the low liquid irrigation rate, structured packings usually are selected for such fractionating sections.

Vacuum distillation also is carried out for the production of lubricating oils. Usually, such lube stills operate at a feed zone pressure of 20 to 35 mm Hg absolute in order to obtain the maximum flash of the feed that enters at a temperature of 690° to 750°F. Above the feed inlet will be a wash bed containing about a 4.5-ft depth of 2-in. Pall rings, or similar packing, whose purpose is to remove carbon and heavy impurities. The principal products from a lube still typically are light lube oil (100 SSU viscosity), medium lube oil (300 SSU viscosity), and heavy lube oil (700 SSU viscosity). These products are removed as sidestreams, which are condensed from the rising vapor stream by a pumparound of cooled condensate. Separation of the products by boiling ranges is accomplished in fractionating beds located between these pumparound sections. Because of the need to maintain a maximum overall pressure drop of 15 mm Hg through such columns, tower packings offer many advantages. For the pumparound sections, modern random packings provide good heat transfer characteristics and low pressure drops. The three to five actual trays formerly installed in the fractionating sections must be replaced to reduce pressure drop, but the height available for the packing is quite restricted. However, structured packings can provide an equivalent number of theoretical stages at a much reduced pressure drop. In this service, the HETP values for fractionation may be up to 90% greater than those obtained in standard test systems for tower packings.

HIGH VACUUM DISTILLATION

Vacuum stills for naturally occurring products, such as fatty acids, vegetable oils, and ester fragrances, typically handle a feed that consists

Figure 8-2. Vacuum distillation of lubricating oils. (Courtesy of Quaker State Refining Company.)

of a homologous series of compounds. These distillations are carried out at pressures below 25 mm Hg absolute at the top of the column for such high molecular weight materials. Pressure drop is severely restricted because the thermal stability of the bottoms products limits column pressure at the bottom. In most cases, a repeated number of distillations is required to obtain product of the purity desired. The first distillation normally removes undesirable low-boiling impurities. Then, a second distillation separates the desired product from a high-boiling residue.

Such a column previously employed trays and was designed from a low-pressure drop restriction; thus, the required column diameter was large. Because the tray efficiency is rather low in these high molecular weight systems, tower packings can be used to revamp such systems with significant advantages. The pressure gradient of IMTP packing is so low that the #25 size packing can be used to meet the hydraulic capacity required, as well as the pressure drop limitation. This size packing provides at least 50% more theoretical stages of separation than the typical trays in the same mass transfer height. These additional theoretical stages permit recovery of the desired product and separation of low-boiling impurities in one distillation operation (see Pasteurization). Not only does such a revamp reduce energy costs, but product purity is better than that previously obtained with trays. There is less decomposition of the products as a result of lower liquid residence time, as well as reduced temperature at the bottom of the column. In addition, the distillation system capacity is increased because double distillation no longer is required.

In the past, some columns have been equipped with grids to obtain a low pressure drop. Although the grid has a very low pressure gradient, it is quite inefficient as a fractionating device. Therefore, the actual pressure gradient per theoretical stage of separation is 60% greater for the grid than for #50 IMTP packing. Further, the grid requires over twice the mass transfer height as this packing, which means a higher column shell.

Structured packings can be used in such an operation; however, deposition of solids is a concern. Many naturally occurring feedstocks contain tars or polymers that may foul a large surface area. Further, if the feed has been hydrogenated prior to distillation, care must be taken to remove any catalyst fines.

TALL OIL FRACTIONATION

Tall oil is the name applied to fatty acids obtained using the Kraft process for manufacturing paper pulp from pine trees. The crude tall oil feed contains many compounds; however, those of principal interest are fatty acids and rosin acids. Many of the feed components are heat sensitive, so that vacuum distillation is used to minimize their exposure to elevated temperatures.

The crude feed initially is dehydrated and then separated from the pitch residue. The first fractionating column removes the rosin acids from the feed as a bottom product. A crude fatty acid product is removed from this column below a pasteurization section. The top distillate contains all the C-14 acids and lower boiling compounds in the feed. The principal separation in this column is between C-18 fatty acids and C-20 rosin acids.

Originally, this separation was made using steam distillation with a top column pressure of 25 to 50 mm Hg absolute. Because of the very low vapor pressure of these fatty acids, as much as six mols of steam were required to vaporize each mol of fatty acid. Modern tall oil plants use a dry distillation system operated at very low top column pressures for this separation [15].

With a condenser pressure of 4 mm Hg absolute, this first column can use #40 IMTP packing in both the stripping and rectifying sections. The pasteurization section uses #50 IMTP packing, as the vapor rate is highest at the column top. This configuration will give a pressure gradient of less than 0.6 mm Hg per theoretical stage. The bottoms product can recover 94% of the rosin acids in the feed, and the sidedraw product can recover 92% of the C-18 fatty acids in the feed. Further, the bottoms temperature will be less than 500°F, thus retarding product degradation.

Tall oil fractionators were among the first operations to recognize the advantages provided by structured packings in vacuum distillations operated at very low absolute pressures. The use of a packing, such as Intalox structured packing #2T, will reduce the pressure gradient per theoretical stage by one-half, as compared to 2-in. metal Pall ring packing. Not only does this structured packing have less than two-thirds the pressure gradient per ft of depth compared to the 2-in. Pall ring, but also this structured packing has a much lower HETP value (higher efficiency). Further, the lower pressure at the bottom of the column provides a lower temperature, which increases the relative volatility between the fatty acids and the rosin acids, thus enhancing their separation. Since the first installation of structured packings in the late 1970s, their use in this service has continued to increase, so that today structured packings usually are specified for this fractionation.

HEAT SENSITIVE MATERIALS

Packed columns are favored in the distillation of thermally unstable materials such as cumene hydroperoxide, acrylic monomers, diisocyanates, amines, and terpenes. Top column pressures below 5 mm Hg absolute frequently are not used because of the high operating and capital costs of the vacuum-producing equipment. Thus, it may be necessary to develop a pressure gradient in the range of only 0.5 to 0.8 mm Hg per theoretical stage of separation. This minimizes the pressure and temperature at the bottom of the column to avoid product degradation. Fortunately, in many cases, only a few theoretical stages are required, so the total pressure drop through the column is only 5 to 10 mm Hg.

The vapor velocity at the column top may be 50% greater than that at the bottom, due to the difference in absolute pressure affecting the vapor density. Usually the column size is determined by the loadings at the top of the packed bed; however, diameter selection must be done carefully. The liquid flow rates may be so low that excessive hydraulic safety factors that increase column diameter will lead to problems in liquid distributor design.

Most chemical changes in products are responses to temperature, time, and reactant concentration. In addition to lowering the temperature, packed columns also greatly reduce the liquid residence time in the fractionator. Average liquid residence time in a column is determined by dividing the total liquid holdup by the volumetric liquid flow rate. In a vacuum fractionator revamped with #40 IMTP packing, the liquid residence time may be only 30% of that experienced with the trays [9]. Even though the concentration profile in the column remains unchanged because of product specifications, the amount of product degradation can be reduced by 85% as compared to a trayed column in typical applications.

In the handling of highly flammable or toxic liquids, local laws may regulate the amount of material that can be contained in a single vessel. In these cases, packed columns of much larger dimensions than trayed columns can be installed. Such columns still can comply with such regulations because of greatly reduced liquid holdup of the packing per unit volume. Further, metal random-dumped packings have been used as flame arresters because of their high surface area and low vapor flow resistance.

In summary, it has been demonstrated that packed columns should be the first choice for vacuum distillation operations. Such a service normally involves a column design restricted by the allowable pressure drop for the number of theoretical stages necessary to produce the specified product. Inherently, modern packed columns always provide a lower pressure drop than a trayed column designed to perform the same function. Only when the trayed column diameter is greatly increased can its pressure drop equal that of a packed column in vacuum service. However, such a design usually is uneconomical.

EXAMPLE PROBLEM

There is a 72-in. ID column separating a mixture of C-12 through C-26 linear alpha olefins. The column contains 26 valve trays on 24-in. spacing and operates at a top pressure of 72 mm Hg absolute. The feed is a liquid of the following composition that enters the column at a rate of 12,900 lb/h and is subcooled by 8°F.

Component (alpha olefin)	Feed (mol %)	Distillate (mol %)	Bottom (mol %)
C-12	24.4	33.2	—
C-14	16.9	23.0	—
C-16	11.5	15.5	—
C-18	8.6	11.6	—
C-20	5.0	6.8	—
C-22	11.1	6.6	23.7
C-24	12.4	3.3	37.7
C-26	10.1	—	38.6

Because recovery of all the C-20 and lighter alpha olefins in the feed is desired, the distillate product rate is fixed at 8,260 lb/h. To assist stripping the lighter components, steam is added to the reboiler, so that the overhead vapor contains 3.55 mol of steam per mol of hydrocarbon. The distillate and bottoms analyses are shown in the preceding table. All analyses in this table are on a water-free basis.

The overall tray efficiency is 60%, so that the present trays are providing 15 to 16 theoretical stages of separation. The vertical height from tray #1 to tray #26 is 51 ft 6 in. Can tower packing be installed to increase the column capacity by at least 50% without losing separating efficiency?

A possible revamp with #50 IMTP packing will be examined. The design HETP for this packing from Equation 7-22 (see Chapter 7), including a suitable safety factor to allow for the presence of an inert (steam) in the vapor phase, is 2.69 ft. To replace 17 actual trays in the rectifying section requires a 27.5-ft-deep bed of #50 IMTP packing. To replace nine actual trays in the stripping section requires a 14.5-ft-deep packed bed. Because sufficient height is available to accommodate this size packing, the column can continue to operate at the present external reflux ratio of 0.55 on a water-free condensate basis. Therefore, the capacity of the #50 IMTP packed column will be determined.

The flow parameter at the top of the column at the present rates is:

$$X = \frac{4543}{16,590} \left[\frac{0.00947}{47.64} \right]^{0.5} = 0.00386 \qquad (8\text{-}A)$$

The standard C_o value from Figure 7-6 is 0.510 ft/s at a flow parameter as high as 0.010 for #50 IMTP packing. After adjustment for physical properties, the design C_s for this packing at the top of the column could be as great as 0.377 ft/s.

The present C_s for the trayed column at the top is only 0.243 ft/s. Thus, the column capacity could be increased by 55% over the present rates after a revamp with #50 IMTP packing.

The flow parameter at the top of the column still has a value of 0.00386 at these higher rates. The ordinate value for Figure 1-16 is now:

$$Y = 0.377 \ (18)^{0.5} \ (0.655)^{0.05} = 1.57 \qquad (8\text{-}B)$$

The pressure gradient for #50 IMTP packing at the top of the column is 0.48 in. H_2O/ft at these higher flow rates and a flow parameter of 0.005. The flow parameter at the bottom of the column at the higher rates is:

$$X = \frac{27{,}657}{26{,}335} \left[\frac{0.0135}{42.51} \right]^{0.5} = 0.0187 \qquad (8\text{-}C)$$

At 55% higher flow rates, the C_s at the bottom of the column is 0.342 ft/s. The ordinate value for Figure 1-16 is:

$$Y = 0.342 \ (18)^{0.5} \ (0.675)^{0.05} = 1.42 \qquad (8\text{-}D)$$

The pressure gradient for #50 IMTP packing at the bottom of the column is 0.44 in. H_2O/ft of packed depth.

Thus, the #50 IMTP packing can revamp the trayed column to obtain a 55% increase in capacity at the same separation efficiency. The total pressure drop through the packed column is only 42 mm Hg, even at a 55% higher feed rate. This is only about one-half the pressure drop through the 26 valve trays at the present lower flow rates. Further, the reduced pressure at the bottom of the column enhances the stripping action and lowers the bottom column temperature.

Another option to provide increased capacity is the use of a structured packing, such as Intalox structured packing 2T. Because the design HETP value is 1.74 ft for this packing, only a 17.8-ft-deep bed is needed for rectifying, and a 9.4-ft-deep bed for stripping. Thus, the packed depth required is reduced, compared to random packing of similar capacity.

The maximum operational C_s value at the top of this column (from Figure 7-7) is 0.462 ft/s at a flow parameter of 0.010, after adjustment for physical properties. Thus, the present flow rates in the trayed column can be increased by as much as 65%. The column top, with Intalox Structured packing 2T at 165% rates, will operate at only 87% of the maximum capacity of this structured packing.

Therefore, replacement of the present valve trays with Intalox Structured packing 2T will permit a 65% increase in column capacity at the same external reflux ratio. Further, the total column pressure drop at

165% of the present rates will be only 29 mm Hg with this structured packing, which is 35% of that of the 26 valve trays at the present flow rates.

NOTATION

C_o Standard Maximum C_s (ft/s)
C_s Capacity factor (ft/s)
HETP   Height equivalent to a theoretical stage (ft)
VLE   Vapor/liquid equilibrium
X   Flow parameter
ΔP Pressure gradient (in. H_2O/ft)
ΔP_B Pressure gradient at bottom (in. H_2O/ft)
ΔP_T Pressure gradient at top (in. H_2O/ft)

REFERENCES

1. Chen, G. K., *Chemical Engineering*, Vol. 91, No. 5, 1984, p. 40.
2. Meier, W. *et al.*, *Institution of Chemical Engineers Symposium Series No. 56*, Vol. 2, 1979, p. 3.3/1.
3. Bravo, J. L. *et al.*, *Hydrocarbon Processing*, Vol. 65, No. 3, 1986, p. 45.
4. Strigle, R. F. and Rukovena, F., *Chemical Engineering Progress*, Vol. 75, No. 3, 1979, p. 86.
5. Chu, J. C., *Distillation Equilibrium Data*, Reinhold Publishing, 1950, p. 22 & 144.
6. Chu, J. C., *Distillation Equilibrium Data*, Reinhold Publishing, 1950, p. 89 & 154.
7. Chu, J. C., *Distillation Equilibrium Data*, Reinhold Publishing, 1950, p. 19.
8. Boundy, R. H. and Boyer, R. F., *Styrene, Its Polymers, Copolymers, and Derivatives*, Reinhold Publishing, 1952.
9. Strigle, R. F. and Perry, D. A., *Hydrocarbon Processing*, Vol. 60, No. 2, 1981, p. 103.
10. McMullan, B. D. *et al.*, *Chemical Engineering Progress*, Vol. 87, No. 7, 1991, p. 69.
11. Murthy, A. and Zudkevitch, D., *Institution of Chemical Engineers Symposium Series No. 56*, Vol. 1, 1979, p. 1.1/51.
12. Strigle, R. F. *et al.*, *Informations Chemie*, Vol. 243, No. 11, 1983, p. 231.
13. Koshy, T. D. and Rukovena, F., *Hydrocarbon Processing*, Vol. 65, No. 5, 1986, p. 64.
14. Watkins, R. N., *Petroleum Refinery Distillation*, 2nd Ed., Gulf Publishing, 1979, p. 100.
15. Knoer, P., "A New Approach of Tall Oil Distillation," Pulp Chemicals Association Naval Stores Meeting, Atlanta, November 1974.

9

PRESSURE DISTILLATION

Distillation usually is carried out under pressure to permit condensation of low-boiling materials at ambient temperatures. Propylene and ethylene of polymer grade have been distilled at pressures as low as 4 atm and 6 atm absolute respectively; however, the condenser must be operated at temperatures of +10°F for propylene and −90°F for ethylene. This latter very low temperature level will be produced by a costly refrigeration system. Propylene usually is distilled at a pressure of at least 16 atm absolute, so that the condenser can be cooled with water. Ethylene normally is distilled at a pressure of about 20 atm absolute, which permits operation of the condenser at a temperature of −20°F and allows the use of less expensive propane or ammonia refrigeration.

Very low-boiling hydrocarbons, such as methane, normally are distilled at pressures of about 70% of their critical pressure. Of course, all distillations must be carried out below critical temperature in order to provide liquid reflux. Ethylene and ethane usually are distilled at 40% to 55% of critical pressure, while propylene and propane are distilled at 35% to 50% of critical pressure. Hydrocarbons in the C-4 and C-5 range normally are distilled at pressures about 20% of critical. Higher hydrocarbons are distilled at pressures up to 25 psig, simply to ensure complete condensation of the overhead vapor. These latter operations usually are considered atmospheric distillations. High molecular weight organic chemical compounds (which have atmospheric boiling points in excess of 320°F) normally are distilled under vacuum. However, refining of petroleum will involve atmospheric pressure distillations for hydrocarbons with boiling points up to 600°F.

As discussed in Chapter 7, the relative volatility in general will decrease as the pressure, and therefore boiling temperature, is increased. Because separation becomes more difficult with reduced relative volatility, the number of theoretical stages required is greater for the same separation at higher pressures. Even though the capacity of a column increases at higher pressure due to the greater vapor density, the number of theoretical stages or the reflux ratio required also will be greater. Usually a distillation column should be designed at the lowest operating pressure that is economically feasible.

CHARACTERISTICS OF PACKINGS AND TRAYS

Modern tower packings provide a much lower pressure drop per theoretical stage than trays; thus packed columns have been accepted readily for vacuum separations. As the operating pressure is increased, pressure drop becomes less important as a basis for selection of the fractionation device. Therefore, we will examine the other characteristics of both packings and trays to ascertain the potential applications for tower packings in high-pressure distillations.

As the distillation pressure is increased, the vapor density increases for any given temperature. When critical pressure is approached, the compressibility factor of a saturated vapor usually has a value less than 0.75. Thus, the density of the gas phase is quite high at pressures greater than 40% of critical. As the operating pressure is increased, for the same C_s value the mass flow of vapor will be much greater than at atmospheric pressure because of the high vapor density; while at the same reflux ratio, the mass flow of liquid also will be greater than for an atmospheric distillation. Therefore, liquid flow rates per unit of column cross-sectional area will be higher as operating pressure increases. The capacity of the fractionating device at high pressure may be dependent on its ability to handle these high liquid flow rates.

In a trayed column, the tower cross-sectional area is the sum of the active area (bubbling area), plus the areas of the downcomer transferring liquid to the tray below and the downcomer receiving liquid from the tray above. The active area required for trays (in which the vapor bubbles through the liquid phase) usually is determined by the vapor flow rate. The downcomer handles a mixture of froth, aerated liquid, and clear liquid. The downcomer area required for trays not only increases with liquid flow rate, but also with the difficulty in achieving separation between the vapor and the liquid phases. The volume required for the downcomer (downcomer residence time) increases at a lower surface tension and a smaller density difference between vapor and liquid. Because of the large downcomer area required to handle the high liquid flow rates typical of high-pressure distillations, a trayed column cross-sectional area may be 40% to 75% greater than the active tray area calculated from the vapor flow rates for such distillations. Thus, the downcomer area becomes a significant factor in the determination of the diameter of a trayed column.

Unlike a trayed column in which a percentage of column cross-sectional area is assigned to the active area handling only vapor flow and another portion to the downcomer area handling only liquid flow, a packed column does not have a fixed geometry. The packed column can use any part of the cross-sectional area for the flow of either phase, provided the sum of the vapor and liquid flow areas required does not exceed the total column cross-sectional area. Thus, the revamp of a trayed high-pressure fractionator with IMTP packing often can increase column capacity by 25% while achieving the same separation into distillate and bottoms products [1].

MAXIMUM COLUMN CAPACITY

For atmospheric pressure or vacuum distillations, the vapor flow rate is limited by the loss of normal separation efficiency due to entrainment of liquid upward in the vapor phase. The amount of entrainment increases rapidly above a threshold C_s value for the particular system. As the vapor flow rate is increased further, the mass of entrained liquid becomes sufficient to reduce the concentration profile established in the column. The maximum operational C_s has been defined as the greatest vapor flow rate attained before loss of normal separation efficiency. Figures 7-6 and 7-7 give a prediction of the maximum capacity for IMTP random packings and Intalox structured packings, respectively, as limited by liquid entrainment.

Table 9-1 gives the pressure drop in inches of operating fluid per foot of packed depth at the maximum operational C_s, as determined at atmospheric pressure for various random packings [2]. The system tested was iso-octane and toluene at total reflux. It is apparent that the pressure drop for larger sizes is lower than for smaller sizes for the same type of packing at equivalent operating conditions. Further, ceramic packings, which have void fractions of 0.72 to 0.75, produce higher pressure drops than metal packings of the same size, which have void fractions of 0.94 to 0.98, even though the vapor flow rates are higher for the metal packings.

Historically, the pressure drop at the onset of flooding was reported to be between 2 in. to 3 in. of water per ft of packed depth for random

Table 9-1

Pressure Drop at Maximum Operational Capacity

Packing	Maximum Operational C_s (ft/s)	Pressure Drop (in. fluid/ft)
#50 IMTP® Packing	0.345	1.29
#40 IMTP® Packing	0.310	1.45
#25 IMTP® Packing	0.278	2.37
2 in. Metal Pall Rings	0.315	1.89
1½ in. Metal Pall Rings	0.287	2.17
2 in. Ceramic Intalox® Saddles	0.279	2.55
1½ in. Ceramic Intalox® Saddles	0.237	2.75

dumped packings [3]. Below the loading point of the packing (as described in Chapter 7), the pressure drop for an irrigated bed will increase at about the 2.4 power of the vapor flow rate in distillation at a fixed reflux ratio. At higher rates, as the column loading approaches the hydraulic limit, pressure drop increases much faster than the second power of the vapor rate. Above the onset of loading, the liquid holdup increases with gas rate as well as with liquid rate. The hydraulic capacity limit of the packing occurs due to excessive liquid holdup, as evidenced by the high rate of pressure drop increase [4]. Increased liquid holdup primarily is responsible for the apparent reduction in void space and the higher pressure drop of smaller size packings shown in Table 9-1. In high-pressure operations, the usable hydraulic capacity of the tower packing may be reached because of excessive liquid holdup before the normally expected maximum operational C_s, as limited by entrainment, is attained. However, this is not the usual case.

The operating holdup of liquid for ceramic Raschig ring or Berl saddle packings has been shown to increase as the liquid flow rate to the 0.57 power [5]. The operating holdup in high voidage open packings, such as IMTP and Intalox Snowflake packings, increases as a higher power of the liquid flow rate [6]. However, these modern packings have a lower amount of liquid holdup than the older ceramic packings. Below the loading region the liquid holdup is not greatly influenced by the vapor rate (see Chapter 1). As the vapor rate is increased above the loading point (see Table 9-3), the downward flow of liquid is retarded by the upward flow of vapor, thereby increasing liquid holdup in the packed bed.

The amount of operating liquid holdup in a packed bed is influenced by the density of the continuous vapor phase. The apparent density of the liquid in the tower is the true liquid density less the actual vapor density, even when there is no aeration of the liquid phase. This buoyancy effect normally is imperceptible at atmospheric pressure because the density of the vapor is only about 0.5% of the liquid density; but at higher pressures this effect becomes significant.

In light hydrocarbon systems, the surface tension of the liquid phase can be less than 6 dyne/cm at the temperatures encountered in high-pressure fractionators. At such a low surface tension, some high density vapor is dispersed into the liquid phase. This aeration of the liquid tends to increase as the surface tension of the liquid becomes lower and as the vapor density increases. Thus, the higher the pressure of operation of a specific system, the greater will be the quantity of vapor dispersed in the liquid phase. Also, the higher the operating pressure, the smaller will be the size of the dispersed vapor bubbles in the liquid phase. This aeration of liquid reduces the effective liquid density; thus, the volume occupied by a given mass of liquid is increased even further. The aeration factor is the ratio of aerated liquid density to clear liquid density. For atmospheric pressure distillations of nonfoaming liquids, the aeration factor normally is not less than 0.9. In light hydrocarbon fractionators operating at 40% of critical pressure, the aeration factor may be as low as 0.7 [17].

From kinetic theory, the viscosity of a gas should be independent of pressure from 60 mm Hg to about 6 atm pressure, but it should increase as the 0.5 power of the absolute temperature. Experimental data confirm this increase in viscosity occurs to about the 0.7 power of the absolute temperature for fixed gases; however, gas mixtures containing more than 25% hydrogen exhibit unusual viscosity characteristics. In systems of light hydrocarbons (methane through pentane), the vapor viscosity increases at the 0.9 power of the absolute temperature, which is more rapid than for fixed gases.

Because liquid viscosity decreases with increasing temperature produced by higher pressures of distillation, and the vapor viscosity increases with temperature, the viscosities of the two phases tend to approach each other in high pressure fractionators. For C-4 or C-5 hydrocarbon fractionators, the vapor viscosity will be only 6% of the liquid viscosity. In C-2 or C-3 hydrocarbon fractionators, the vapor viscosity is about 11% of the liquid viscosity. In distillations involving methane, the vapor viscosity can be 35% of the liquid viscosity.

The high ratio of vapor density to liquid density, the low values of the aeration factor for the liquid phase, and the high ratio of phase viscosities all tend to increase the volume of liquid holdup in a packed bed. As the liquid holdup increases, the void fraction in the packed bed becomes lower with a resultant increase in pressure drop.

PRESSURE DROP CONSIDERATIONS

The pressure drop for high-pressure distillations of light hydrocarbons in commercial columns has been found to be much higher than that predicted from the generalized correlation (Figure 1-15 or Figure 1-16). In depropanizers and C-2 splitters, the vapor density can be about 10% of the liquid density. In demethanizers, the vapor density may be as much as 18% of the liquid density. As the ratio of vapor density to liquid density increases, the liquid holdup will increase, thus increasing the true gas velocity and the pressure drop. The actual measured pressure drop from bottom to top of a column represents not only the pressure loss through the packing, but also the static head of vapor in the tower. Thus, when the 140 trays were replaced with #40 IMTP packing in a C-2 splitter, the vapor head accounted for up to 40% of the overall measured pressure drop. After correcting for this vapor head, the pressure drop through the packed beds averaged 0.51 in. H_2O/ft, which was equivalent to 1.17 in. fluid/ft. However, this corrected measured pressure drop was twice that calculated using the generalized pressure drop correlation.

As shown in Table 9-1, the pressure drop is greater for small-size packings than for larger packings of the same type at the maximum operational C_s. This leads to the conclusion that in actual operation the total void fraction in a bed of small-size packing must be less than in a bed of larger-size packing. These values of C_s from Table 9-1 were used in the preparation of Figure 7-6, with corrections to the C_s values to adjust them to a liquid surface tension of 20 dyne/cm and a liquid viscosity of 0.20 cps. Table 9-2 gives the void fractions of the packings themselves. This table shows that the void fraction does not vary significantly by size for the same type of packing. Increased liquid holdup with smaller packing sizes must account for the greater pressure drop. The use of a larger-size packing will minimize the possibility of reaching maximum hydraulic capacity, as determined by excessive liquid holdup, before reaching maximum operational capacity, as determined by liquid entrainment.

Table 9-2

Void Fractions of Random Tower Packings

Packing	Void Fraction
#50 IMTP® Packing	0.978
#40 IMTP® Packing	0.972
#25 IMTP® Packing	0.964
2 in. Metal Pall Rings	0.960
1½ in. Metal Pall Rings	0.953
1 in. Metal Pall Rings	0.940
2 in. Ceramic Intalox® Saddles	0.754
1½ in. Ceramic Intalox® Saddles	0.747
1 in. Ceramic Intalox® Saddles	0.726

Table 9-3 shows the pressure drop for the same system as Table 9-1 at the maximum efficiency C_s (minimum HETP value) and at the onset of the loading region of the packing [7]. Note that the pressure drops are the same for 2-in. ceramic Intalox saddles, 1½- in. metal Pall rings, and #25 IMTP packing at equivalent rates. A generalized pressure-drop equation would indicate that all three packings have nearly the same total void fraction in the operating packed bed.

SELECTION OF COLUMN DIAMETER

Because of the high cost of the vessel shell needed for high-pressure operation, the design of such a column should be approached in a conservative manner. The recommended capacity correlation has been developed from data on organic systems in distillation operations.

Table 9-3

Pressure Drop as a Function of Column Loading

Packing	Pressure Drop at Maximum Efficiency (in. Fluid/ft)	Pressure Drop at Onset of Loading (in. Fluid/ft)
#50 IMTP® Packing	0.76	0.32
#40 IMTP® Packing	0.88	0.38
#25 IMTP® Packing	1.41	0.60
2 in. Metal Pall Rings	1.19	0.53
1½ in. Metal Pall Rings	1.39	0.60
2 in. Ceramic Intalox® Saddles	1.41	0.60
1½ in. Ceramic Intalox® Saddles	1.60	0.83

Because of the limited amount of high-pressure data available, the correlation in this area may not be as accurate as at lower operating pressures. The following procedure has been used for the design of several hundred high-pressure distillation columns. It is possible that operation of high-pressure columns in aqueous systems or with nonboiling liquids could be carried out at higher rates than suggested by this method.

The recommended design procedure uses a design maximum vapor rate (C_s), which is a percentage of the maximum operational capacity of the packing (as determined from Figures 7-6 and 7-7) for a system with a surface tension of 20 dyne/cm and a liquid viscosity of 0.20 cps. This maximum C_s value must be adjusted for the effects of liquid viscosity and surface tension. The maximum operational capacity of the tower packing, as shown in these figures, varies directly as the 0.16 power of the surface tension of the liquid phase. This effect does not increase the capacity beyond that which applies to liquids of 32 dyne/cm surface tension. The holdup in the packed bed will be a function of liquid viscosity, although high liquid viscosity normally is not a limiting factor in high pressure distillations. Capacity of a packing is increased as the reciprocal of liquid viscosity to the 0.11 power. This capacity increase is limited to liquid viscosities not less than 0.09 cps.

If a trayed column in high pressure service does not have sufficient downcomer residence time to clarify the liquid phase, the vapor/liquid mixture will be carried down to the next lower tray. This recycling of vapor lowers the capacity, as well as the separation efficiency, of the trays. Conditions preventing rapid disengagement of vapor and liquid in a tray downcomer are high liquid viscosity, low surface tension, and a small density difference between liquid and vapor. Also, any tendency for the liquid to foam will increase the downcomer residence time required.

In a packed column, the hydraulic capacity will be restricted as the liquid holdup volume increases. At atmospheric or slightly higher operating pressures, the actual vapor velocity will become sufficient for the vapor to entrain liquid upward, because of the reduction of total void fraction in the packed bed. This entrainment will result in a lower degree of separation produced by the column. In high-pressure distillations, the liquid holdup can become great enough for the packing to reach its hydraulic capacity limit, as evidenced by a rapid increase in pressure drop. A packed column does not suffer reduction in capacity in a foaming system to nearly the extent exhibited by a trayed column. The presence of a foaming liquid, however, will raise the pressure drop compared to a non-foaming system.

A design C_s should be selected that provides the added capacity necessary for fluctuations in normal column operation, as well as temporary surges in feed rate and reboiler heat input. Usually this requires 15% to 25% additional capacity above the design rate; thus, the design C_s will be between 80% and 87% of the maximum operational C_s for the packing selected. This design criterion is based on loss of separation efficiency due to excessive liquid entrainment; however, in high-pressure fractionators liquid holdup may limit the hydraulic capacity. Because pressure drop is an indication of liquid holdup, Equation 1-5 (see Chapter 1) can be used to obtain an indication of the maximum hydraulic capacity (flooding point) of a random packing. From the author's experience in high-pressure distillations, it is suggested that the column size selected from the use of the maximum operational capacity also be checked against this maximum pressure drop limitation. The C_s value equivalent to the ΔP flood can be calculated using Figure 1-16 (Chapter 1). The design C_s value should not exceed 85% of the C_s value at flood.

As critical conditions are approached, the liquid holdup will increase dramatically because the vapor density will approach the difference between the aerated liquid density and the vapor density. If the pressure of distillation is so high as to give a vapor density that is greater than 20% of the liquid density, the maximum capacity of the column probably will be determined by system properties, as well as by the vapor/liquid contacting device.

TYPICAL DESIGN EFFICIENCY

As might be expected, the vapor phase may offer the controlling resistance to mass transfer in high-pressure distillations. The liquid-phase temperature has increased, which reduces liquid density and viscosity. Thus, liquid diffusivity should be increased. The vapor phase, on the other hand, increases in density and viscosity at higher pressures and temperatures, so that the diffusivity in the vapor phase will be reduced. High-pressure distillations of light hydrocarbons may involve separations of low relative volatility. Thus, ethylene/ethane splitters may have an average α of 1.45, while propylene/propane splitters have an average α of only 1.11. In such separations, we should not expect any increase of HETP typical of a high lambda system (as discussed in Chapter 7).

Increasing the operating pressure changes the physical properties in a manner that should increase the efficiency of separation. However, the efficiency of trayed columns has been shown to increase only from atmospheric pressure up to a pressure of 165 psia. At higher operating pressures, the efficiency of the trays decreases with increasing pressure. Hoek and Zuiderweg report that there is an entrainment of vapor in the liquid phase that is carried back down the column [8]. They have calculated that the entrained vapor increases from 0.05 mol vapor/mol liquid at 165 psia to 0.43 mol vapor/mol liquid at a pressure of 400 psia for a C-4 hydrocarbon separation. This recycle of vapor reduces the separation efficiency as well as column capacity. These investigators predict that tray efficiency will be reduced by 16% as the pressure is raised from 165 psia to 400 psia.

The HETP values in high pressure separations of similar light hydrocarbons are very low. Separation efficiency appears to be greatest in C-3 splitters. The same packing in a C-2 splitter will have up to a 20% higher HETP value. In C-4 fractionations, the packing will have an efficiency intermediate between these other two separations. Table 9-4 gives typical design HETP values for fractionations of C-3 and C-4 hydrocarbons at pressures of 18 atm and 6 atm absolute, respectively. In fractionators separating similar light hydrocarbons, the efficiency in the stripping section may be lower (as much as a 10% higher HETP value) than in the rectifying section with the same packing. The HETP for 2-in.-size packing will be about 40% greater than the HETP for 1-in.-size packing of the same type.

In the stripping of light hydrocarbons from heavier ones, such as deethanizing natural gas liquids, the HETP value normally will be greater than for fractionators separating hydrocarbons of similar molecular weights, as given in Table 9-4. For #40 IMTP packing, the design value of HETP in such an operation is given by the following empirical equation:

Table 9-4

Separation Efficiency of IMTP® Random Packing in C-3 andC-4 Fractionations

Packing Size	HETP (in.)
#25	14 to 16
#40	16 to 19
#50	19 to 22

$$HETP = 4.90 - 0.7 \ln L_{MW} \tag{9-1}$$

In Equation 9-1, the HETP value is expressed in feet. Equation 9-1 applies to a liquid phase with a molecular weight between 22 and 72. The #25 size IMTP packing will give an HETP lower than #40 IMTP packing by 0.47 ft, while the #50 size will give an HETP value 0.53 ft higher. In those applications with high methane or hydrogen concentrations in the rectifying section, the HETP can be up to 30% greater than that predicted by Equation 9-1 for the stripping section. In separations of aliphatic hydrocarbons of 84 to 114 molecular weights, the HETP will decrease by up to 10% compared to the values given by Equation 9-1 for $L_{MW} = 72$. Higher molecular weight compounds normally are not fractionated at pressures above 4 atm absolute.

Aromatic hydrocarbons normally are fractionated at a pressure not greater than 75 psia, which is less than 15% of the critical pressure. HETP values for such distillations are about 5% greater than those obtained in C-4 fractionations for the same type and size of packing.

Structured packings to date have not been used widely in high pressure distillations. Proprietary tests conducted by Fractionation Research, Inc. on Intalox Structured packing 2T using a system of i-butane/n-butane did not produce consistent results for either capacity or separation efficiency at pressures above 300 psia [9].

However, satisfactory operation of Intalox Structured packing 2T has been reported for a C-3/C-4 splitter operating at a pressure of 320 psia [10]. In this 48-in. ID crude unit depropanizer, 16 trays in the stripping section were replaced in order to obtain a 25% capacity increase. Data, taken during 18 months of operation after replacing the stripping section trays, demonstrate that this structured packing is producing a 17-in. average HETP value.

THEORETICAL STAGES AND REFLUX RATIO

The number of theoretical stages required for separation of light hydrocarbons can be calculated by the usual methods, as described in Chapter 7. C-4 and heavier paraffin and mono-olefin hydrocarbons generally act like ideal compounds in the liquid phase. In C-3 splitters, the relative volatility between propylene and propane tends to decrease as the concentration of propylene increases; thus, α may go from 1.14 in the bottom of the stripping section to 1.08 in the top of the rectifying section in the production of polymer grade propylene. In C-2 splitters the relative volatility (therefore the number of theoretical stages) varies with the methane content of the feed. The K value for ethylene may be less than unity at the top of the column; thus, ethylene enrichment of the vapor is not occurring. The actual separation taking place in this portion of the column is between the methane impurity and ethylene. The top of the column functions as a pasteurization section so that the methane in the feed can be removed from the product, which is recovered as a sidedraw liquid stream. Because of the large number of theoretical stages required for C-2 and C-3 fractionations, the same VLE as was used to evaluate the HETP value of the packing must be used to design the column. Small changes in VLE can change significantly the number of theoretical stages calculated that would result in a considerable difference in HETP values for the same packing.

Usually it is desirable to operate near the minimum reflux ratio if energy costs are more important than capital costs of equipment. However, unless there is actual operating experience, columns should be designed to operate at a reflux ratio at least 112% of the calculated minimum reflux ratio. Designs at a closer approach to minimum reflux ratio may result in a column operating below the actual minimum reflux ratio, due to inaccuracy of the VLE data. In such a case, the product specifications never will be achieved.

OLEFINS PLANT COLD SECTION

The cold section of an olefins plant illustrates a significant application of high pressure distillation operations. Figure 9-1 illustrates a flow diagram of a conventional olefins plant in which hydrocarbons are recovered beginning with lower molecular weight compounds (methane) and ending with higher molecular weight compounds (C-5s+). The cold section begins with series coolers and flash drums following the drying of the high-pressure cracked-gas stream. Typically, the condensates from the flash drums are fed to a demethanizer at several different locations from the top of this column downward, in order of increasing molecular weights. The bottoms from the demethanizer is fed to the deethanizer. The overhead product from this column is fed to the C-2 splitter, while the bottoms serve as feed to the depropanizer. The overhead from this column is fed to the C-3 splitter, while the bottoms serves as feed to the debutanizer. The overhead from the debutanizer contains butanes, butenes, and butadienes, which are separated in other equipment. The bottoms from this column consists of C-5 and heavier compounds. This material is valuable as a gasoline blending stock. Alternately, the bottoms can be combined with the hydrocarbon condensate from the water quench tower and processed to recover its aromatic content.

DEMETHANIZERS

The primary function of this column is removing methane from the heavier hydrocarbons in the condensed liquid feed streams. Any methane

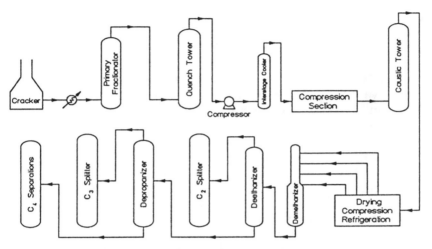

Figure 9-1. Typical ethylene plant flow diagram.

remaining in the bottoms otherwise will be eliminated in the pasteurization section at the top of the C-2 splitter. The ethylene can be recovered by recycling this C-2 splitter overhead vapor stream through the last two compression stages for return to the demethanizer. However, this vapor stream consists of 10 to 16 times as many mols of ethylene as methane. This large recycle gas stream consumes additional energy for compression, as well as for reboiling in the demethanizer. A second function of the demethanizer is the recovery of C-2 and higher molecular weight hydrocarbons from the liquid feeds.

One of the most difficult high-pressure separations for a trayed column is the separation of methane from a light hydrocarbon feed. In an olefins plant, the demethanizer typically is operated at a top pressure of 430 to 520 psia. This column has a partial condenser that is cooled by an ethylene refrigeration system and operates at a temperature of $-130°$ to $-145°F$. Usually, an olefins plant demethanizer has a smaller diameter upper section than the lower section because the majority of the feed leaves the bottom of the column. A trayed column typically contains 50 to 70 actual trays with 50% to 60% of these trays located below the lowest feed point. At the bottom of the column, the liquid rate will be at least 25 gpm/ft^2, which produces a flow parameter of greater than 0.80 on the generalized pressure drop correlation (Figure 1-15). At the top of the column, the flow parameter will be about 0.20; however, the liquid irrigation rate will be only 50% to 60% of that in the bottom section. Achieving separation of the vapor from the liquid in downcomers is difficult because of the approach of vapor density to liquid density. In such a column, the vapor density usually will be between 12% and 18% of the clear liquid density. Aeration of the liquid at high pressure will reduce further the difference between the actual operating liquid density and the vapor density. Also, the surface tension is low (below 4 dyne/cm), which increases the difficulty of obtaining phase separation in the downcomers. As the vapor density approaches the liquid density and the surface tension of the liquid phase becomes low, the residence time required for vapor and liquid separation increases. Therefore, the downcomer area required may be as much as 40% of the total cross-sectional area in a trayed column.

In most cases where additional capacity is not required, a demethanizer can be revamped with #25 IMTP packing, thereby gaining a 50% to 60% increase in the number of theoretical stages available. Such a revamp of the 8-ft diameter bottom section of an olefins plant demethanizer operating at 30 atm top pressure has been described by Buffenoir [11]. The 29 trays on 18-in. spacing were replaced with two beds of #25 IMTP packing. The bottom (highest molecular weight) feed was piped down the column and introduced between these two packed beds at a location that continued to provide the same number of theoretical stages of stripping as the trays. The revamped column thus had additional rectifying stages that produced an 87% reduction in the ethylene loss overhead. At the same time, the reflux ratio required was lowered by 18%, thereby reducing the −140°F refrigeration load on the condenser. All of this was accomplished while actually reducing the methane concentration in the bottoms liquid. The pay-out time for this revamp was reported to be less than one year (see Figure 9-2).

When the lowest feed point is not changed, the use of #25 IMTP packing will increase the number of theoretical stages stripping. In such a case, the methane content of the bottoms in a naphtha-fed olefins plant was reduced by 80%. Packed demethanizers routinely provide a bottoms liquid containing far less methane than the 150 ppm typical for trayed columns.

In those cases where a capacity increase is desired, the #40 IMTP packing has been employed in the revamp of a trayed olefins plant demethanizer. This packing has permitted the column feed rate to be increased by 20% over that for the original tower, which was equipped with single-pass valve trays on 600 mm spacing in the upper section and two-pass valve trays on the same spacing in the lower section. Even when handling 120% of the trayed column rates, the #40 IMTP packing was utilizing only 84% of its maximum operational capacity.

The trays in such a column have a relatively low efficiency compared to more common fractionation operations. This could be the result of vapor entrainment through the downcomer, as previously discussed. The physical properties of the system that lower the tray efficiency do not have as drastic an effect on the efficiency of packed columns. Thus, the #40 IMTP packing used to revamp this demethanizer also increased the number of theoretical stages developed by 13%. By design, this revamp was carried out so that two-thirds of these additional theoretical stages were located in the upper section of the column in order to permit a reduction in the reflux ratio with the accompanying energy savings.

The use of a predemethanizer is becoming increasingly popular. This column is a stripper that is fed with the liquid that normally would go to the lowest feed point of a demethanizer. The overhead vapor from this column enters the main demethanizer at the lowest feed point location. This arrangement greatly reduces the loading in the stripping section of the main demethanizer, while not increasing its condenser duty. Further, because bottoms from the main demethanizer are of a lower molecular weight, they can be fed to the deethanizer part-way up the rectifying section so as to reduce the reflux required for that column.

DEETHANIZERS

Bottoms from the demethanizer, at a temperature of 30° to 50°F, is fed to the deethanizer. The primary function of this column is recovery of ethylene and ethane from the feed. The overhead vapor also contains all the methane and acetylene present in the feed, as well as some propylene that is stripped to ensure complete C-2 recovery.

The deethanizer in a naphtha-fed olefins plant also is a column with a smaller diameter upper section than lower section. This column operates at a pressure between 340 and 410 psia with a top temperature of 0° to 20°F. A trayed column typically contains 45 to 70 actual trays. Again the liquid surface tension is very low, and the density difference between the liquid phase and the vapor phase is small. Therefore, the capacity of a trayed column usually is limited by the downcomers. In a trayed tower, the cross-sectional area is rather large compared to vapor flow rate. Replacing trays with an IMTP system increases the capacity by about 35% above the design rate for the trays.

If no additional capacity is needed, revamp of a trayed column with a smaller size IMTP packing increases the number of theoretical stages by up to 20%. These additional theoretical stages permit operation at a lower reflux ratio. This, in turn, reduces the condenser's refrigeration requirement.

ETHYLENE/ETHANE FRACTIONATOR

The overhead from the deethanizer, after hydrogenation to convert any acetylene to ethylene, serves as a superheated vapor feed to the C-

Figure 9-2. Olefin plant demethanizer. When this tower was revamped to IMTP packing, overhead ethylene losses were reduced.

2 splitter. The primary function of this tower is production of a polymer-grade ethylene. The secondary function is recovery of ethylene from the feed, because the bottoms from this column usually is reprocessed by recycling to an ethane/propane cracking furnace.

The C-2 splitter normally operates at a pressure of 260 to 320 psia with a top temperature of $-30°$ to $-10°F$. The C-2 splitter typically consists of two columns, operated in series, that are equipped with a total of 120 to 160 actual trays. The feed enters the first column that has a reboiler at its base. The overhead vapor from this column goes to the bottom of the second column. Liquid from the bottom of the second column is pumped to the top of the first column. The upper 8 to 11 actual trays in the second column serve as a pasteurization section that removes the small amount of methane present in the feed. The ethylene product is withdrawn as a liquid sidestream below the pasteurization section. Any propylene in the feed leaves in the bottoms from the first column.

In the past, the polymer-grade product specification called for 99.90% pure ethylene. However, there recently has been an increased demand for greater purities, up to 99.97% ethylene. Impurities in the product consist of methane and ethane, usually in the ratio of 2.4 to 3.0 mol of ethane per mol of methane. The ethylene recovered as product should not be less than 94% of that present in the feed stream.

A revamp of a 10-ft 3-in. ID C-2 fractionator with IMTP packing provided a 27% increase in feed rate over the design capacity of the original trayed column. In addition, the packed column developed almost 25% more theoretical stages than the trayed column. This permitted an 11% reduction in reflux ratio, while simultaneously increasing product purity from 99.92% to 99.95% ethylene. This C-2 splitter used an external heat pump system that condensed propylene in the reboiler and evaporated it in the condenser. The revamp reduced the energy consumption for this system as a result of the lower reflux ratio. Further, the lower fractionator pressure drop provided by the packing reduced the propylene condensing pressure required, thereby saving energy on the external vapor compressor. Thus, the IMTP system provided the desired increase in column capacity as well as in product purity.

DEPROPANIZERS

The bottoms liquid from the deethanizer serves as the principal feed to the depropanizer. A second feed stream to this column consists of the bottoms liquid from the condensate stripper for the fourth and fifth compression stages. The primary function of this column is propylene and propane recovery from these two feeds. The column operating pressure typically will be 240 to 340 psia, which is sufficient to condense the overhead vapor with cooling water or ambient air. The overhead from this column contains all of the C-3 hydrocarbons present in the feed, as well as some C-4 hydrocarbons that are stripped to provide complete recovery of C-3 components. C-2 hydrocarbon content in the distillate is negligible due to the overstripping commonly carried out in the preceding deethanizer.

A depropanizer normally contains 35 to 55 actual trays and has a uniform diameter. In these systems, the surface tension of the liquid phase is below 6 dyne/cm, the liquid density is near 30 lb/ft, and the vapor density is about 8% of the liquid density. Under such conditions, the downcomer residence time required can be a significant factor in the specification of the tower diameter for a trayed column. The downcomer normally is designed so that the froth height is no more than 70% of the tray spacing; therefore, downcomer area must be large to avoid the need for excessively tall columns.

In high-pressure distillations where column size is critical, the advantages of packed columns can be substantial. One such installation, located on a remote offshore platform, is processing natural gas liquids. The depropanizer in this unit produces HD-5 propane as distillate. The addition of new wells to the gathering system would increase the quantity of natural gas liquids to be processed by 50%. The depropanizer was among the columns that had to handle this higher feed rate. At 250 psia operating pressure, the shell thickness and column weight would increase substantially if a larger-diameter column were installed. Overall tower height was restricted by wind load, foundation requirements, and platform space.

The existing column contained 43 actual trays on 24-in. spacing and developed 72% overall tray efficiency. This column was revamped using IMTP packing to provide the required fractionation and accommodate a 50% greater feed rate than the original trayed tower. Because the packed column developed 18% more theoretical stages than the trayed column, operation at a lower reflux ratio enhanced the feed capacity. There was no significant difference in the operating weight for the trayed tower and for an IMTP packed column because of the low liquid holdup of this packing.

In a depropanizer, diene polymers may tend to form in the stripping section of the column. This polymer formation is a function of time, temperature, and diene concentration in the column. The temperature and concentrations in both trayed and packed columns are similar; however, the liquid holdup with the IMTP packing is reduced by 70% to 75% compared to trays. This greatly decreases liquid residence time in the depropanizer. As on tray surfaces, there may be a slow deposition of polymer on the packing elements, however, because of the accessibility of all IMTP packing surfaces, polymer buildup has been removed simply by circulating a solvent over the packed bed.

PROPYLENE/PROPANE FRACTIONATOR

Overhead from the depropanizer is fed to the C-3 splitter, after hydrogenation to convert the highly unsaturated methyl acetylene and propadiene to propylene. The primary function of this tower is production of polymer grade or, in some cases, chemical grade propylene. A secondary function is propylene recovery because the bottoms from this column either is recycled to an ethane/propane cracking furnace or is used as propane fuel.

A C-3 splitter producing polymer grade propylene normally consists of two columns in a series containing a total of 150 to 180 actual trays. The feed usually enters the first column, which has a reboiler at its base. Overhead vapor from the first column goes to the bottom of the second column. The liquid from the bottom of the second column is pumped back to the top of the first column. The C-3 splitter normally operates at a minimum pressure of 230 psia, which is sufficient to condense the overhead vapor at a temperature of 100°F with available cooling water. Because the bottom column temperature is only about 120°F, the lower pumparound water from the water quench tower can serve as an energy source for this column. To use this source of heat, as well as to keep the relative volatility as high as possible, operating pressure for this column normally does not exceed 290 psia.

The polymer grade product is 98.4% to 99.6% propylene, with propane as the major impurity. The distillate also contains the small amount of ethane present in the feed; however, a pasteurization section usually is not required to meet the product specifications. Chemical grade has a wide range of purities, but typically contains around 93% propylene. Normally, about 98% of the propylene in the feed is recovered in the product.

Because of the very high percentage of propylene recovery, plus high product purity specified for polymer grade, the reflux ratio required for a C-3 splitter usually is greater than 10 to 1. This system also is complicated by a shift in relative volatility of propylene to propane with the liquid-phase composition. The relative volatility drops from 1.14 in the propane-rich bottom section of the column to only 1.08 in the propylene-rich top section. Revamping such a column with an IMTP system provides up to a 20% increase in the number of theoretical stages available (as compared to the trayed tower) without reduction in column capacity.

Where capacity is the primary interest, revamping the tower with an IMTP system permits an increase of 15% in the feed rate without any operational changes. However, because IMTP packing provides more theoretical stages of separation, the reflux ratio can be reduced. This combination of higher allowable vapor rate and lower reflux ratio provides a 25% increase in the available product rate for a column revamped with an IMTP system.

In some situations, refinery feedstock is fractionated to polymer grade propylene. In such a case, surplus energy is not available as 170° to 190°F water from a hot section. Lower reflux ratios, therefore, are desired to reduce energy consumption. In these situations, a heat-pumped fractionator offers a viable option when a packed column is used, because of the lower operating pressure drop [12]. A heat-pumped system can operate at a reduced column pressure (150 to 180 psia), which increases the relative volatility between propylene and propane. The lower permissible reflux ratio, as well as the pressure drop of only 2.6 psi per 100 theoretical stages for IMTP packing, keeps energy input to a minimum and permits the use of a single-stage vapor compressor.

DEBUTANIZERS

The bottoms liquid from the depropanizer is fed to the debutanizer. The primary function of this column is recovery of all C-4 compounds from the feed. This column usually operates at a pressure from 70 to 130 psia and is equipped with 25 to 40 actual trays. The distillate product contains 98% to 99% of the C-4 hydrocarbons present in the feed. This distillate also contains all the propane present in the feed, plus a small amount of C-5 hydrocarbons.

Replacing the trays with an IMTP system provides up to a 30% increase in the number of theoretical stages compared to a trayed column with the same capacity. These additional theoretical stages can be used to reduce the reflux ratio. This lower reflux flow, plus the increased vapor handling capacity of IMTP packing, permits an increase in product rate up to 30%. In addition, the greatly reduced liquid residence time provided by IMTP packing minimizes any formation of diene polymers in the rectifying section.

C-4 SEPARATIONS

The C-4 hydrocarbons are gaining increased commercial importance with both the demand for 1-butene as a comonomer and the interest in MTBE as a motor fuel additive. The distillate from a debutanizer usually is processed first to remove butadiene, which is a valuable monomer used in the production of elastomers and plastics. The separation of butenes from butanes is carried out by distillation in a series of columns. The first

Figure 9-3. High pressure debutanizer. (Courtesy of Placid Refining Company.)

separation removes the low-boiling iso-butane as distillate, while the second separation recovers the 1-butene as distillate from the high-boiling n-butane.

In order to increase the recovery of 1-butene, two columns, each containing 70 trays on 16-in. spacing, were converted to #25 IMTP packing using three packed beds per column. Individual bed depths varied from 27 ft to 30 ft to accommodate existing manhole locations. The recovery of 1-butene after packing these columns increased from 75% to 93% with a high butane feed, and from 86% to 96% with a low butane feed, due to an increase of over 50% in the number of theoretical stages obtained [13]. This separation involved a relative volatility of only 1.10 between 1-butene and iso-butane, which produced a temperature rise of only 0.1°C per theoretical stage.

OTHER OLEFIN FRACTIONATING ARRANGEMENTS

The processing scheme just discussed is the most common sequence of fractionating columns in the cold section of an olefins plant; however, it is not the only sequence in industrial use. The process offered by Linde A.G. uses the deethanizer as the first column in the cold section [14]. The overhead from this column contains all the hydrogen, methane, and C-2 hydrocarbons present in the feed. This stream is hydrogenated to remove the acetylene, then cooled to condense the hydrocarbons, leaving a gaseous hydrogen product. The condensed liquid fractions serve as feeds to the demethanizer in which the methane is stripped overhead. The demethanizer bottoms is fed to the C-2 splitter for fractionation of the ethylene product. The bottoms from the original deethanizer is the feed to the depropanizer, and the balance of the fractionation train uses the same sequence as previously described.

A different scheme is offered by C. F. Braun and Co., which takes the effluent vapor from the acid gas removal system and, after drying and cooling, feeds it to the depropanizer [15]. The overhead from this column is compressed to around 540 psia, hydrogenated to remove the dienes, and chilled to separate a hydrogen stream from the condensed hydrocarbons. Liquid condensates contain methane, plus the C-2 and C-3 hydrocarbons present in the feed to the depropanizer. These liquids are fed to the demethanizer, which strips the methane overhead. The demethanizer bottoms serve as feed to the deethanizer. The overhead from that column goes to the C-2 splitter, while the bottoms is the feed to the C-3 splitter. The bottoms liquid from the original depropanizer is sent to the debutanizer for separation of the C-4 hydrocarbons from the aromatic gasoline fraction.

CHEMICAL SEPARATIONS

Nonhydrocarbon distillations of chemicals usually do not operate at pressures greater than about 15% of the critical pressure. Table 9-5 gives typical operating pressures for purification of some of these commercially important chemicals. Only a few chemical separations qualify as high-pressure distillations (greater than 80 psia operating pressure). One of the principal reasons for operating chemical fractionators under pressure is to raise the condensing temperature for low-boiling compounds. In addition, a high-pressure column can be of a smaller diameter than an atmospheric column because the higher vapor density produces a lower C_s capacity factor for the same mass vapor rate.

Table 9-5

Chemical Separations at High Pressure

Chemical Product	Distillation Pressure (psia)
Carbon Disulfide	40
Ethylene Oxide	60
Fluorinated Refrigerants	65
Methanol	90
Methyl Amines	120
Methylene Chloride	100
Vinyl Chloride	50

In summary, tower packings are used instead of trays, or to revamp trayed columns, in high pressure distillations to accomplish the following objectives:

1. To increase the capacity of downcomer limited trayed columns.
2. To improve product purity or yield by providing a greater number of theoretical stages than developed by the trays.
3. To conserve energy by providing a greater number of theoretical stages in order to reduce the reflux ratio.
4. To permit the use of vapor recompression due to the reduced pressure drop produced by tower packings as compared to that developed by trays in the separation of close-boiling materials [16].
5. To reduce energy use by operation of columns in parallel, which because of the low pressure drop of tower packings, permits the overhead vapor from the first column to supply reboiler heat to the second column.
6. To lower the residence time for materials that degrade or polymerize.

7. To reduce the inventory in the column of flammable or hazardous materials.
8. To increase product recovery in batch distillations due to the lower liquid holdup in a packed column.

EXAMPLE PROBLEM

It is desired to recover the C-3 components from a feed of the composition listed below. The distillate is to contain 1.0 mol % maximum C-4 hydrocarbons while the bottoms is to have a maximum of 2.0 mol % C-3 hydrocarbons. There is available a 5-ft. ID column containing 22 actual trays on 24-in. spacing. The vertical height from tray #1 to tray #22 is 43.5 ft. Can this column be revamped with IMTP packing to perform the separation? If so, what will be the column capacity?

Feed Analysis

Component	mol %
propylene	62.4
propane	24.6
iso-butane	4.0
1-butene	6.0
iso-pentane	0.5
n-hexane	2.0
n-heptane	0.5

The column will be operated at a top pressure of 220 psia and a 98°F condenser temperature. The feed to the column is a liquid at a temperature of 115°F. This feed will undergo a 2.4 mol % flash to vapor on entering the column.

A computer simulation indicates that seven theoretical stages rectifying and seven theoretical stages stripping, plus the reboiler, will satisfy the separation requirements at an external reflux ratio of 1.70. If #50 IMTP packing is selected for the revamp, from Equation 9-1 we obtain a design HETP of 2.78 ft rectifying and 2.63 ft stripping. These design HETP values include an ample safety factor when compared to the values in Table 9-4. Thus, a 19.5-ft-deep rectifying bed and an 18.5-ft-deep stripping bed will be specified.

The computer simulation indicates that the maximum loading in this column occurs at the top of the stripping section. The vapor rate here is 0.975 times the overhead vapor flow, while the liquid rate is 1.675 times the reflux flow rate. The flow parameter at the top of the stripping section is:

$$X = \frac{1.675\,(1.70)}{0.975\,(2.70)}\left[\frac{1.99}{30.5}\right]^{0.5} = 0.276 \tag{9-A}$$

The standard maximum C_s value (C_o) from Figure 7-6 for #50 IMTP packing at this flow parameter is 0.266 ft/s. Adjustment for physical properties gives a maximum operational C_s of 0.238 ft/s. Because the vapor density is 6.5% of the clear liquid density, the hydraulic capacity limit will be checked using Equation 1-5 (from Chapter 1).

$$\Delta P \text{ flood} = 0.115 \ (18)^{0.7} = 0.870 \text{ in. H}_2\text{O/ft} \tag{9-B}$$

From Figure 1-16 this pressure drop represents a C_s value of 0.286 ft/s at flood. The design C_s should not exceed 85% of this value, or 0.243 ft/s. However, allowing a 15% safety factor from the MOC value of 0.238 ft/s gives a C_s value of 0.207 ft/s. Therefore, the usable column capacity is controlled by the maximum operational capacity, and the design C_s will be set at 0.207 ft/s. At the top of the stripping section, the vapor flow will be 110,210 lb/h and the liquid flow will be 119,210 lb/h. From Figure 1-16, the pressure drop at the top of the stripping section with #50 IMTP packing will be 0.23 in. H$_2$O/ft, which is equivalent to 0.47 in. fluid/ft.

The maximum loading in the rectifying section also is at the top where the flow parameter is:

$$X = \frac{1.70}{2.70}\left[\frac{2.02}{30.0}\right]^{0.5} = 0.163 \tag{9-C}$$

The C_o value for #50 IMTP packing at this flow parameter is 0.312 ft/s. The maximum operational C_s corrected for physical properties is 0.280 ft/s. From the design loadings previously fixed at the top of the stripping section, the flow rates at the top of the rectifying section are 113,040 lb/h of vapor and 71,170 lb/h of liquid. The C_s at the top of the rectifying section is 0.213 ft/s, which is only 76.1% of the MOC value of 0.280 ft/s. These flow rates give a pressure drop for #50 IMTP packing of 0.20 in. H$_2$O/ft, or 0.42 in. fluid/ft at the top of the rectifying section.

By material balance, this 5-ft ID column can accept a maximum feed rate of 50,870 lb/h when equipped with #50 IMTP packing, while providing the desired separation of C-3 components from C-4 and heavier components.

NOTATION

C_o	Standard maximum C_s (ft/s)
C_s	Capacity factor (ft/s)
F	Packing factor
HETP	Height equivalent to a theoretical stage (ft)

K   Equilibrium ratio
L_{MW} Molecular weight of liquid
MOC   Maximum operational capacity (ft/s)
VLE   Vapor/liquid equilibrium
X   Flow parameter
α Relative volatility
ΔP Pressure drop (in. H_2O/ft)
ρ_G Gas density (lb/ft)
ρ_L Liquid density (lb/ft)

REFERENCES

1. Robinson, K., "High Pressure Distillation Using Random Packings," European Federation of Chemical Engineers Meeting, Amsterdam, June 1985.
2. Strigle, R. F. and Rukovena, F., *Chemical Engineering Progress*, Vol. 75, No. 3, 1979, p. 86.
3. Leva, M., *Tower Packings and Packed Tower Design*, 2nd ed., United States Stoneware, 1953, p. 57.
4. Billet, R., *Chemical Engineering Progress*, Vol. 43, No. 9, 1967, p. 53.
5. Shulman, H. L. *et al.*, *A.I.Ch.E. Journal*, Vol. 1, No. 2, 1955, p. 259.
6. Strigle, R. F., *Canadian Process Equipment and Control News*, April 1989, p. 68.
7. Strigle, R. F., *Chemical Engineering Progress*, Vol. 81, No. 4, 1985, p. 67.
8. Hoek, P. J. and Zuiderweg, F. J., *A.I.Ch.E. Journal*, Vol. 28, No. 4, 1982, p. 535.
9. Rukovena, F. and Strigle, R. F., "Effect of Pressure on Structured Packing Performance," American Institute of Chemical Engineers Meeting, Houston, March 1989.
10. Hausch, G. W. *et al.*, *Hydrocarbon Processing*, Vol. 71, No. 4, 1992, p. 67.
11. Buffenoir, M. H., *Oil and Gas Journal*, Vol. 80, No. 36, 1982, p. 78.
12. Danziger, R., *Chemical Engineering Progress*, Vol. 75, No. 1, 1979, p. 58.
13. Strigle, R. F. and Fukuyo, K., *Hydrocarbon Processing*, Vol. 65, No. 6, 1986, p. 47.
14. *Petrochemical Handbook, Hydrocarbon Processing*, Vol. 58, No. 11, 1979, p. 161.
15. Clancy, G. M. and Townsend, R. W., *Chemical Engineering Progress*, Vol. 67, No. 2, 1971, p. 41.
16. Strigle, R. F. and Perry, D. A., *Hydrocarbon Processing*, Vol. 60, No. 2, 1981, p. 103.
17. Strigle, R. F., *Chemical Engineering Progress*, Vol. 89, No. 8, 1993, p. 79.

10

COLUMN INTERNALS

Modern tower packings, as well as the refined design concepts now available, have generated an increasing need to update the technology concerning column internals. No longer are packed columns designed at only one-half their maximum capacity, nor is a 50% safety factor added to the calculated packed depth. In today's competitive environment, the column internals must function as an integral part of the total packed column design, rather than limit the performance of the packing.

The most commonly employed column internals are:

1. Packing support plates
2. Vapor distributors
3. Bed limiters and hold-down plates
4. Feed and reflux distributors
5. Liquid redistributors
6. Wall wipers
7. Liquid collectors

Not all of these internals are used in every column. In addition, some plates may serve more than one function.

PACKING SUPPORT PLATES

The primary function of the packing support plate is to serve as a physical support for the tower packing plus the weight of the liquid holdup. In the design of the packing support plate, no allowance is made for the buoyancy due to the pressure drop through the packed bed nor for the support offered by the column walls. In addition, the packing support plate must pass both the downwardly flowing liquid phase as well as the upwardly flowing gas phase to the limit of the capacity of the tower packing itself.

The first packing support plates for random dumped packings were slotted or perforated, flat ceramic plates. The use of 1-in. to 2-in. size ceramic Raschig ring packings, common in those days, required small holes or narrow slots that gave the plate a low open area of only 15% to 25%. Even though these plates were very heavy (up to 2½-in. thick), they did not have sufficient strength to support deep beds of ceramic tower packings.

This same type of design also was used in large cast iron grids for supporting stacked packings in the ammonia-soda industry. Similar grids of cast iron also were used in the manufacture of sulfuric acid. In addition, sections of subway grating sometimes were used as packing support plates where the corrosion resistance of the metal was adequate. The then commonly used Raschig ring packing tended to align along these slots or orifices in such support plates, thus leaving very little effective free area for gas and liquid passage. Flooding of the packed bed frequently was initiated from the bottom of the bed, and progressed upward, until eventually the column became inoperable.

Until about 1952, tower internals were designed specifically for each individual column. Many times these designs emphasized the mechanical requirements for the internal, with the process function of the internal receiving only secondary consideration. The first standardized line of column internals was marketed about 1960. For the most part these internals were made from ceramics, then later the designs were adapted for fabrication from metals.

With the increasing use of ceramic saddle packings, the older support plates proved inadequate. Leva proposed a gas injection weir-type support plate design to circumvent previous limitations [1]. This design injected the gas phase into the packed bed above the level where the liquid phase left the packing. Such a design avoids the difficulty of trying to pass the two phases in opposite directions through the same openings.

This type of support plate proved adequate for ceramic packings up to a 2-in. size, which then were in wide use. However, when 2-in. metal Pall ring packing was tested by an independent research organization in the early 1960s, it was found that the pressure drop through the packing support plate and first two feet of packing was much higher than the average pressure drop for the balance of the packed bed. Thus, the packing capacity was limited by the packing support plate.

Further development work resulted in the improved multibeam gas injection packing support plate design. Repeated tests in the later 1960s verified the capacity of this design, again using 2-in. metal Pall ring packing. Figure 10-1 shows the pressure drop developed by this improved support plate as compared to the original design.

As the output of the chemical industry grew, column sizes became larger. With columns of 42-in. or larger diameter, a man could enter the column easily; thus, the packing support plate also had to hold a man's weight. Further, it was impractical to use removable heads on these larger size columns. Therefore, the tower internals had to enter the column through a manhole. The multibeam support plate, shown in Figure 10-2, met the desired criteria for most applications. This plate uses

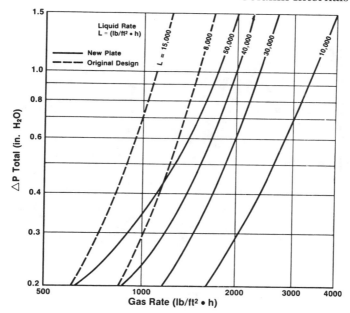

Figure 10-1. Performance of packing support plates. (Courtesy of Norton Chemical Process Products Corporation.)

the gas injection principle to put the gas phase into the packed bed through openings in the almost vertical sidewalls of each beam. The liquid phase flows down along the sides of the beams to the horizontal bottom legs where it leaves the bed through perforations. Thus, the gas phase flows through one set of openings, while the liquid phase passes through a different set of openings.

The beam-style design provides a high mechanical strength permitting single spans 12 ft long or greater. The modular design allows installation through standard 18-in. manholes and permits its use in any column 48-in. ID and larger. A modification of this multibeam support plate is available for use in smaller diameter columns. Pressure drop through this packing support plate is very low for the current design. In fact, its pressure drop actually has been included in the packing factor, which is calculated from a measurement of the pressure drop through a 10-ft depth of tower packing resting on such a support plate.

In extremely corrosive services, ceramic support plates (as shown in Figure 10-3) may be required. In larger diameter columns (such as sulfuric acid plant towers), a series of ceramic grids is installed resting on brick arches or piers. Then a layer of cross-partition rings or grid blocks is stacked on these grid bars to support the dumped ceramic packing, as shown in Figure 10-4.

Figure 10-2. Multibeam packing support plate. (Courtesy of Norton Chemical Process Products Corporation.)

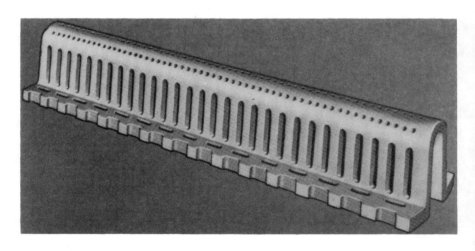

Figure 10-3. Ceramic packing support plate. (Courtesy of Norton Chemical Process Products Corporation.)

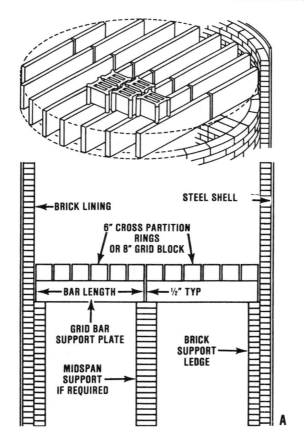

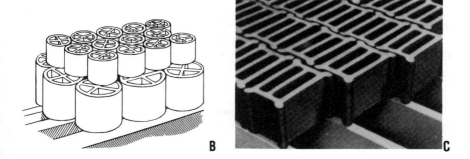

Figure 10-4. (A) Ceramic grid support system. (B) Typical arrangement of cross partition rings. (C) Typical arrangement of Norton grid blocks. (Courtesy of Norton Chemical Process Products Corporation.)

Plastic packing support plates also are available. Thermoplastic support plates are similar in design to metal plates. Fiberglass reinforced plastic internals use metal internal designs adapted for hand lay-up. These plates are designed for use with plastic tower packings because their load-bearing capabilities are limited. Generally free-span length does not exceed 4 ft, due to possible high-temperature creep.

Packing support plates usually are designed to rest on a continuous ledge. This ledge should be level and perpendicular to the tower's vertical axis. Also, the ledge must be flat to provide a uniform load-bearing surface if a ceramic support plate is used. The width of this ledge should not exceed the values shown in Table 10-1 if the column is to be operated near maximum capacity. For columns smaller than 48-in. ID, continuous ledges may restrict the ultimate capacity of the tower packing. Support plates for columns over 12 ft in diameter usually require at least one mid-span supporting beam or truss. The sidewall of the column must be sufficiently rigid to support the point loading imposed at the beam seats.

Table 10-1

Support Ledges for Tower Internals

Tower ID (in.)	Support Ledge Width (in.)
48	1½
60	2
72	2
84	2½
96	2½
120	3
144	3½

In columns 72-in. or larger diameter, the packing support plates usually are clamped to the supporting ledge at both ends. This prevents movement of the individual beams during operating upsets that could allow some packing pieces to fall out of the packed bed.

A more simple design of support plate can be used for structured packings, because such packings are installed in discrete modules. Support plates for such packings provide a horizontal contact surface designed to prevent distortion of the packing while possessing sufficient structural strength to support the weight of the packing and liquid holdup over the length of the span. Such support plates have a very high open area for gas and liquid passage and do not add any significant pressure drop.

VAPOR DISTRIBUTORS

Because a packing support plate usually is located immediately above the gas inlet in an absorber or the reboiler return in a distillation column, this plate could be used to control vapor distribution. Obviously, vapor maldistribution can reduce column efficiency in the same way as liquid maldistribution; although due to the turbulence in the vapor phase, its rate of radial cross-mixing is at least three times that of the liquid phase. The potential for vapor maldistribution increases as column diameters or operating pressures increase. Fortunately, the vapor phase tends to maintain a uniform distribution once it has been established. Thus, usually only the packing support plate immediately above the vapor inlet needs to act as a vapor distributor. This support plate should be located at least one vapor-inlet diameter plus 12-in. above the centerline of the vapor inlet nozzle.

A vapor sparger could be used to produce uniform flow of vapor up the column. This approach to vapor distribution control frequently is used for high-pressure stripping steam where there is available a sufficient pressure gradient to permit the use of multiple vapor orifices. When the column exceeds 48-in. ID, an H-shaped or ladder arm pipe sparger design, often is used in order to inject the steam in a more uniform pattern. However, in many cases (such as with a thermosiphon reboiler vapor return) it is not desirable to take a sufficiently high pressure drop on the inlet gas stream to permit use of a sparger.

With a simple radial vapor inlet perpendicular to the vertical axis of the column, the potential for gas maldistribution is a function of the kinetic energy of the inlet vapor. Whenever the vapor inlet nozzle operates at an F_s vapor capacity factor greater than 22 $lb^{0.5}/ft^{0.5} \cdot s$ in high-pressure service, or the kinetic energy of the inlet vapor exceeds eight times the pressure drop through the first foot of packing, or the pressure drop through the packed bed is less than 0.08 in. H_2O/ft, vapor distribution should be considered. Vapor flow control usually is accomplished by establishing a pressure drop across the packing support plate or by use of another type of vapor distributor. The pressure drop through a multibeam support plate is too low for it to be used to control vapor distribution.

In a column using trays, the pressure drop across the trayed section normally is about 0.15 psi for each actual tray [2]. This is about twice the usual kinetic energy in the inlet vapor. However, when trays are replaced with tower packings, the pressure drop is significantly reduced. If structured packings are installed, their pressure drop typically will be only 10% of that of the trays replaced. Thus, gas distribution must be critically reviewed whenever trays are replaced by packings. Further, if vapor rates are increased to utilize the additional capacity provided by pack-ings, the problem of vapor distribution can be compounded.

One design of vapor-distributing support plate uses vapor orifices beneath perforated gas risers (see Figure 10-5). The liquid phase will pool on the horizontal deck to a depth equal to the pressure drop causing flow through the liquid orifices plus the gas-phase pressure drop through the plate. The gas phase will be injected into the packed bed through the perforations in the upper part of the gas risers. The lower part of the gas risers is left unperforated to accommodate the liquid pool.

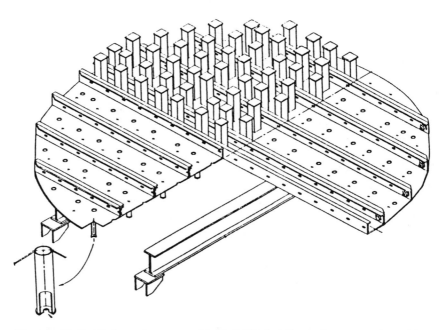

Figure 10-5. High performance Model 796 distributor/support plate. (Cour-tesy of Norton Chemical Process Products Corporation.)

The use of non-radial (tangential or offset) vapor inlet nozzles often leads to vapor distribution problems. Whenever two reboiler return nozzles are required, they should be installed radially and located 180 degrees apart so as to cancel kinetic energy effects. The invert of the vapor inlet nozzle should be at least 8 in. above the maximum liquid level in the bottom of the column. Submerging the vapor inlet into the liquid can lead to premature flooding of the packed bed caused by massive liq-uid entrainment.

BED LIMITERS AND HOLD-DOWN PLATES

Normally, the upper surface of the packed bed is at least 6 in. below a liquid distributor or redistributor. The bed limiter or hold-down plate is located on top of the packed bed in this space. It is important to provide such a space to permit gas disengagement from the packed bed. Such a space allows the gas to accelerate to the velocity necessary to pass through the distributor without exceeding the capacity of the packing.

Bed limiters commonly are used with metal or plastic tower packings. The primary function of these devices is to prevent expansion of the packed bed, as well as to maintain the bed top surface level. In large diameter columns, the packed bed will not fluidize over the entire surface. Vapor surges fluidize random spots on the top of the bed, so that after return to normal operation the bed top surface is quite irregular. Thus, the liquid distribution can be affected adversely by such an occurrence.

Bed limiters are fabricated as a light weight metal or plastic structure. Usually a mesh backing is used to prevent passage of individual pieces of tower packing (see Figure 10-6). Because the bed limiter rests directly on the top of the packed bed, structurally it must be only sufficiently rigid to resist any upward forces acting on this packed bed.

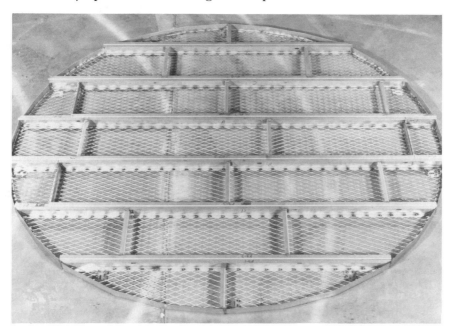

Figure 10-6. Bed limiter, Model 823. (Courtesy of Norton Chemical Process Products Corporation.)

Usually the bed limiter is fastened to clips on the column wall or it is restrained by the column internal located immediately above it. A slight settling of the packed bed below the bed limiter is not a concern [3]. It is not recommended that a continuous ledge be used to support the bed limiter. This ledge can interfere with the liquid distribution to the top of the packed bed. Likewise, the bed limiter should not contain horizontal structural members that can intercept and divert the downflowing liquid.

Hold-down plates are weighted plates used with ceramic or carbon tower packings. With these packings, it is especially important to prevent fluidization of the packed bed top surface. These brittle materials can be fractured during an operating upset or at high vapor loadings, so that the resulting fragments migrate down into the packed bed where they can severely reduce column capacity.

The hold-down plate must rest freely on the top of the packed bed because beds of ceramic and carbon packings tend to settle during operation. These plates usually act by their own weight to prevent bed expansion; therefore, the plates weigh 20 lb to 30 lb per sq ft.

Both bed limiters and hold-down plates should be of sectional construction to permit entry into the column through a manhole. These plates must fit closely to the column wall to prevent passage of individual packing pieces. The free space through these plates must be high enough not to restrict the capacity of the tower packing.

FEED AND REFLUX DISTRIBUTORS

From a process standpoint, the most important column internals are the liquid distributors. A liquid distributor is required at all locations in the tower where an external liquid stream is introduced. In addition to providing a uniform liquid distribution pattern to the top of the packed bed, the distributor also must provide sufficient gas passage area to avoid a high pressure drop or liquid entrainment. The liquid distributor should have a flow range suitable for the application and be resistant to fouling.

Figure 7-5 (see Chapter 7) demonstrates the effect of liquid distributor performance on the separation efficiency of a packed bed. Curve II shows the performance typical of commercial liquid distributors available in the 1970s. Curve I represents the operation of high-performance liquid distributors now available. In evaluating distributor performance, the following points should be considered:

1. Uniformity of liquid flow from each point of irrigation.
2. Geometric uniformity of the location of each point of irrigation.
3. Uniformity of liquid flow to each square foot of cross-sectional area at the packed bed top.

4. Number of liquid irrigation points per square foot of column cross-sectional area.
5. Wetted area compared to dry area at the column wall.

To maintain uniform flow from each irrigation point, the orifice or weir controlling the liquid flow rate must be manufactured to a high tolerance. The minimum pressure loss through this flow control device should be established to allow for variations in levelness, distributor deflection due to mechanical loading, and head gradients required to flow liquid throughout the entire distributor. In addition, the minimum head must take into account the gas-phase pressure loss through the distributor. High-performance distributors provide a flow rate variation per irrigation point that is a maximum of ±5% of the average flow.

Every liquid irrigation point must be located in a uniform geometric pattern. This pattern must not be sacrificed to insert the necessary gas risers into the distributor. Thus, the designer of such a device is faced with an intriguing challenge that becomes more complex as the gas rate, and thus the gas riser area required, increases.

If the flow per irrigation point is uniform, there must be the same number of irrigation points for every square foot of bed cross-sectional area. This causes the liquid flow to every square foot of the packed bed surface to be the same. To ensure conformance with these criteria, the design can be checked by any of several methods. One method involves dividing the column into quadrants plus concentric circles of equal areas. Thus, a 7-ft 6-in. ID column uses eight equal areas to be evaluated, while an 11-ft 0-in. ID column uses 12 areas, and a 15-ft 0-in. ID column uses 16 areas. The number of distribution points in each of these equal areas must be the same.

Usually, the area adjacent to the column wall requires special consideration to accomplish such uniform liquid irrigation. As is visualized by the point-circle method described by Moore and Rukovena, liquid from an adjacent irrigation point may spread onto the column wall [4]. However, with a normal spacing of irrigation points, some part of the column wall will not be wetted. It is desirable to locate the irrigation points near the column wall in such a manner that the wetted and unwetted portions of the column wall are equal. Also, it is necessary to ensure that this uniform distribution pattern extends under the ledge supporting the liquid distributor. If a high-purity distillate product is specified, all of the vapor phase must be rectified by contact with the liquid phase to prevent high-boiling components from being carried overhead.

The number of distribution points per square foot of column cross-sectional area usually is six to nine for 1-in. and larger sizes of random packings, as well as for structured packings. For very small sizes of these packings or for wire gauze packing where very low HETP values are expected, up to 12 distribution points per square foot may be used. A larger number than this does not improve packed bed efficiency. The geometric uniformity of liquid distribution has more effect on packing efficiency than the number of distribution points per square foot.

The size of the orifice or weir required depends on the total liquid flow and the number of irrigation points per square foot. If the liquid to be distributed is perfectly clean, the minimum orifice diameter or weir width should be 0.14 in. For fouling services this minimum dimension should be increased to 0.20 in. or larger. Such size orifices or weirs may require a reduction in the number of irrigation points per square foot when handling low liquid rates. Packed bed efficiency normally can be maintained with a minimum of five distribution points per square foot, if the other four criteria are maintained.

In the past, it had been thought that the necessity for uniform liquid distribution was reduced as the liquid irrigation rate per square foot increased. However, it has been found that regardless of the liquid rate, the necessity for uniform irrigation increases as the number of theoretical stages per packed bed is increased. For less than five theoretical stages per bed, the column is not so sensitive to the uniformity of liquid distribution; however, this depends on the sensitivity to stage count of the process [5]. For over five theoretical stages per bed, liquid distribution

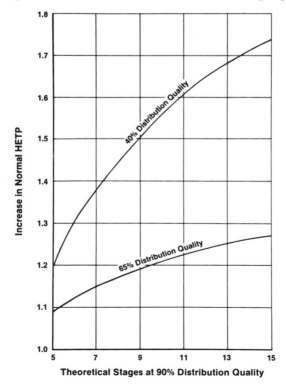

Figure 10-7. Effect of liquid distribution quality.

has a significant effect on packing efficiency, as shown in Figure 10-7. In this figure, the increase in the value of HETP is shown as a function of liquid distribution quality. With 15 or more theoretical stages per bed, liquid distribution uniformity is extremely critical to the attainment of the desired packing efficiency.

Thus, for packed beds of equal depth, the larger packing sizes are less sensitive to the uniformity of liquid distribution than smaller size packings. This occurs because the large packings have higher HETP values and develop fewer theoretical stages than smaller packings in the same

Table 10-2

Comparison of Commercial vs. High-Performance Distributors

Pall Ring Size (in.)	Possible Number of Theoretical Stages	Percent Efficiency Loss for Commercial Distributor
1	14.3	47
1½	10.5	36
2	8.6	29
3½	5.8	17

Packed bed depth of 19 ft.

bed depth. Table 10-2 illustrates the performance loss of various sizes of metal Pall ring packings with a typical commercial distributor, compared to a high performance distribution system in a distillation operation with a 19-ft bed depth.

With the advancements in liquid distribution technology, packed bed depths are being increased in order to better utilize the available column height. Packed depths up to 40 ft, which develop over 25 theoretical stages, are becoming more common with the use of high-performance liquid distributors.

Ideally, each individual piece of packing on the top surface of the bed should be irrigated by a liquid stream. This could be accomplished for a bed of 3½- in. size Pall ring packing, but would be impractical for the 1-in. size of this packing. Albright found that every packing has a natural liquid flow distribution [6]. Perfect initial distribution will degrade to the natural pattern. Initial maldistribution of liquid will improve slowly to the natural distribution, given sufficient bed depth. He concluded that there exists an initial liquid distribution pattern that will minimize the depth of packing required to attain the natural distribution pattern.

Bemer and Zuiderweg showed that a significant maldistribution of liquid occurred in a bed of Raschig ring packing [7]. Local flow rates differed from a normal pattern when measured at various liquid flows and with different size packings. They concluded that the bulk of the liquid

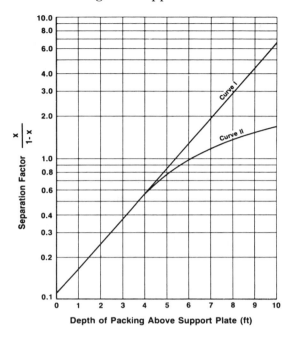

Figure 10-8. Effect of liquid distribution on separation.

flows in stable channels. Further, a high percentage of the radial liquid mixing is due to this irregular flow distribution.

Later experiments in small diameter columns have shown that a bed of random dumped packing develops a definite number of preferred paths of internal liquid flow [8]. If liquid is distributed onto the packed bed with a greater number of streams per square foot than number of preferred liquid paths, the liquid streams within the bed coalesce until the number of preferred liquid paths is reached. If liquid is distributed onto the packed bed with a smaller number of streams per square foot than the number of preferred liquid paths, the packing redistributes the liquid until the number of preferred liquid paths is established. In this latter case, the upper portion of the packed bed has a lower-than-normal separating efficiency. Figure 10-8 shows the performance of such a packed bed in a binary distillation. Curve I represents the separation obtained with a high-performance liquid distribution system. Curve II shows the effect of inadequate liquid distribution to the top surface of the 10-ft deep packed bed.

In spite of the irregularity of the internal liquid streams, the overall liquid residence time in a packed bed exhibits a normal curve. This has been verified in a commercial column using radioactive tracers that demonstrated that the average liquid residence time was the same as for plug flow of liquid.

It has been well established that the efficiency of random packings is significantly affected by the quality of liquid distribution onto the packed bed. As was true when saddle-type packings first were developed, initially structured packings were assumed to be able to rectify the initial inferior liquid distribution quality. More recent work has shown that liquid distribution quality also is critical to achieving high mass transfer efficiency with structured packings [9].

Liquid distributors are of two general types: the gravity-fed distributor and the pressure-fed distributor. Gravity-fed distributors are more common and are illustrated in Figures 10-9 through 10-12. These distributors for towers larger than 36-in. ID may use a deck that is sealed to the supporting ledge with orifices for metering the liquid flow (Figure 10-9). This type of distributor can use either long, narrow channels for gas risers or a series of individual gas riser tubes. This latter design provides a greater degree of liquid cross-mixing. The high cross-flow capacity of the orifice deck distributor is especially useful with very high liquid flow rates. For smaller diameter columns, the orifice pan distributor usually is used (Figure 10-10). Due to the restricted gas riser area available, this distributor may not be used with extremely high vapor rates.

Because they are inherently liquid-tight, trough-type distributors are useful for low liquid flows. These distributors can be equipped with orifices or weirs as the liquid flow-metering device. Such a distributor with sidewall orifices combines a high flow turndown range with the ability to span large tower diameters without additional support (Figure 10-11). When there is a possibility of fouling an orifice in the bottom, an orifice

Figure 10-9. Orifice deck liquid distributor. (Courtesy of Norton Chemical Process Products Corporation.)

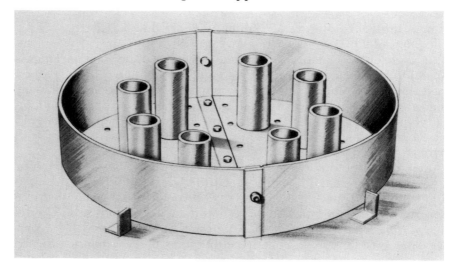

Figure 10-10. Orifice pan liquid distributor. (Courtesy of Norton Chemical Process Products Corporation.)

Figure 10-11. Orifice trough distributor with side-wall orifice, Model 137. (Courtesy of Norton Chemical Process Products Corporation.)

Figure 10-12. Weir trough liquid distributor. (Courtesy of Norton Chemical Process Products Corporation.)

located in the sidewall of the trough can be used. However, for severe fouling, a weir trough distributor can be used (Figure 10-12). However, because weirs are more sensitive than orifices to variations in liquid head, the uniformity of liquid distribution may be degraded by their use.

Pressure-fed distributors typically are of the ladder-type that may use pipe arms containing liquid-metering orifices, as shown in Figure 10-13. Another design uses a formed box-shape in which orifices have been pre-punched into the horizontal bottom. This design provides a closer tolerance on orifice shape and diameter than a hole drilled into a pipe. Because of the greater pressure drop available, the orifice sizes in these distributors usually are smaller than in gravity-fed distributors. The feed liquid first should be passed through a fine strainer to remove any materials that would foul these smaller orifices. While gravity-fed bottom-orifice distributors usually are limited to a 2-to-1 turn-down ratio, because of the limitations of gas riser height due to the manhole size, sidewall orifices located at multiple levels can provide much wider flow ranges. However, pressure-fed distributors can operate at a 3-to-1 or greater turn-down ratio. This type distributor is useful where column height is limited or a support ledge is not available. It has the disadvantage of not being able to mix feed with any downflowing liquid. Also, it should not be used with flashing liquids.

In addition, spray-nozzle distributors have been used to irrigate packed beds (Figure 10-14). Spray nozzles for distributing liquid usually are not used in fractionating columns or absorbers. Their use is limited to heat transfer operations where liquid entrainment from the bed top is not

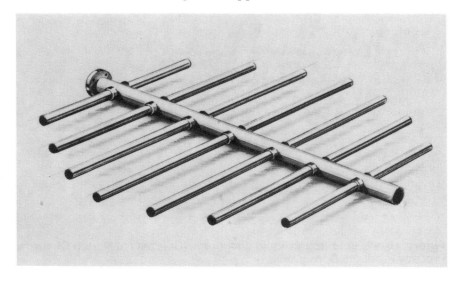

Figure 10-13. Orifice ladder liquid distributor. (Courtesy of Norton Chemical Process Products Corporation.)

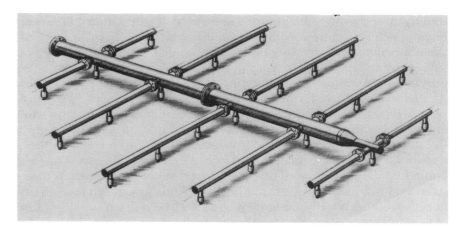

Figure 10-14. Spray nozzle liquid distributor. (Courtesy of Norton Chemical Process Products Corporation.)

likely to occur or will not constitute an operational problem. Spray nozzles do not generate a uniformly distributed liquid-flow pattern. Further, tests at high pressures have shown that the spray cone angle may vary with system properties.

As we have discussed, uniformity of liquid distribution is essential to the attainment of the maximum packed bed efficiency. In those cases where a mixed vapor/liquid feed is used, or where the liquid feed would flash on entering the column, special designs are necessary. To avoid excessive turbulence in the liquid distributor, it is customary to install a device that separates the vapor and liquid phases ahead of the final distributor. Such a device used for small columns is located immediately above the distributor (Figure 10-15). For large diameter towers where feed

Figure 10-15. Vapor/liquid separator. (Courtesy of Norton Chemical Process Products Corporation.)

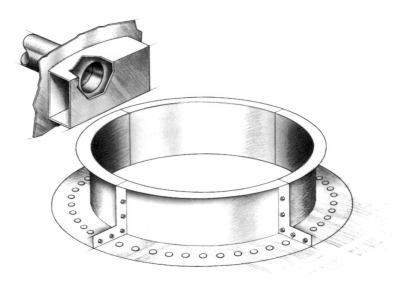

Figure 10-16. Metal flashing feed gallery. (Courtesy of Norton Chemical Process Products Corporation.)

rates are much greater, the usual parting boxes above the distributor can be replaced with a gallery, as illustrated in Figure 10-16. For these mixed vapor/liquid feeds, a gravity-fed liquid distributor should be used.

LIQUID REDISTRIBUTORS

A liquid redistributor is required at the top of each packed bed. The liquid flow from a typical support plate is not sufficiently uniform to properly irrigate the next lower packed bed. The multibeam type of packing support plate, which is widely used, tends to segregate the liquid downflow from a packed bed into a pair of parallel rows of liquid streams about 2-in. apart with a 10-in. space between adjacent pairs. Gas-distributing support plates, likewise, do not give a sufficiently uniform liquid irrigation pattern, because gas riser locations take precedence in the design of such a plate.

Liquid redistributors must operate in the same manner as gravity-fed distributors. To intercept all of the liquid downflow, these distributors usually have a deck that is sealed to a supporting ledge, as shown in Figure 10-17. If liquid-tight pans or boxes are used for a redistributor, gas riser covers and wall wipers must be used, or a collector plate must be installed above it, to intercept all the liquid downflow. Whenever the liq-

Figure 10-17. Orifice deck liquid redistributor. (Courtesy of Norton Chemical Process Products Corporation.)

uid falls directly onto a deck-type redistributor, the gas risers must be provided with covers to prevent liquid from raining into this area of high vapor velocity [10]. To avoid excessive disturbance of the liquid pool on the deck, the redistributor should be located no more than 2 ft below the support plate for the bed above it.

In any mass transfer operation, the compositions of the liquid and vapor phases are assumed to follow the relationship illustrated by the column operating line. This line represents the overall calculated profile down the column; however, the composition on each individual square foot of a particular column cross-section may vary from that represented by the operating line. These variations are the result of deviations in the hydraulic flow rates of the vapor and liquid phases, as well as incomplete mixing of the phases across the entire column.

One of the functions of a liquid redistributor is to remix the liquid phase so as to bring the entire liquid flow onto the next lower bed at a more uniform composition. To perform this function, the liquid redistributor must intercept all the liquid that is flowing down the column, including any liquid on the column walls. If a new feed is to be introduced, a feed sparger or parting box must be used to predistribute this feed onto the redistributor. The redistributor must maintain the uniform vapor distribution that should have been established at the column bottom. To perform these functions, the redistributor must have a large flow area available that is transverse to the gas risers, because only very low gradient heads are available for cross-mixing of the liquid. In addition, the vapor flow area must be sufficient to avoid a high pressure drop in the gas phase.

There has been considerable speculation regarding the depth of packing that could be installed before liquid redistribution is required. Silvey and Keller found no loss of efficiency in distillation with 18-ft deep beds of 1½-in. ceramic Raschig rings and 35-ft deep beds of 3-in. ceramic Raschig rings [11]. On the basis of their reported average HETP values, these beds were developing only seven and ten theoretical stages, respectively. Strigle and Fukuyo showed that with high performance redistributors over 20 theoretical stages per packed bed could be obtained repeatedly with 1-in. size packing [12].

Packed bed heights typically vary from 20 ft to 30 ft [3]. Many times the location of manholes to provide access to the redistributor will determine the packed depth. Whenever more than 15 theoretical stages are required in one packed bed, good liquid distribution is critical.

WALL WIPERS

In small diameter columns the tower wall surface area is substantial when compared to the total packing surface area. As the column diameter becomes larger, the wall area diminishes in significance compared to the packing area. Thus, in a 6-in. ID column perhaps as much as 30% of the liquid feed could flow down the column wall. However, in a 60-in. ID column as little as 3% of the liquid feed may flow down the column wall. The amount of wall flow will depend upon the ability of the tower packing to transfer liquid onto and away from the tower wall, as well as upon the liquid irrigation rate.

There have been many questions raised about the effect of wall flow in a packed column. If the liquid reaching the column wall continues to flow down the wall, it represents a bypassed stream that reduces the overall separation efficiency. Furzer showed that 1-in. Lessing rings (and presumably 1-in. Raschig rings) were poor at transferring liquid to and from the column wall with a distributor having three distribution points per square foot [13]. Later work using a distributor having 6.5 distribution points per square foot with the same packing indicated that the wall flow frequently interchanged with the liquid in the packed bed.

Liquid flowing on the wall must be in dynamic equilibrium with the liquid in the packed bed, or the overall separation will be reduced. In small columns with a high percentage of wall flow, wall wipers frequently are installed. Wall wipers fit tightly against the column wall to intercept all of the liquid flowing down the wall. If the bottom product is to be of high purity, all of the low-boiling component must be removed in the column stripping section. Any liquid feed that flows down the column wall may not be completely stripped. The wall wiper is used to remove this liquid from the wall and place it into the packed bed where it will be adequately contracted with the rising vapor phase. Generally, wall wipers are required only in the lower portion of the stripping section. These devices usually are spaced apart by about two theoretical stages of packed height.

Because wall wipers are installed within the packed bed itself, they must be designed carefully to avoid severely reducing the column capacity. As illustrated by Table 10-1, any ledge installed must be rather narrow; thus, the ledge itself is incapable of returning the intercepted liquid a sufficient distance back into the packed bed to ensure its mixing with the main liquid phase. Figure 10-18 illustrates a patented design for such a

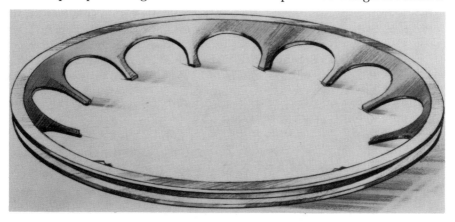

Figure 10-18. "Rosette" wall wiper. (Courtesy of Norton Chemical Process Products Corporation.)

plate that overcomes this problem. This design maintains a constant, very high percentage of the column cross-sectional area open to vapor and liquid flows. The finger extensions convey the intercepted liquid back into the packed bed and the main downflowing liquid phase.

Wall flow of liquid also is a concern with structured packings. The angular corrugations in the metal sheets tend to direct the liquid 45 degrees downward in a series of parallel planes in each layer of packing. The structured packings are carefully spaced away from the column wall; therefore, a wall wiper is installed on each layer of structured packing to return the liquid flowing down the wall back into the packed bed.

LIQUID COLLECTORS

Sometimes it is necessary to intercept all of the liquid flowing down the column. This may occur due to an enlargement or contraction of the column diameter when operating at liquid rates in excess of 15 gpm/ft². If the lower portion of the column is of a larger diameter than the upper portion, the liquid must be collected at the bottom of the smaller diameter section. It then is fed to a redistributor located at the top of the larger diameter section to irrigate uniformly the lower section. If the lower portion of the column is of a smaller diameter than the upper portion, the liquid must be collected at the bottom of the larger diameter section. It then is fed to a redistributor at the top of the smaller diameter section to prevent excessive wall flow in the lower section.

In a number of applications liquid pumparound sections are installed. Such sections are used in caustic scrubbers where only a small addition of sodium hydroxide is required to neutralize the absorbed acid gas. However, the liquid irrigation rate of each section must be adequate to ensure good gas scrubbing in the packed bed. In absorbers where the solute has a high heat of vaporization or heat of solution, the downflowing liquid progressively increases in temperature. This heated liquid must be removed from the column and cooled before it is returned to irrigate the next lower packed bed. The absorption otherwise is limited by the high vapor pressure of the solute above the hot rich solution. In some operations, liquid is removed and recirculated back to the top of the same packed bed after cooling. Such a situation is common when the packed bed is used as a total, or partial, condenser.

In applications that must use a feed location that will not match the internal liquid composition (see Chapter 7), the feed must be mixed with the downflowing liquid. One method to accomplish this is the use of a collector plate that is installed beneath the rectifying section of the column. The liquid feed then is added to the pool of downflowing liquid on this collector plate. Such an arrangement provides at least partial mixing of the feed with the rectifier effluent in the liquid downcomer to give a more uniform composition of liquid onto the distributor irrigating the stripping section of the column. In other cases, a liquid cross-mixing device is installed in the column at the feed elevation.

For columns in which there is a substantial flash of the feed liquid, or in which the feed is a vapor of a different composition than the internal vapor, a collector plate can be installed above the feed point. The purpose of this plate is to provide mixing of the vapor phase in the gas risers so that a more uniform vapor composition enters the rectifying section of the column.

Figure 10-19 shows a typical liquid collector plate for a column that uses one side downcomer to withdraw the liquid. The maximum diameter for such a design is about 12 ft, which is limited by the hydraulic gradient necessary for such a liquid flow-path length. For larger diameter columns, two opposite side downcomers or a center downcomer normally is used unless the total amount of liquid collected is relatively small.

A liquid collector plate must be of gasketed construction so that it can be sealed to the supporting ledge and will be liquid-tight. The sections could be seal-welded together; however, future removal would be difficult. There must be sufficient liquid head available to cause the liquid to flow out the side nozzle in the column shell. The use of sumps pro-

Figure 10-19. Liquid collector plate. (Courtesy of Norton Chemical Process Products Corporation.)

vides such a liquid head without pooling liquid across the entire plate, where leakage and the weight of liquid to be supported would be greater.

The gas risers must have a sufficient flow area to avoid a high gas-phase pressure drop. In addition, these gas risers must be uniformly positioned to maintain proper gas distribution. The gas risers should be equipped with covers to deflect the liquid raining onto this collector plate and prevent it from entering the gas risers where the high gas velocity could cause entrainment. These gas riser covers must be kept a sufficient distance below the next packed bed to allow the gas phase to come to a uniform flow rate per square foot of column cross-sectional area before entering the next bed [14].

Where only about 5% or less of the liquid downflow is to be withdrawn from the column, a special collector box can be installed within the packed bed. This box can remove small quantities of intermediate boiling components that otherwise would accumulate in a sufficient quantity to interfere with the fractionation operation. Such a collector box must be designed very carefully to avoid interference with the vapor distribution above it or reduction in the quality of liquid distribution below it.

REFERENCES

1. Leva, M., *Tower Packings and Packed Tower Design,* 2nd ed., United States Stoneware, 1953, p. 25.
2. Chen, G. K. and Chuang, K. T., *Hydrocarbon Processing,* Vol. 68, No. 2, 1989, p. 37.
3. Harrison, M. E. and France, J. J., *Chemical Engineering,* Vol. 96, No. 4, 1989, p. 121.
4. Moore, F. and Rukovena, F., *Chemical Plants + Processing, European Edition,* August 1987, p. 11.
5. Spiegel, L. and Yuan, H. C., "The Influence of Maldistribution at Partial Reflux," World Congress II of Chemical Engineering, Montreal, October 1981.
6. Albright, M. A., *Hydrocarbon Processing,* Vol. 63, No. 9, 1984, p. 173.
7. Bemer, G. G. and Zuiderweg, F. J., *Chemical Engineering Science,* Vol. 33, No. 12, 1978, p. 1637.
8. Hoek, P. J., "Large and Small Scale Liquid Maldistribution in a Packed Column," Ph.D. Thesis, Delft University, June 1983.
9. Martin, C. L. *et al.,* "Performance of Structured Packings in Distillation Service," A.I.Ch.E. Meeting, New Orleans, March 1988.
10. Fadel, T. M., *Chemical Engineering,* Vol. 91, No. 1, 1984, p. 71.
11. Silvey, F. C. and Keller, G. J., *Institution Chemical Engineers Symposium Series,* No. 32, 1969, p. 4:18.
12. Strigle, R. F. and Fukuyo, K., *Hydrocarbon Processing,* Vol. 65, No. 6, 1986, p. 47.
13. Furzer, I. A., *Chemical Engineering Science,* Vol. 39, No. 7/8, 1984, pp. 1283 and 1301.
14. Chen, G. K., *Chemical Engineering,* Vol. 91, No. 3, 1984, p. 40.

11

LIQUID-LIQUID EXTRACTION

Many industrially important solutions of liquids form constant boiling mixtures (azeotropes) or have components with such close boiling points that separation of these liquids by ordinary distillation is not practical. Separation of high molecular weight organic materials by distillation may cause degradation even under low pressures. Evaporation of very dilute solutions of product may be prohibitively expensive. Various other methods of separation have been applied to such systems, including liquid-liquid extraction. While most mass transfer operations separate components based on differences in physical properties, liquid-liquid extraction separates components based on chemical differences. Compared to distillation as a means of separation, liquid-liquid extraction is a more recent operation. It has reached industrial significance only since 1930 [1].

Liquid-liquid extraction involves the contacting of a solution with another solvent, which is immiscible with the original solvent, in which a desired solute in the original solution is soluble. Thus, two liquid phases are formed after addition of the new solvent. These two immiscible phases separate because of a difference in densities. Some component of the original solution will be more soluble in the new solvent than in the original solvent; thus, this component will be extracted from the original solution through contact with the new solvent.

GENERAL CONSIDERATIONS

In liquid-liquid extractions, at least one component in the original mixture to be separated must be soluble in the new solvent, while the other components are not as soluble. Thus, we are concerned with two separate immiscible, or only partially miscible, liquid phases and at least one solute component. These two phases must be mutually insoluble or exhibit a very limited mutual solubility. However, the transferred component that is to be separated is soluble in both liquid phases.

Systems using liquid-liquid extractions fall into two categories:

1. Those systems in which mass transfer takes place because of differences in solubility of the solute in the two solvents.
2. Those systems in which mass transfer takes place due to a subsequent chemical reaction of one or more of the solutes in the original mixture with a component of the new solvent.

Examples of some liquid-liquid extractions are given in Table 11-1.

Table 11-1

Typical Liquid-Liquid Extractions

Original Solvent	Solute	New Solvent
Water	Acetic Acid	Benzene
Water	Adipic Acid	Diethyl Ether
Reformate	Aromatics	Diethylene Glycol
Vacuum Residue	Asphaltenes	Propane
Water	Benzoic Acid	Carbon Tetrachloride
Water	Diethylamine	Toluene
Natural Oils	Fatty Acids	Propane
LPG	H_2S	MEA
Naphtha	Mercaptans	NaOH Solution
Water	MEK	Toluene
Lubricating Oil	Naphthenes	Furfural
Water	Phenol	Chlorobenzene
Water	Rare Earths	MIBK

It is necessary that we define the terms customarily used in connection with extraction. The mixture that is to be separated consists of the solute C to be recovered, which is present in solvent A. This solution is the feed to the extractor. This solvent A feed, after removal of at least some solute C, is called the raffinate as it leaves the extractor. The second liquid phase (with which the original mixture is contacted) consists of solvent B, containing little or no solute C, and is termed the solvent. This solvent B, after being enriched in solute C, is called the extract as it leaves the extractor. Thus, in an extractor operating in the usual countercurrent manner, the feed is in contact with the extract leaving at one end and the solvent is in contact with the raffinate leaving at the other end. The solute C, which is separated from the feed mixture, leaves in the extract phase mixed with solvent B. It is apparent that the solute cannot be recovered in highly pure form by a liquid-liquid extraction, as may be possible in a distillation. Thus, to recover the solute, the extract must be subjected to some additional purifying operation such as evaporation, distillation, crystallization, or adsorption. Further, the raffinate may contain some dissolved solvent B, which for economic reasons must be recovered by another mass transfer operation.

EXTRACTOR OPERATION

Extraction is carried out in three classes of equipment:

1. mixer-settlers
2. contacting columns
3. centrifugal contractors

Mixer-settlers are devices in which immiscible liquids are mixed together in an attempt to bring the system to equilibrium. The two phases then are separated (settled) and removed. While such devices can provide high stage efficiencies, they require a large floor area and have high liquid inventories.

Centrifugal contractors are rotating mechanical devices in which the less dense liquid is contacted with the more dense liquid under the influence of centrifugal force. These devices can process liquid phases with small density differences and have low liquid holdups. Such devices particularly are useful when the difference between the density of the light phase and the density of the heavy phase is 4% or lower. Principally, such contactors are used to recover high value products where a large number of equilibrium stages are required.

Contacting columns operate in a continuous manner with counter-current flow of the two liquid phases. The more dense phase is introduced into the top of the column and the less dense phase is introduced into the bottom. To achieve mass transfer of solute C between solvent A and immiscible solvent B, these solvents must be in intimate contact; thus, one phase must be dispersed in the other phase. The dispersed phase travels through the continuous phase in the form of droplets. It follows that in order to obtain flow of the dispersed phase through the continuous phase, the two phases must be of different densities. Further, for continuous, countercurrent contacting this density difference between phases must exist throughout the entire tower, because the density of the phases may change significantly due to transfer of the solute. A typical arrangement of a contacting column is shown in Figure 11-1.

Where columns with tower packings or sieve trays are used, the difference in densities between the liquid phases is the force causing flow, as well as dispersion of one phase into the other. However, mechanically agitated columns are equipped with a series of radial mixers driven by a vertical shaft, which produce the dispersion. Also, there is a hybrid device that uses radial mixers separated by wire mesh packing.

CHOICE OF DEVICE

Interfacial tension, difference between phase densities, and viscosity are the principal limiting factors in the selection of the type of equipment

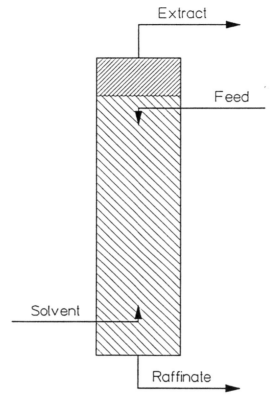

Figure 11-1. Typical contacting column.

used. Very low interfacial tension can result in formation of an emulsion, unless power input is limited. Small differences in the densities of the two phases require more than gravitational force to attain reasonable flow capacities. High liquid viscosities and high interfacial tensions require increased power input to achieve rapid rates of mass transfer.

The problem of coalescence of the dispersed phase also must be considered. This phenomenon is affected by interfacial tension and viscosity. Entrainment of the dispersed phase can occur if the droplets of this phase are too small. Obviously, an emulsion can require an excessive time to produce phase separation. High viscosity of the continuous phase also retards the rate of coalescence of the dispersed phase.

When only one theoretical stage is required, a liquid mixer followed by a settling tank usually is used. This probably was the earliest device used for liquid extraction; however, it requires a large inventory of solvents.

Spray columns can be used where the density difference between phases is large. However, such towers become excessively tall if N_{OL} is three or greater, because of the large values of H_{OL}. This low efficiency partially is due to axial mixing, which shows an increasing effect as column diameter becomes larger.

Whenever three to nine theoretical stages are necessary, packed columns are the preferred devices. The packing provides a tortuous flow path for the dispersed phase, thereby increasing contact time between phases. The packing also restricts axial mixing of the continuous phase. Sieve-plate columns also have been employed for these same applications. The perforations in the trays serve to produce the dispersion, while the downcomers (or upcomers) conduct the continuous phase from tray to tray. Sieve plates create a series of short spray columns with the continuous phase being partially mixed in the downcomers. Because packed and sieve-trayed columns impart only a minimum of energy to the system, they are preferred for low interfacial tension systems (less than 12 dyne/cm) to avoid emulsification.

When ten or more theoretical stages are required, the packed depth needed may make the tower excessively tall; therefore, specifying a mechanical contactor may permit the use of a shorter column. These contactors use rotating disks or impellers to disperse one phase into the other.

DEPICTION OF LIQUID EXTRACTION

Because it is difficult to represent a system of three components on a rectangular diagram, a triangular diagram frequently is used. In Figure 11-2, A and B are the two solvents, and C is the solute. A feature of the triangular diagram is that at any point the summation of the concentrations of components A, B, and C always is 100%.

A common characteristic of liquid extraction systems is that the mutual solubility of the solvents A and B increases with an increase in the concentration of solute C. This is illustrated in Figure 11-2, where, at a sufficiently high concentration of solute C, solvents A and B become completely miscible, and a single-phase system results.

MUTUAL SOLUBILITIES

Figure 11-2 is a triangular diagram representing a system in which water and benzene are the two solvents (A and B, respectively) and an organic acid is the solute C. Benzene is contacted with the aqueous feed solution to extract the organic acid. Point J represents the solubility of benzene in water, and point K represents the solubility of water in benzene. Curve JRPEK represents the equilibrium among these three components

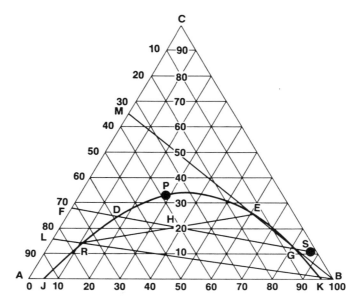

Figure 11-2. Equilibrium relation—triangular diagram.

at a particular temperature. Any point under this curve represents a mixture that will separate into two liquid phases. A point above the curve represents the composition of a single homogeneous phase.

There exists a definite concentration relationship between the two liquid phases at equilibrium. In Figure 11-2 the feed to the extractor is a solution of organic acid in water, represented by point F. The solvent to the extractor is partially stripped benzene of a composition represented by point S. The feed and solvent form a mixture of the composition represented by point H. If the extractor consists of one equilibrium stage, mixture H will separate into two phases, so that the composition of the extract will be represented by point E and the composition of the raffinate by point R. The composition at point E will be in equilibrium with the concentration at point R.

The ratio of the concentration of solute in benzene to the concentration of solute in water is called the distribution coefficient for this temperature:

$$K_D = \frac{x_E}{x_R} \tag{11-1}$$

This distribution coefficient is similar to the Henry's Law constant in absorption operations. For a single solute, which is only sparingly soluble in the two solvents, the distribution coefficient would be the ratio of the solubilities of the solute in each of the two liquid phases. For more soluble materials (higher solute concentrations), the distribution coefficient may be significantly different than the ratio of the solubilities in the two solvents. The distribution coefficients for some typical aqueous solutions with various solvents are shown in Table 11-2 [2].

Table 11-2

**Distribution Coefficient Between Solvent and Water
For Various Solutes at 25°C**

Solvent	Solute	K_D
Benzene	Acetic Acid	0.023
Benzene	Benzoic Acid	1.8
Benzene	Diethylamine	0.63
Benzene	Ethanol	1.1
Benzene	Isopropanol	0.50
Benzene	Phenol	2.3
Carbon Tetrachloride	Acetic Acid	0.059
Carbon Tetrachloride	Acetone	0.44
Carbon Tetrachloride	Phenol	0.36
Diethyl Ether	Acetic Acid	0.45
Toluene	Acetone	0.50
Toluene	Aniline	7.7
Toluene	Isopropanol	0.21
Xylene	Aniline	3.0
Xylene	Diethylamine	0.20
Xylene	Phenol	1.4

Note: Concentrations are in grams of solute per liter of solution.

In Figure 11-2, line ER connects the composition of an extract phase with the composition of a raffinate phase with which it is in equilibrium. Such lines are known as tie lines. These tie lines move vertically as the compositions of the two phases approach each other, until only a single phase exists (as shown in Figure 11-3). The point on curve JRPEK where a single liquid phase is formed is called the plait point (point P). The interfacial tension approaches zero as the plait point is approached.

EFFECT OF TEMPERATURE AND PRESSURE

In most cases solubility of the solute increases at higher temperatures; however, the change in solubility with temperature may not be the same in both solvents. Thus, the distribution coefficient for a solute between two solvents may increase or decrease as the temperature rises. When more than one solute is present in the feed, the temperature of operation should be fixed to give the largest distribution coefficient for the preferred solute to be recovered.

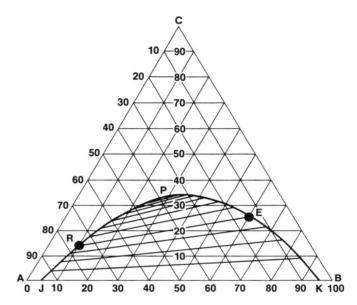

Figure 11-3. Tie lines on triangular diagram.

Because solubility usually increases at higher temperatures, above some temperature normally there will exist one homogeneous phase, regardless of composition. This temperature is known as the critical solution temperature. At lower temperatures, both the composition of the mixture and the temperature will determine whether one or two liquid phases exist. However, the vapor pressure of the solvents also increases at higher temperatures. In some systems, vaporization of the liquid phase occurs before the critical solution temperature is reached. The contactor must be operated at a high enough pressure to keep all components liquid.

The temperature of operation should be high enough to ensure solubility of all solutes at the concentrations encountered in both liquid phases. Solubility of a solute is only slightly influenced by pressure. This effect can be predicted from the principle of Le Chatelier. If the volume of the liquid phase increases with an increase in solute concentration, a higher pressure of operation will decrease solubility.

INTERFACIAL TENSION

There exists an interfacial tension between the two liquid phases. Quite often the interfacial tension between the two solvents is altered markedly by the presence of the solute. Surface active materials may cause a sharp change in interfacial tension. While high values of interfacial tension tend to increase the difficulty of dispersing one phase in another, a large value of interfacial tension will promote coalescence of the dispersed phase droplets. On the other hand, low values of interfacial tension may produce an emulsion of the dispersed phase. The tiny droplets of such an emulsion do not separate easily from the continuous phase, which makes operation of the extractor very difficult.

The interfacial tension between the two phases cannot be calculated as the difference between the individual phase surface tensions measured against air. Generally, interfacial tension is reduced by the presence of a dissolved solute. Donahue and Bartell empirically correlated interfacial tension and mutual solubilities of binary pairs of liquids in the absence of a solute [3]. Treybal reported that this correlation also predicted eight different ternary systems from available data [4]. His modified correlation is shown as Figure 11-4. In this figure, x_{AB} is the mol fraction of solvent A dissolved in solvent B, x_{BA} is the mol fraction of solvent B dissolved in solvent A, x_{CA} is the mol fraction of solute C dissolved in solvent A, and x_{CB} is the mol fraction of solute C dissolved in solvent B. For binary liquid systems, Girifalco and Good showed that there is a relationship between interfacial tension and the hydrogen-bonding characteristics and molal volumes [5].

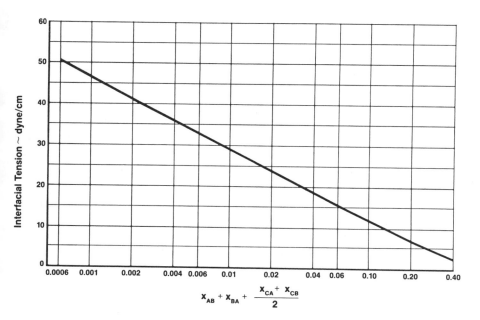

Figure 11-4. Treybal correlation for interfacial tension (From Treybal [3]. Reprinted from *Liquid Extraction* by permission. Copyright © 1963, McGraw-Hill.)

SOLVENT SELECTION

For practical purposes the two solvents should be immiscible; however, in most cases there is some mutual solubility of the solvents such as is indicated in Figure 11-2. The solvent selected should exhibit a high selectivity—it must dissolve the maximum amount of the solute and a minimum amount of the other solvent. The distribution coefficient should be large to reduce the number of theoretical stages required in the extractor. Because the solute C must be recovered from solvent B in the extract and any dissolved solvent B recovered from the raffinate, lines from point B on Figure 11-2 can be extended through the extract and raffinate compositions to intersect line AC at points M and L, respectively. The farther the displacement of points M and L from the feed (point F), the greater the selectivity of the solvent and the larger the amount of separation obtained per theoretical stage.

The capacity of the solvent for dissolving the solute must be large, otherwise the solvent circulation rate required may be uneconomical. Also, the solvent selected must be separated easily from the solute. The cost of separation and recovery of the solute and solvent significantly influences the economics of the entire liquid-liquid extraction operation. As an example, liquid-liquid extraction may not be practical for recovery of low concentrations of solute from aqueous waste streams if the volume of the extract exceeds the volume of the waste treated. However, extraction may be used when the distribution coefficient strongly favors the solvent, and this solvent can be recovered at low cost by evaporation.

The solvent must have a significant difference in density from the feed, otherwise the hydraulic capacity of the extractor will be low. Further, this density difference still must exist after transfer of the solute. Thus the extract and raffinate phases across any tie line (as shown in Figure 11-3) must be of different densities if contacted in a continuous manner. Francis suggests that the formation of two phases of equal density can occur in many ternary systems [6, 7].

The solvent should have a low viscosity, otherwise the column capacity will be reduced and the rate of settling of the dispersion will be slow. Sometimes modifiers can be added to the solvent to reduce its viscosity. Also, increasing the temperature of operation will lower liquid viscosity. The solvent chosen must not produce such a low interfacial tension after solute transfer that an emulsion is formed. In addition, the solvent selected should be readily available and inexpensive. Many organic solvents pose special restrictions in their use due to flammability or high vapor pressure. Also, the solvent selected should be nontoxic and noncarcinogenic and should not corrode common materials of construction, so as to improve ease of handling and reduce capital cost of equipment.

Oberg and Jones present a simplified method for determining the miscibility of various solvents [1]. Typical solvents are listed in order in Table 11-3. Water at the top of this table is virtually immiscible with n-heptane at the bottom of the table. Each solvent is completely miscible with those located within two positions of it in the table. There is a relatively high miscibility with those located three positions away from it in the table. On the other hand, there is a relatively low miscibility with those located four positions away from it in the table. Any liquids located five or more positions away from each other in the table are practically immiscible. Blumberg proposes the use of dielectric constant as the property for comparison of non-aqueous solvents or diluents [8].

Table 11-3

Miscibility of Various Solvents

1. Water
2. Diethylene Glycol
3. Triethylene Glycol
4. Furfural
5. Diethyl Ether
6. Benzene
7. Cyclohexane
8. n-Heptane

ALTERNATE DEPICTION OF EXTRACTION

In distillation calculations, the system is depicted by rectangular coordinates that plot the concentration of light key in the vapor vs. the concentration of light key in the liquid. It is possible to depict a liquid-liquid extraction in a similar manner. As shown in Figure 11-5, the concentration of solute in the extract phase can be plotted against the concentration of solute in the raffinate phase. The slope of this equilibrium curve is represented by the distribution coefficient. The distribution coefficient of solute C is not affected by its concentration. The distribution coefficient of solute E is a significant function of its concentration, while the distribution coefficient of solute D is a lesser function of its concentration. As illustrated, at low concentrations of solute, the shape of the distribution curve has diminished importance.

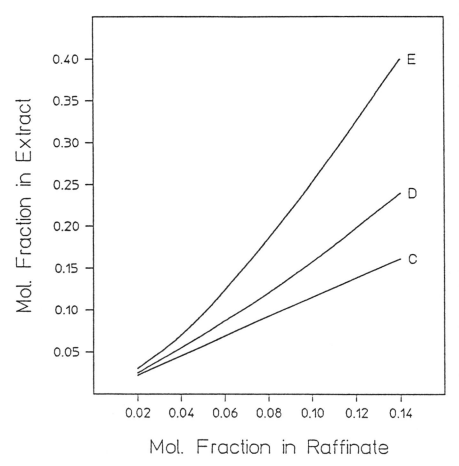

Figure 11-5. Equilibrium relationship for multiple solutes.

EQUILIBRIUM CONSIDERATIONS

The equilibrium between the extract and the raffinate is characterized by the same activity in both phases, although the concentrations are not the same in both phases. Therefore, at equilibrium:

$$\gamma_{CE} = \gamma_{CR} \tag{11-2}$$

where γ_{CR} is the activity coefficient for solute C in the raffinate and λ_{CE} is the activity coefficient for solute C in the extract.

If the purpose of the extraction operation is the separation of two solutes (component C and component D) that are present in the feed mixture, the selectivity of the solvent B for each of the two solutes must be considered. The degree of separation of the two solutes is given by:

$$S_D = \frac{(K_D)_C}{(K_D)_D} \tag{11-3}$$

which is the ratio of the distribution coefficients for the two solutes. In such systems, activities can vary due to interactions between components. The degree of separation can vary substantially with concentration, as the two solutes vie for the same limited amount of solvent. As shown in Figure 11-5, the degree of separation between solutes D and E is greatly influenced by the concentration. The lowest value of the distribution coefficient over the range of operation of the extractor will control the ratio of solvent to feed.

In systems with multiple solutes, those with higher K_D values (solute E) than the key solute (solute D) will be diluted in the extract by transfer of the key solute. Those solutes with lower K_D values (solute C) than the key solute will be only partially extracted from the feed.

RATES OF MASS TRANSFER

To produce mass transfer of solute between the two solvents, a driving force is necessary. This driving force usually is expressed in terms of the concentrations of solute in the two phases and the departure from equilibrium values. The two-film theory of mass transfer developed in Chapter 3 for gas absorption also can be applied to liquid extraction. The rate of mass transfer of solute C from the feed (solvent A) to the extract (solvent B) is:

$$N = K_E \, aAZ \, (x_E{}^* - x_E) \tag{11-4}$$

Alternately, the rate of mass transfer of solute C for the raffinate phase is:

$$N = K_R \, aAZ \, (x_R - x_R{}^*) \tag{11-5}$$

These relationships are illustrated diagrammatically in Figure 11-6.

If we consider the mass transfer from the two-film theory, the transfer through the extract liquid film from the interface is:

$$N = k_E \, aAZ \, (x_E{}' - x_E) \tag{11-6}$$

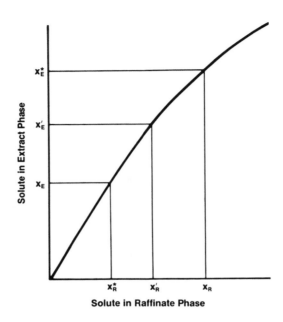

Figure 11-6. Equilibrium relationship by two-film theory.

Likewise, the transfer through the raffinate liquid film to the interface is:

$$N = k_R \, aAZ \, (x_R - x_R')$$ (11-7)

The resistance to mass transfer through each film is the reciprocal of the film mass transfer coefficient. As is true in other forms of mass transfer, the resistances in the two films are additive. Thus, we have the overall resistance in the extract phase:

$$\frac{1}{K_E} = \frac{1}{k_E} + \frac{m}{k_R}$$ (11-8)

Similarly, in the raffinate phase:

$$\frac{1}{K_R} = \frac{1}{k_R} + \frac{1}{m k_E}$$ (11-9)

In these equations, m is the slope of the equilibrium curve as illustrated in Figure 11-5.

If the distribution coefficient representing the concentration of solute in the extract to the concentration of solute in the raffinate is large, m will have a value greater than unity, and the main resistance to mass transfer will be in the raffinate phase. If the distribution coefficient is small, m will have a value less than unity, and the main resistance to mass transfer will be in the extract phase.

REACTIVE SYSTEMS

If solvent B is a solution that contains a material that will react with solute C, the solubility in the extract phase will increase. If the reaction is rapid, the reactant in solvent B will diffuse toward the liquid film and react there with the solute C diffusing through the interface. In this case, the diffusion of the reactant in solvent B may control the mass transfer rate. However, systems exhibiting fast reactions in the extract phase usually exhibit the main resistance to mass transfer in the raffinate phase. If the reaction is slower, solute C will diffuse some distance into the main body of solvent B before the reaction is completed. In most cases, a chemical reaction in the extract phase increases the rate of mass transfer.

When the reaction between solvent B and solute C is irreversible, the value of x_E^* approaches zero. Such would be the case if H_2S were extracted from LPG using an aqueous solution of caustic soda as the solvent. However, if the chemical reaction is reversible, so that the solute can be recovered, then x_E^* will have a low value that is dependent on the concentrations of the reactants and the temperature. Such a system might be the extraction of H_2S from LPG using an aqueous ethanolamine solvent. The extract phase subsequently would be regenerated to permit reuse of the amine solvent. As shown in Figure 11-6, the equilibrium concentration in the extract approaches a constant value limited by the concentration of the reactant in the solvent and the stoichiometry.

DISPERSED PHASE

In designing an extractor, it is necessary to select which of the two solvent phases will be dispersed with the object of maximizing the rate of mass transfer. Some criteria for this selection are

1. maximize interfacial area.
2. minimize mass transfer resistance.
3. maximize column capacity.
4. avoid coalescence within the packed bed.

A consideration in the rate of mass transfer is the interfacial area available. If the phase with the largest volumetric flow is dispersed, the surface area available for mass transfer from the droplets is maximized. If the volumetric flow rates are greatly different, choosing the greater flow as the continuous phase may cause backmixing of the dispersed phase. However, if the continuous phase flow is almost zero, the drag exerted by the dispersed phase may reduce mass transfer.

In most systems, dispersion of the organic phase into the aqueous phase results in the formation of stable, normal-shaped, dispersed phase droplets. However, Blanding and Elgin reported that in certain systems irregular-shaped, dispersed phase droplets were produced when the aqueous phase was dispersed into the organic phase [9]. They also reported that nonuniformity of the droplet shape affected the flooding rate.

If one of the liquid films offers the major resistance to mass transfer, that high-resistance phase should be dispersed to maximize mass transfer rates. This is done to reduce the required distance the solute must be diffused in the phase in which resistance is greater.

If one of the phases is hazardous or highly flammable, it may be desirable to disperse that phase, as the inventory of dispersed phase usually is less than that of the continuous phase.

PACKED EXTRACTORS

One of the primary functions of tower packing in extractors is to increase the flow path length for the dispersed phase. This increases the contact time between phases, thus producing a greater amount of solute transfer. The tower packing also maintains a relatively uniform distribution of flow of both phases throughout the entire column cross-section. Further, the packed bed distorts the dispersed phase droplets, which results in fresh surfaces being made available that promote increased mass transfer. Another important function of the tower packing is to eliminate backmixing of the continuous phase, which would result in a reduced mass transfer driving force. The extent of axial mixing in a packed tower is considerably less than in an empty spray tower [10]. To accomplish these functions, the packed bed must not contain too large size interstitial voids or have too few pieces of packing per unit volume. For these reasons, the packing selected normally is no larger than 2-in. size, and many times 1½-in. size is the desired maximum.

If the higher viscosity solvent is the continuous phase, the dispersed phase droplet rate of rise will be reduced. This increases the contact time between phases and the total mass of solute transferred; however, a high viscosity continuous phase lowers the column capacity. If the higher viscosity solvent is the dispersed phase, the rate of diffusion of solute in the dispersed phase will be reduced. Breckenfeld and Wilke reported that dispersed phase viscosity had little effect on hydraulic capacity [11].

Treybal states that it is important to choose a packing material that is preferentially wetted by the continuous phase [12]. Because the dispersed phase will not wet the packing, coalescence of the dispersed droplets by contact with the packing pieces is minimized. When the dispersed phase wetted the packing, investigators found that it formed rivulets or flowed as a film over the surface of the packing. Ceramic packings are wetted preferentially by aqueous solvents, while plastic packings are wetted preferentially by organic solvents. Metal packings will wet by either an aqueous or an organic solvent, depending on the initial exposure of the metal surface. However, since the packing elements do not create interfacial area, it may only be necessary to avoid packing materials that are strongly wetted by the dispersed phase.

COLUMN CAPACITY

Flooding correlations for packed liquid extractors have been developed in a manner similar to those used for gas/liquid systems. Just like the air/water system used to evaluate the maximum hydraulic capacity for a gas absorption operation, the capacities in liquid-liquid systems are based on hydraulic flow rates for immiscible solvents in the absence of any mass transfer. As has been stated, the transfer of a solute can change the properties of the extract and raffinate phases in a significant manner. For this reason, it may be that flooding has been experienced in commercial operations at flow rates well below those predicted by the flooding correlation. Clearly, more research is needed to explain the effect of mass transfer on the capacity of a liquid extractor. Nevertheless, the application of a widely used flooding correlation will be reviewed. However, the designer should consider the limitations of this correlation and apply appropriate safety factors in the specification of equipment.

If the dispersed phase flow is increased gradually, drop frequency per unit of column volume becomes greater. Eventually the number of dispersed phase droplets becomes so great that this phase fills the interstitial voids in the packed bed, so that coalescence and flooding occurs. If the continuous-phase flow is increased, eventually its velocity will become as large as the velocity of the dispersed phase. Because the dispersed phase no longer can flow in the opposite direction to the continuous phase, dispersed-phase holdup increases rapidly, and flooding occurs.

Most investigations of the flooding rates in packed columns have been carried out using binary pairs of solvents without solute transfer. Thus, such correlations represent the maximum possible flow rates, because solute transfer usually affects the properties of the two phases so as to reduce hydraulic capacity.

Crawford and Wilke determined the maximum hydraulic flows in a 12-in. diameter column packed with Raschig rings [13]. They reported the flooding velocities of each phase based on the column cross-sectional area. The capacity of the column decreased significantly as the packing size was reduced. The sum of the square roots of the continuous and dispersed phase velocities at flooding was found to be constant for a given packing and pair of liquids. The limiting velocity for each system, therefore, was taken to be the square of this sum. These limiting velocities were expressed as a Reynolds number and used as the ordinate of a flooding correlation. The characteristic packing diameter was expressed as the reciprocal of the packing surface area.

Crawford and Wilke found that the best empirical fit of their data was obtained when these Reynolds numbers were related to the expression:

$$\left[\frac{\mu_c}{\Delta\rho}\right]^{0.5}\left[\frac{\sigma_i}{\rho_c}\right]^{0.1}\left[\frac{a_p}{\varepsilon}\right]^{0.75}$$

To expand the scale of their log-log plot, the square of this relationship was used as the abscissa.

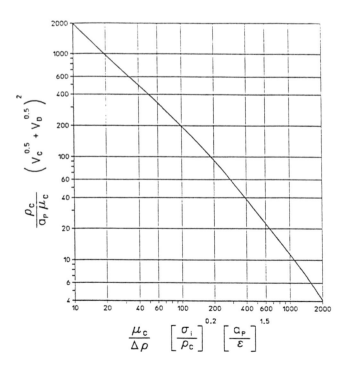

Figure 11-7. Crawford-Wilke correlation for extractor flooding capacity. (From Crawford [13]. Reproduced by permission of the American Institute of Chemical Engineers.)

The Crawford-Wilke flooding correlation for liquid-liquid contactors is shown as Figure 11-7. The values for surface area and void fraction for commonly used random dumped packings are given in Tables 11-4, 11-5, and 11-6. The correlations to predict maximum capacity of liquid-liquid contactors do not provide the same degree of reliability as offered by correlations for gas-liquid columns.

Table 11-4

Flooding Correlation Values for Metal Packings

Packing	Surface Area (ft^2/ft^3)	Void Fraction (ε)
#25 IMTP® Packing	63	0.964
#40 IMTP® Packing	46	0.972
#50 IMTP® Packing	30	0.978
#1 Hy-Pak® Packing	53	0.959
#1½ Hy-Pak® Packing	36	0.964
#2 Hy-Pak® Packing	26	0.971
1 in. Pall Rings	63	0.940
1½ in. Pall Rings	39	0.953
2 in. Pall Rings	31	0.960

Table 11-5

Flooding Correlation Values for Plastic Packings

Packing	Surface Area (ft^2/ft^3)	Void Fraction (ε)
#1 Super Intalox® Saddles	63	0.900
#2 Super Intalox® Saddles	33	0.928
1 in. Pall Rings	63	0.902
1½ in. Pall Rings	39	0.914
2 in. Pall Rings	31	0.923

Table 11-6

Flooding Correlation Values for Ceramic Packings

Packing	Surface Area (ft^2/ft^3)	Void Fraction (ε)
¾ in. Intalox® Saddles	102	0.722
1 in. Intalox® Saddles	78	0.726
1½ in. Intalox® Saddles	59	0.747
2 in. Intalox® Saddles	36	0.754
¾ in. Raschig Rings	74	0.705
1 in. Raschig Rings	58	0.714
1¼ in. Raschig Rings	45	0.722
1½ in. Raschig Rings	37	0.730
2 in. Raschig Rings	28	0.738

The Crawford and Wilke correlation was based on eight different binary liquid systems, which are listed in Table 11-7. The void fractions for packings tested had a maximum value of 0.74. The liquid properties varied as follows:

liquid viscosity	0.58 to 7.8 cps
density difference between phases	9.4 to 37.2 lb/ft^3
interfacial tension	8.9 to 44.8 dyne/cm

All of these flooding data were based purely on hydraulic flow data with no mass transfer of solute occurring. The extrapolation of Figure 11-7, or its use outside the range of applicable physical properties, should be done with considerable caution. If the continuous phase velocity (V_C) is less than 40 ft/h, efficiency of mass transfer can be reduced. Likewise, as the dispersed phase velocity (V_D) is increased, the holdup of dispersed phase increases until coalescence occurs with loss of interfacial area. Regardless of the allowable flow rate from the correlation, the dispersed phase velocity should be limited to 200 ft/h.

Table 11-7

Experimental Systems for Capacity Correlation

Continuous Phase	Dispersed Phase
Water	Gasoline
Glycerine	Gasoline
Carbon Tetrachloride	Water
Carbon Tetrachloride	Glycerine
Water	Methylisobutylketone
Glycerine	Toluene
Naphtha	Water
Water	Naphtha

The transfer of solute can alter the density and viscosity of each of the two phases. If the volumetric flows or physical properties change substantially due to solute transfer, the approach to flooding could be significantly altered. However, in all cases, the approach to flooding should be checked both at the bottom and at the top of the column.

With the development of newer random dumped packings (such as Intalox Metal Tower packing) void fractions exceed 0.96, while the packing surface area is similar to a metal Pall ring packing of the same size. Siebert *et al.* have conducted tests on both #25 and #40 IMTP packings, which permit evaluation of their flooding capacities [14].[1] The #25 IMTP packing's flooding capacities were about 25% higher than the Craw-

---

[1] Reprinted with permission from *Industrial & Engineering Chemistry Research*, 1990, American Chemical Society.

ford-Wilke correlation, while the #40 IMTP packing reached flooding at about the rates predicted by that correlation.

In addition, Siebert also conducted tests on Intalox Structured packing 2T using a system of toluene/acetone/water with the toluene phase dispersed. These tests gave flooding rates for this structured packing that were about the same as the values predicted from the correlation of Crawford and Wilke. Properties of this packing are given in Table 11-8. Until more data becomes available, it would be prudent to design liquid-liquid contactors using high-voidage random packings or structured packings based on the Crawford-Wilke correlation.

Table 11-8

Flooding Correlation Values for Metal Structured Packings

Packing	Surface Area (ft²/ft³)	Void Fraction (ε)
Intalox® Structured Packing 1T	95	0.976
Intalox® Structured Packing 2T	66	0.984
Intalox® Structured Packing 3T	52	0.987

Nemunaitis *et al.* report that flooding in two commercial treaters removing mercaptans from gasoline using an aqueous caustic soda solution occurred at 20% of the values given by Figure 11-7 [15]. More recent commercial experience with treaters removing H_2S from LPG using an aqueous ethanolomine solution also showed flooding occurs at 20% of the values given by that correlation. For these treaters—in which the hydrocarbon phase is dispersed and the aqueous continuous phase flow velocity (V_C) is only 5% to 10% of the dispersed phase flow rate (V_D)—it is suggested that design flows not exceed 12% of the flooding velocity given by Figure 11-7. These practical observations indicate that additional work is needed to provide a more precise basis for design of such extractors.

PRESSURE DROP

In liquid-liquid systems, the pressure drop primarily is due to the hydrostatic head through which the phase must flow. The average fluid density is slightly different from that of the continuous phase, due to the volume occupied by the dispersed phase holdup. Of course, there is a resistance to flow; however, this frictional pressure drop normally is much less than the hydrostatic head. In extractors, the operating temperature should be chosen to prevent crystallization of solute or freezing of solvents. Also, the operating pressure must be high enough to prevent any vaporization at the point of minimum column pressure.

PACKING SIZE

The use of Figure 11-7 is limited to extractors with packings selected to provide interstitial spaces that are larger than the dispersed phase droplet size. Gaylor and Pratt show that for each pair of liquids there is a critical packing size [16]. The critical packing size is a function of the interfacial tension and the difference between the densities of the two phases. The dispersed phase droplet size is independent of flow rate as long as the packing is larger than this critical size. Liebson and Beckmann report that the critical packing size frequently is near ½ in. [17]. Because of this effect, packing of ¾-in. or larger size ordinarily should be specified. To avoid channeling and reduced contacting efficiency at the column wall, packing size should not exceed ⅛ the column diameter [1].

DETERMINATION OF STAGES

Any design procedure requires a calculation of the number of mass transfer stages required and then a determination of the packed depth required to achieve such a stage. The use of the equilibrium stage concept in liquid-liquid extraction is similar to its use in distillation operations. A theoretical stage of mass transfer is one from which the extract and the raffinate leave in equilibrium. Stated in a different manner, the ratio of the concentration of solute in the extract to the concentration of solute in the raffinate equals the distribution coefficient.

If the solvent A and the solvent B are immiscible or only slightly miscible, then their flows through the extractor essentially are constant. In this case, Figure 11-2 can be redrawn as illustrated by Figure 11-8. On the abscissa are values of mol fraction solute C in the solvent A on a solvent B free basis. These values represent raffinate compositions such as from J to P in Figure 11-2. On the ordinate are values of the mol fraction of solute C in solvent B on a solvent A free basis. These values represent extract compositions in equilibrium with the raffinate compositions, which are connected by tie lines as illustrated on Figure 11-3. They are compositions such as from K to P on the curve JRPEK in Figure 11-2.

The equilibrium curve in Figure 11-8 is obtained from the distribution coefficients. The values for K_D must be known between the extract and feed and the solvent and raffinate. If these values differ significantly, K_D values for three or four intermediate points must be determined.

The number of theoretical stages required can be determined from Figure 11-8 by means of a stepwise procedure similar to the McCabe-Thiele method used in distillation calculations (see Chapter 7). An operating line, QT, first must be constructed below the equilibrium curve, NO, developed from equilibrium data. Line QT can be drawn by material balance on the solute quantities in the feed and solvent because these rates and compositions are known. Point T represents the composition of solvent B entering the column and the composition of the raffinate leaving the column. Point Q represents the composition of the extract leaving the column and the composition of the feed in solvent A entering the extractor. The ratio of x_E to x_R on curve NO is the distribution coefficient. The value of x_R at point T usually is fixed by a specification for percentage recovery of the solute in the feed.

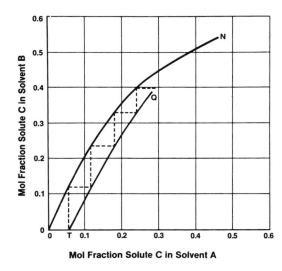

Figure 11-8. Determination of number of equilibrium stages.

As an example, assume a feed containing 28 mol % solute C and 72 mol % solvent A enters the extractor at the top. The solvent is pure immiscible solvent B entering the bottom of the extractor at the rate of 375 mols solvent per 1,000 mols feed. It is desired to recover 85% of solute C in the feed as extract leaving the top of the column. By material balance on the streams leaving the extractor, the raffinate will contain 5.5 mol % solute and the extract will contain 38.8 mol % solute. In Figure 11-8, the top column conditions are represented by $x_R = 0.280$ and $x_E = 0.388$. The bottom column conditions are $x_R = 0.055$ and $x_E = 0$. The operating line is slightly curved because the flow of solvent A phase decreases from 1,000 mols to 762 mols, while the flow of solvent B phase increases from 375 mols to 613 mols, due to solute transfer. From a stepwise procedure, it is determined that this extraction requires 3.8 theoretical stages.

Cusack *et al.* show a graphical solution for the number of theoretical stages based on the extraction factor,

$$F_E = K'_D \left[\frac{S}{F} \right] \tag{11-10}$$

where S and F are the solvent and feed flows, respectively, on a solute-free basis, and K'_D is the distribution coefficient based on lb solute/lb solvent [18]. They show that values of F_E less than 1.3 require more than 12 theoretical stages to effect 99% solute recovery, which may be impractical for many commercial applications. Equation 11-10 applies to systems in which the equilibrium curve and the operating line essentially are straight lines.

Where the transfer of solute is followed by a rapid, irreversible chemical reaction in the extract phase, the value of x_E* approaches zero. The preponderant resistance to mass transfer will occur in the raffinate phase. In this case, the use of a transfer unit rather than a theoretical stage is more helpful for design purposes (see Chapters 3 and 4). The number of transfer units required may be calculated directly from the concentrations of solute in the feed and raffinate:

$$N_{OL} = \ln\left[\frac{x_F}{x_R}\right] \qquad (11\text{-}11)$$

Thus, removal of 99.5% of the H_2S from a hydrocarbon liquid feed by contacting it with an aqueous alkaline solvent will require 5.3 transfer units.

STAGE EFFICIENCY

The problem of specifying the depth of packing in an extractor is not a straightforward determination. As discussed by Nemunaitis *et al.*, their tests produced a lower apparent H_{OL} value for beds of 1-in. size packings when 2-ft deep beds were used than when the bed depth was 5 ft [15]. This work showed that the efficiency is practically independent of velocity as long as the continuous phase velocity is at least 80 ft/h. At lower rates backmixing of the continuous phase tended to reduce the efficiency. The dispersed-phase velocity produced only a very minor effect on efficiency. These data for three types of packing are shown in Table 11-9. Further, this work indicates that 1-in. metal Pall ring and 1-in. ceramic Intalox saddle packings develop H_{OL} values that are only about 40% of the values for empty spray columns.

Table 11-9

**Transfer Units Developed With 1 in. Packing
MEK-Kerosine-Water System**

Packing	2 ft Bed Depth	5 ft Bed Depth
Metal Pall Rings	1.20	1.86
Ceramic Intalox® Saddles	1.11	1.86
Ceramic Raschig Rings	—	1.42

Eckert indicated that the rate of mass transfer decreased rapidly as the residence time of the dispersed-phase droplets in the continuous phase increased [19]. Thus, the act of formation of the dispersed-phase droplets contributes significantly to the overall mass transfer. Therefore, the use of packed beds of 8 to 12 ft depth followed by redispersion tends to minimize column height. Seibert *et al.* ran tests using two beds of packing, each 11.5 ft deep, in a 16.7- in. ID extractor [14]. With #25 IMTP packing, they found a 40% improvement in the overall mass transfer coefficient when redispersion of the organic phase occurred between the two packed beds.

Eckert further showed that the packed depth necessary to achieve an equilibrium stage of mass transfer decreased only slightly with an increase in the continuous-phase velocity when this rate was greater than 80 ft/h. However, he found a small increase in the depth required to achieve an equilibrium stage with an increase in the dispersed phase velocity. Sherwood has postulated that at low rates the interfacial area increases with the dispersed phase flow rate; while at higher rates the interfacial area attains a nearly constant value [20].

Seibert *et al.* reported that the overall volumetric mass transfer coefficient varied directly with flow rates; however, it was much more affected by the dispersed phase rate compared to the continuous phase rate [21]. These investigators also observed that the overall mass transfer coefficient initially increased rapidly with an increase in continuous-phase velocity; however, above a continuous-phase velocity of 40 ft/h, the mass transfer coefficient approached a fixed value. The overall mass transfer coefficient increased almost linearly with the dispersed-phase velocity. Their data for #15 IMTP packing is shown in Figure 11-9 with the aqueous-phase being continuous.

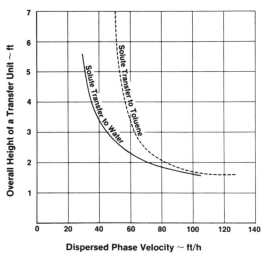

Figure 11-9. Efficiency of IMTP® packing with acetone-toluene-water system and with the water phase continuous. (From Seibert [21]).

Sherwood stated that the rate of mass transfer may depend on whether the extract or raffinate is the dispersed phase for systems in which mass transfer occurs because of differences in solubility. Seibert *et al.* observed that the overall mass transfer coefficients were significantly greater for a system of low interfacial tension (butanol and water) than for a system of high interfacial tension (toluene and water). They also found a tendency for mass transfer efficiency to be dependent on the direction of solute transfer.

Treybal points out that the presence of surface active agents in very small concentrations can reduce markedly the rate of mass transfer [22]. Such substances can act as a third liquid film through which the solute must pass in series with the raffinate and extract liquid films.

Mass transfer coefficients generally increase with temperature rise. For instance, in the removal of sulfuric acid from alkylate by washing with water, the high heat of solution of the acid in water can produce a significant increase in the temperature at the interface. Also, mass transfer rates can be affected by a change in interfacial tension during the solute transfer. If the solute in Figure 11-8 were acetone, which was being transferred from water to dispersed toluene, the interfacial tension as given by Figure 11-4 would decrease by 18 dyne/cm from the bottom to the top of the extraction column.

Based on commercial experience, Table 11-10 has been prepared to show the packed depth required for various numbers of transfer units per bed. This table is based on mobile organic/aqueous systems and the use of metal slotted-ring or ceramic saddle packings, together with high-performance dispersion plates. Generally, a single packed bed is not deeper than 12 ft before another dispersion plate is installed. The use of deeper beds results in a relative loss of efficiency for each additional foot of depth of a random dumped packing.

The tests by Seibert *et al.* on #25 and #40 IMTP packings using dispersed toluene to extract acetone from water showed the H_{OL} for the #40 size to be 17% greater than the H_{OL} for the #25 size at continuous phase rates greater than 37 ft/h [14]. These investigators also tested a sheet metal

Table 11-10

Packed Bed Depths Required For Modern Random Packings

Transfer Units Per Bed	Packing Size		
	1 in.	1½ in.	2 in.
1.5	4.4 ft.	5.3 ft.	6.2 ft.
2.0	7.2	8.6	10.1
2.5	9.9	11.9	14.0

structured packing (Intalox Structured packing 2T) in the same system. The H_{OL} for this structured packing was 35% lower than that of #25 IMTP packing, even though the surface areas of these two packings are about the same as shown in Tables 11-4 and 11-8. Because this random dumped packing and this structured packing also have high void fractions, their capacities were found to be similar, as would be predicted from Figure 11-7. Structured packings can be used to increase the efficiency of existing extractors without loss of capacity.

EXTRACTOR INTERNALS

Because of the differences between gas-liquid contacting and liquid-liquid contacting, column internals of somewhat different design from those described in Chapter 10 are required. Of course, the light phase enters the bottom of the column, and the heavy phase enters the top of the column. The most common manner of operating an extractor is with the light phase dispersed. Thus, the interface between phases will be located at the top of the column above the beds of packing.

At the bottom of the packed bed, it is necessary to form the light-phase dispersion. While this dispersion could be produced by one device, and a separate packing support plate used to hold the packed bed, such an arrangement is not desirable because the support plate commonly used for random dumped packings can affect adversely the light-phase dispersion rising through it. Therefore, the packing support plate and the light-phase dispersion plate can be combined, as illustrated in Figure 11-10. By design, the light phase pools beneath this plate to a sufficient depth necessary to cause it to flow through the orifices in the plate due to the difference in densities between the two phases. These orifices set the light-phase dispersion into the random packed bed that rests on the top surface of this plate. The continuous phase enters the downcomers above this plate at the bottom of the packed bed. The heavy phase is discharged from the downcomers below the pool of light-phase liquid under this plate. Structured packing bundles are supported on the structural frame on top of each of the sections of this disperser support plate.

The design of a disperser/support plate involves specifying the number, location, and size of the orifices that disperse the light phase. The velocity of the dispersed phase through these orifices usually is limited to not more than 70 ft/min to avoid possible formation of an emulsion. Such emulsions consist of very fine droplets that do not coalesce nearly as quickly as a conventional dispersion of larger size drops. Orifice sizes of 0.18-in. to 0.25-in. diameter commonly are used, although sizes as small as 0.14-in. and as large as 0.31-in. diameter have been used. When the dispersed-phase superficial velocity (V_D) exceeds 130 ft/h, generally the number of orifices per square foot is increased, rather than enlarging the orifice size. If the continuous-phase superficial velocity (V_C) exceeds 60 ft/h, additional downcomers should be installed through the disperser plate. Obviously, these additional downcomers displace some number of the light-phase dispersion orifices, so that the light-phase flow capacity is reduced.

Because disperser plates of the design shown in Figure 11-10 operate by difference of densities between the two phases, this same plate can be used for redispersion under each succeeding bed of packing through which the light phase passes while traveling up the column. Obviously, these plates must be sealed with a gasket to the supporting tower ledge to prevent leakage.

Each packed bed usually is equipped with a bed limiter at the top to prevent disturbance of the upper surface of the bed due to operational upsets. The heavy phase is introduced into the column through an orifice ladder distributor similar in appearance to those shown in Chapter 10. However, the orifices in such a continuous phase distributor are sized to provide a low entrance velocity (not greater than 170 ft/min) so as to avoid disturbing the dispersed phase that is rising through it. A similar design of feed sparger is used in the inverted position to introduce the light phase below the bottom dispersion plate. Risers are added to this sparger so as to discharge the light phase about 1 in. above the bottom of the continuous-phase downcomers. Again, the entrance velocity is low to avoid creating turbulence on the lower surface of the light-phase pool below the disperser plate.

In those cases where the heavy phase is dispersed, a different arrangement of column internals is necessary. Now the interface between phases

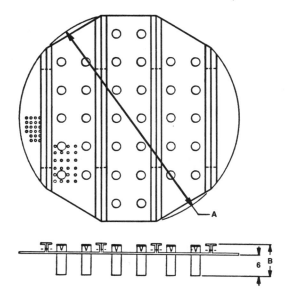

Figure 11-10. Disperser support plate. (Courtesy of Norton Chemical Process Products Corporation.)

will be located at the bottom of the column below the beds of packing. In such cases, the packed beds are supported on conventional packing support plates, as illustrated in Chapter 10. Again, a bed limiter may be installed on the top of each bed of packing.

The heavy-phase dispersion is formed at the top of the packed bed by use of a modified design of the dispersion plate (shown in Figure 11-10). This plate is installed in an inverted position using a gasket on a ledge located 8 in. to 12 in. above the top of the packed bed. Similar plates are installed above each packed bed to reproduce the heavy-phase dispersion. The light phase is introduced into the column through a distributor, similar to the orifice ladder type, which is installed in the inverted position below the bottom packing support plate. The heavy phase is fed to the top disperser plate through a sparger of similar design to that previously described.

COALESCENCE OF DISPERSED PHASE

In general, the higher the interfacial tension, the more rapidly coalescence will occur. The more viscous the continuous phase, the slower will be the rate of coalescence of the dispersed phase. The coalescing zone of the column must be designed from settling principles. This may require enlarging the column diameter in order to reduce the velocities if the packed bed is operating at high flow rates.

The interface between phases should be kept several feet away from the column outlet to avoid entrainment of continuous phase droplets in the coalesced dispersed phase. If coalescence is difficult to achieve, a small size packing or a mesh that is wetted preferentially by the dispersed phase may be employed to help coalesce the dispersed phase droplets.

The presence of trace impurities may have a pronounced effect on column operation. Many times such impurities collect at the interface between the two phases. Modification of the liquid properties at the mass transfer interface can affect both the capacity and efficiency of an extractor. It is common practice to provide a means of removing a small quantity of liquid from the interface between coalesced phases periodically in order to purge impurities from the system.

INDUSTRIAL APPLICATIONS

Although liquid-liquid extraction usually is not the first choice of separating processes, it has been employed in the following commercial applications:

1. Removal of sulfur compounds from liquid hydrocarbons.
2. Recovery of aromatics from liquid hydrocarbons.
3. Removal of waxes and resins from lubricating oils.

4. Separation of butadiene from other C-4 hydrocarbons.
5. Separation of homogeneous aqueous azeotropes.
6. Separation of asphaltic compounds from oil.
7. Manufacture of hydrogen peroxide.
8. Removal of phenolic compounds from waste water.
9. Extraction of glycerides from vegetable oils.
10. Recovery of acetic acid from digesters and fermenters.
11. Refining of tall oil and methylated tall oil.
12. Recovery of rare earths in phosphor manufacture.
13. Extraction of tar acids from coal tar.
14. Recovery of hormones, vitamins, and antibiotics.
15. Purification of uranium, tantalum, and columbium.
16. Recovery of copper from leach liquor.
17. Manufacture of caprolactam.
18. Purification of phosphoric acid.
19. Separation of cresol isomers.
20. Recovery of essential oils.

EXAMPLE PROBLEM

An aqueous process effluent contains 3.4 lb of a valuable organic compound per 1,000 lb of H_2O. Because the organic material has a somewhat higher boiling point than water, an extraction of this organic with a solvent appears to be the least expensive method for recovery of the solute. This organic solute is highly soluble in aromatic solvents that are almost immiscible in water. In order to enable recovery of the solute from the extract by means of a simple stripping operation, a high boiling aromatic liquid (cumene) will be used as the solvent.

Laboratory tests conducted at the effluent temperature of 80°F give the following distribution coefficients when the compositions of each phase are expressed in lb solute per 1,000 lb solvent.

Concentration in Water	Concentration in Cumene	K'_D
2.1	21.1	10.05
1.7	14.2	8.35
1.2	8.7	7.25
0.7	4.3	6.14
0.2	1.2	6.00

What would be the column diameter and packed depth required to recover at least 95% of the solute present in 41,140 lb/h of aqueous effluent?

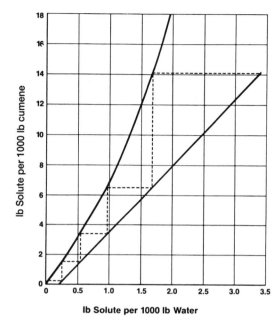

Figure 11-11. Equilibrium diagram for example problem.

The data from the laboratory tests can be used to construct an equilibrium diagram on rectangular coordinates, as in Figure 11-11. To recover 95% of the solute would give a concentration of 0.17 lb solute per 1,000 lb H_2O in the raffinate. Assuming the solvent is solute-free, we can establish the condition at the bottom of the extractor. This condition will lie on the X-axis of the equilibrium diagram.

Because cumene and H_2O are almost immiscible and the amount of solute transferred is small compared to the total mass-flow rates of the solvents, the operating line for this column will be essentially a straight line. Next, we will fix the slope of the operating line by choosing the solvent flow rate so as to avoid a pinch against the equilibrium curve. Further, because we are using a packed column, we will attempt to specify a sufficient solvent flow rate so that no more than five theoretical stages of mass transfer are required. For this extraction, therefore, the solvent flow rate will be set at 9,400 lb/h.

By material balance, the concentration of solute in the extract will be 14.1 lb solute per 1,000 lb cumene. We now have established the condition at the top of the extractor that can be located on the equilibrium diagram. The operating line will join the compositions at the top of the tower with the compositions at the bottom of the tower on this diagram.

A McCabe-Thiele procedure is used to step off the equilibrium stages required, as has been illustrated in Figure 11-11. For this extraction, 4.3 theoretical stages are necessary for 95% solute recovery.

Because the volume of aqueous feed solution is much greater than the volume of solvent, the water phase will be dispersed into the solvent phase in order to generate the maximum interfacial area for mass transfer. The packing selected will be #40 IMTP packing, which will be wetted initially with solvent. From Table 11-4, this packing has a surface area of 46 ft^2/ft^3, and the void fraction is 0.972.

Now that all flow rates have been determined, the Crawford-Wilke Correlation (Figure 11-7) can be used to calculate the required column diameter. The following physical properties are needed:

Physical Property	Top of Column	Bottom of Column
Continuous phase density	53.42 lb/ft³	53.58 lb/ft³
Dispersed phase density	62.32 lb/ft³	62.33 lb/ft³
Continuous phase viscosity	0.86 cps	0.78 cps
Interfacial tension	32.0 dyne/cm	42.4 dyne/cm

The abscissa value for Figure 11-7 at the top of the column is:

$$X = \frac{0.86}{8.90}\left[\frac{32.0}{53.42}\right]^{0.2}\left[\frac{46}{0.972}\right]^{1.5} = 28.4 \qquad (11\text{-}A)$$

The ordinate value at flood from the correlation is 720, therefore:

$$\frac{53.42}{46(0.86)}\left[V_C^{0.5} + V_D^{0.5}\right]^2 = 720 \qquad (11\text{-}B)$$

Thus, $V_c^{0.5} + V_D^{0.5} = 23.09$ \qquad (11-C)

From the flow rates of feed and extract, the ratio of V_C to V_D is determined to be 0.270. Therefore, at flood, V_D is 231 ft/h and V_C is 62.4 ft/h.

If we select a 54-in. ID column, the dispersed-phase rate will be 41.5 ft/h and the continuous-phase rate 11.2 ft/h. At the top, this column will operate at 18.0% of flooding velocities.

The abscissa value for Figure 11-7 at the bottom of the column is:

$$X = \frac{0.78}{8.75}\left[\frac{42.4}{53.58}\right]^{0.2}\left[\frac{46}{0.972}\right]^{1.5} = 27.7 \qquad (11\text{-}D)$$

The ordinate value at flood from the correlation is 730, therefore:

$$\frac{53.58}{46(0.78)}[V_C^{0.5} + V_D^{0.5}]^2 = 730 \qquad (11\text{-}E)$$

Thus, $V_c^{0.5} + V_D^{0.5} = 22.11$ (11-F)

At flood, the dispersed phase velocity is 213 ft/h, and the velocity of the continuous phase is 56.7 ft/h. For this 54-in. ID tower, the bottom will be operating at 19.5% of flooding rates. These operating rates provide an adequate safety factor, because Figure 11-7 has been found to predict the capacity of #40 IMTP packing quite well, and the densities and viscosities of the phases do not change greatly throughout the column.

A design HETP of 5.0 ft for #40 IMTP packing was chosen based on the use of Equations 7-18 and 7-23 (see Chapter 7) and values from Table 11-10. From Table 11-10, it is apparent that a significant amount of the mass transfer will occur during the initial dispersion of the aqueous phase. An experienced designer probably will specify two beds each 9.5 ft deep for this 54-in. ID column as being adequate to provide 4.3 theoretical plates. Each packed bed would be equipped with a high-performance dispersion plate at the top, a bed limiter, and a conventional packing support plate.

NOTATION

A	Column cross-sectional area (ft^2)
a	Interfacial area (ft^2/ft^3)
a_p	Surface area of packing (ft^2/ft^3)
F	Feed flow on a solute-free basis (lb/h)
F_E	Extraction factor
H_{OL}	Overall height of liquid transfer unit (ft)
k_E	Extract liquid-film mass transfer coefficient (lb-mol/h · ft^2 · Δx)
k_R	Raffinate liquid-film mass transfer coefficient (lb-mol/h · ft^2 · Δx)
K'_D	Distribution coefficient
$K_E a$	Overall mass transfer coefficient for extract (lb-mol/h · ft^3 · Δx)
$K_R a$	Overall mass transfer coefficient for raffinate (lb-mol/h · ft^3 · Δx)
m	Slope of equilibrium curve
N	Solute transferred (lb-mol/h)
N_{OL}	Number of liquid transfer units
S	Solvent flow on solute-free basis (lb/h)
S_D	Degree of separation
V_C	Continuous phase superficial velocity (ft/h)
V_D	Dispersed phase superficial velocity (ft/h)
x_E	Mol fraction solute in extract
x_E^*	Equilibrium mol fraction solute in extract

x_E' Mol fraction solute in extract liquid film
x_F Mol fraction solute in feed
x_R Mol fraction solute in raffinate
x_R^* Equilibrium mol fraction solute in raffinate
x_R' Mol fraction solute in raffinate liquid film
Z Packed depth (ft)
γ Activity coefficient
$\Delta\rho$ Density difference between phases (lb/ft^3)
ε Void fraction of packing
μ_C Continuous phase viscosity (cps)
ρ_C Continuous phase density (lb/ft^3)
σ_i Interfacial tension (dyne/cm)

REFERENCES

1. Oberg, A. G. and Jones, S. C., *Chemical Engineering*, Vol. 70, No. 15, 1963, p. 119.
2. *International Critical Tables*, Vol. 3, McGraw-Hill, 1928, p. 418.
3. Donahue, D. J. and Bartell, F. E., *Journal of Physical Chemistry*, Vol. 56, 1952, p. 480.
4. Treybal, R. E., *Liquid Extraction*, 2nd ed., McGraw-Hill, 1963, p. 132.
5. Girifalco, L. A. and Good, R. J., *Journal of Physical Chemistry*, Vol. 61, 1957, p. 904.
6. Francis, A. W., *Industrial and Engineering Chemistry*, Vol. 45, 1953, p. 2789.
7. Francis, A. W., *Industrial and Engineering Chemistry*, Vol. 46, 1954, p. 205.
8. Blumberg, R., *Liquid-Liquid Extraction*, Academic Press, 1988, p. 61.
9. Blanding, F. H. and Elgin, J. C., *Transcripts of American Institute of Chemical Engineers*, Vol. 38, 1942, p. 305.
10. Gier, T. E. and Hougen, J. O., *Industrial and Engineering Chemistry*, Vol. 45, 1953, p. 1362.
11. Breckenfeld, R. R. and Wilke, C. R., *Chemical Engineering Progress*, Vol. 66, 1942, p. 305.
12. Treybal, R. E., *Liquid Extraction*, 2nd ed., McGraw-Hill, 1963, p. 486.
13. Crawford, J. W. and Wilke, C. R., *Chemical Engineering Progress*, Vol. 47, No. 8, 1951, p. 423.
14. Seibert, A. F. *et al.*, *Industrial & Engineering Chemistry Research*, Vol. 29, No. 9, 1990, p. 1901.
15. Nemunaitis, R. R. *et al.*, *Chemical Engineering Progress*, Vol. 67, No. 11, 1971, p. 60.
16. Gaylor, R. N. and Pratt, H. R. C., *Transactions of Institution of Chemical Engineers*, London, Vol. 35, 1957, p. 267.

17. Liebson, I. and Beckmann, R. B., *Chemical Engineering Progress,* Vol. 49, No. 8, 1951, p. 423.
18. Cusack, R. W. *et al., Chemical Engineering,* Vol. 98, No. 2, 1991, p. 66.
19. Eckert, J. S., *Hydrocarbon Processing,* Vol. 55, No. 3, 1976, p. 117.
20. Sherwood, T. K., *Absorption and Extraction,* McGraw-Hill, 1937, p. 256.
21. Seibert, A. F. *et al., Separation Science and Technology,* 22 (2 & 3), 1987, p. 281.
22. Treybal, R. E., *Liquid Extraction,* 2nd ed., McGraw-Hill, 1963, p. 178.

APPENDIX

Metric Conversion Table

Term	Convert From	Convert To	Multiply By
Absolute Temperature	°R	°K	0.5556
Area	ft^2	m^2	0.09290
Capacity Factor	ft/s	m/s	0.3048
Density	lb/ft^3	kg/m^3	16.02
Diameter	ft	mm	304.8
Diffusivity	ft^2/h	cm^2/s	0.2581
Enthalpy	Btu/lb	kcal/kg	0.5556
Gas-Film Mass Transfer Coefficient	lb-mol/ $h \cdot ft^2 \cdot atm$	kg-mol/ $h \cdot m^2 \cdot atm$	4.883
Gravitational Constant	ft/s^2	m/s^2	0.3048
Heat Capacity	Btu/ $lb \cdot °F$	kcal $kg \cdot °C$	1.000
Heat Flow	Btu/h	kcal/h	0.2520
Heat Transfer Coefficient	Btu/ $h \cdot ft^3 \cdot °F$	kcal $h \cdot m^3 \cdot °C$	16.02
Height Equivalent to a Theoretical Stage	ft	mm	304.8
Height of a Transfer Unit	ft	mm	304.8
Humidity	lb H_2O/ lb BDG	kg H_2O/ kg BDG	1.000
Interfacial Area	ft^2/ft^3	m^2/m^3	3.281
Kinematic Viscosity	ft^2/h	cSt	25.81
Kinetic Energy	ft-lb	kg-m	0.1383
Length	ft	m	0.3048

(continued)

328

Metric Conversion Table

Term	Convert From	Convert To	Multiply By
Liquid-Film Mass Transfer Coefficient	lb-mol/ h · ft^2 · mol/ mol	kg-mol/ h · m^2 · mol/ mol	4.883
Liquid Flow	gpm	m^3/h	0.2271
Liquid Rate	gpm/ft^2	m^3/m^2 · h	2.445
Mass	lb	kg	0.4536
Mass Flow	lb/h	kg/h	0.4536
Mass Velocity	lb/ft^2 · h	kg/m^2 · h	4.883
Mass Velocity	lb/ft^2 · s	kg/m^2 · s	4.883
Molar Flow	lb-mol/h	kg-mol/h	0.4536
Overall Gas Mass Transfer Coefficient	lb-mol/ h · ft^3 · atm	kg-mol/ h · m^3 · atm	16.02
Overall Liquid Mass Transfer Coefficient	lb-mol/ h · ft^3 · mol/ mol	kg-mol/ h · m^{3}mol/ mol	16.02
Packed Depth	ft	mm	304.8
Packing Diameter	in.	mm	25.40
Pressure	atm	kg/cm^2	1.033
Pressure	psi	kg/cm^2	0.07031
Pressure	in. H$_2$O	mm Hg	1.872
Pressure Drop	in. H$_2$O/ft	mm H$_2$O/m	83.33
Superficial Velocity	ft/s	m/s	0.3048
Surface Tension	lb/in.	dyne/cm	175,100
Temperature	°F	°C	0.5556 (°F−32)
Vapor Capacity Factor	lb$^{0.5}$/ ft$^{0.5}$ · s	kg$^{0.5}$/ m$^{0.5}$ · s	1.220
Viscosity	lb/ft · h	cps	0.4134
Volume	ft^3	m^3	0.02832

GLOSSARY

Absorption factor—Ratio of the slope of the operating line to slope of the equilibrium curve in absorption operations.

Absorption operation—Boiling mixture that has the same vapor composition as the liquid composition.

Bed limiter—A column internal on top of a packed bed to prevent expansion of the bed.

Bottoms—The high boiling liquid product effluent from a distillation column.

Capacity factor—Superficial vapor velocity corrected for vapor and liquid densities.

Concurrent scrubber—Scrubber in which the gas and liquid flow in the same direction.

Condenser—Heat exchanger that condenses a vapor to provide reflux for a distillation operation.

Countercurrent scrubber—Scrubber in which the gas and liquid flow in opposite directions.

Critical pressure—Pressure required to liquify a gas at its critical temperature.

Critical solution temperature—Temperature above which two liquids are completely miscible.

Critical temperature—Temperature above which a liquid phase will not exist regardless of pressure.

Cross-flow scrubber—Scrubber in which the gas and liquid flow in perpendicular directions.

Debutanizer—Column that removes C-4 hydrocarbons from the feed.

Deethanizer—Column that removes C-2 hydrocarbons from the feed.

Demethanizer—Column that removes methane from the feed.

Depropanizer—Column that removes C-3 hydrocarbons from the feed.

Diatomic gas—Gas whose molecules consist of two atoms.

Disperser plate—Tower internal that produces dispersed drops of one liquid phase in the other liquid phase.

Distillate—That portion of the condensed overhead vapor from a distillation column that is withdrawn as product.

Distillation—Separation of feed components by differences in boiling temperatures at a fixed pressure.

Distribution coefficient—Ratio of solute concentration in extract phase to solute concentration in raffinate phase.

Drag coefficient—Measure of a force exerted on a body in the direction of fluid flow.

Driving force—Force responsible for producing a change.

Dry line—Line on a plot that represents a property of a packed bed with gas flow only.

Dumped packing—Bed of individual packing elements that are randomly oriented.

Entrained liquid—Liquid droplets transported in a flowing gas.

Equilibrium curve—Line on a plot that represents the compositions of two phases that are in equilibrium.

Equilibrium ratio—Ratio of the composition of one phase to another phase with which it is in equilibrium.

Extract—The effluent of an extractor that has been enriched in dissolved solute.

Extractive distillation—Distillation in which a high boiling solvent is added to alter the relative volatility of components in the feed.

Extractor—Device for transferring a solute between two immiscible liquid phases.

Feed point—Location in a column at which the feed is introduced.

Flash zone—Portion of a column in which a liquid is partially vaporized.

Flooding—A liquid holdup sufficient to invert phases within the interstices of a packed bed.

Flow parameter—Square root of the ratio of liquid kinetic energy to gas kinetic energy.

Fluidized bed—Bed in which the solid elements are suspended in a rapidly moving gas phase.

Foam—A cellular mass of gas bubbles fixed by liquid films.

Form drag—Force exerted on a body by parallel flowing fluid due to the shape of the body.

Fractionator—Device that physically separates a mixture of components in the feed, usually by distillation.

Froth—A layer on the surface of a liquid which contains dispersed vapor.

Fume scrubber—Device used to remove an offensive substance from a gas stream.

Gas-film-controlled—Mass transfer operation in which the principal resistance is in the gas film.

Gas quench tower—See Quench tower.

Gas scrubber—See Fume scrubber.

Generalized pressure drop correlation—A method of prediction of the pressure gradient through a packed bed.

Geometric area—Surface area determined by the geometric shape.

Heavy key—Principal high boiling component of a feed mixture.

HETP value—Mass transfer height that provides one theoretical stage of separation.

Hold-down plate—A heavy tower internal used to prevent fluidization of the top surface of a packed bed.

HTU value—Mass transfer height that provides one transfer unit of change in compositions.

Hydraulic loading—Degree of maximum fluid handling capacity of the device.

Hyperbolic tower—A column whose shell takes the shape of a hyperbola in a longitudinal section.

Interfacial area—Area of contact between two different phases.

Interfacial tension—Resultant of cohesive forces acting at the interface between two immiscible liquids.

Irrigation points—Openings from which discrete streams of liquid flow.

Irrigation rate—Volumetric liquid flow per unit of column cross-sectional area.

Lambda factor—Ratio of slope of equilibrium curve to slope of operating line.

Lean solution—Solvent that contains a small quantity of solute.

Light key—Principal low boiling component of a feed mixture.

Liquid distributor—Tower internal that provides uniform liquid flow onto a packed bed.

Liquid-film-controlled—Mass transfer operation in which the principal resistance is in the liquid film.

Liquid holdup—Quantity of liquid present in a packed bed.

Loading region—Flow rates at which the liquid holdup also is a function of the vapor rate.

Logarithmic average—Mathematical average based on a logarithmic function.

Lower loading point—Maximum flow rates at which the pressure drop is proportional to the square of the gas rate for a packed bed.

Mass transfer coefficient—Rate of solute transfer from one phase to another based on unit time, interfacial area, and driving force.

Mass velocity—Mass flow rate based on column cross-sectional area.

Maximum operational capacity—Maximum vapor rate that provides normal efficiency of a packing.

Overhead—Low boiling vapor product from a distillation column.

Packed bed—Confined volume of elements designed to improve contacting between two phases.

Packed depth—Vertical height of a packed bed.

Packing factor—Number relating the pressure drop to flow rates through a particular tower packing.

Pasteurization—Removal of small quantities of low-boiling components at the top of a distillation column.

Pressure distillation—Distillation at pressures greater than 5.5 atmospheres.

Pressure drop—Reduction in pressure due to resistance to flow through a device.

Pressure gradient—Reduction in pressure per unit depth.

Pumparound—Section of a column over which the liquid is recirculated.

Quench tower—Column that rapidly cools a hot gas stream.

Raffinate—Effluent of an extractor from which dissolved solute has been stripped.

Reboiler—Heat exchanger that vaporizes a liquid to provide energy to a distillation operation.

Rectifying section—Section of a column that condenses high-boiling components in the vapor.

Reflux—Condensate returned to a distillation column to rectify the rising vapor.

Reflux ratio—Ratio of reflux flow to distillate product flow.

Regeneration—Removal of solute from a rich solution to permit reuse of the solvent.

Relative volatility—Ratio of the equilibrium ratio of one component to that of another component.

Removal efficiency—Degree of elimination of a substance.

Rich solution—Solvent that contains a large quantity of solute.

Sensible heat load—Difference in heat content due to a temperature change with no change of phase.

Single-component vapor—Vapor phase that contains but one chemical substance.

Solvent—A liquid that is capable of dissolving a solute.

Splash deck—Row of separated horizontal slats onto which liquid rains.

Split stream—Operation in which a fluid stream is divided into two or more streams.

Static holdup—Quantity of liquid remaining in a packed bed after discontinuance of feeds.

Stripping factor—Ratio of the slope of the equilibrium curve to the slope of the operating line in stripping operations.

Stripping operation—Transfer of solute from a liquid phase to a gas phase.

Stripping section—Section of a column that vaporizes low-boiling components in the liquid.

Structured packing—Tower packing that is installed in a column in a precise array.

Superficial velocity—Rate of flow based on the column cross-sectional area.

Support plate—Tower internal that is located at the bottom of a packed bed to carry the weight of the packing.

Theoretical stage—A mass transfer stage from which the two phases leave in equilibrium.

Tower internals—Devices used to facilitate performance of tower packings.

Tower packing—Elements designed to promote contact between two phases.

Transfer unit—A mass transfer stage that produces a change in composition equal to the driving force causing that change.

Trayed columns—Towers containing a series of horizontal plates for contacting two phases.

Trays, angle—Trays consisting of a series of separated horizontal angle irons.

Trays, baffle—Trays consisting of a series of staggered horizontal baffles that are vertically offset.

Trays, counterflow—Trays on which the vapor and liquid flow countercurrently either through the same or separate openings.

Trays, sieve—Trays that are perforated to allow vapor flow upward through liquid flowing horizontally from the inlet to the outlet downcomer.

Trays, valve—Trays in which the perforations have caps that deflect the upwardly flowing vapor that passes through liquid flowing horizontally from the inlet to the outlet downcomer.

Turndown ratio—Ratio of maximum hydraulic flow to minimum flow at a constant efficiency.

Vacuum crude still—A vacuum tower that processes the bottoms from an atmospheric pressure distillation of crude oil.

Vacuum deaeration—Removal of dissolved air from a liquid at pressures less than atmospheric.

Vacuum distillation—Distillation at pressures less than 0.4 atmospheres.

Vapor capacity factor—Superficial vapor velocity corrected for vapor density.

Vapor distributor—Tower internal that produces uniform vapor flow into a packed bed.

Vapor/liquid equilibrium—Relationship of vapor composition to the liquid composition with which it is in equilibrium.

VOC stripper—Column which removes volatile organic compounds from water.

Void fraction—Proportion of unoccupied space in a bed of tower packings.

Wall flow—Quantity of liquid that flows down the wall of a column.

Wall wiper—Tower internal designed to intercept liquid flowing down the column wall.

Wash bed—Packed bed used to remove minor contaminants from a gas stream by scrubbing with a liquid.

Water cooling tower—Column that reduces water temperature by partial evaporation into an air stream.

Wire-gauze packing—Structured packing formed from loosely woven, thin metal wire.

INDEX

RETURN TO ➡

CHEMISTRY LIBRARY
100 Hildebrand Hall • 642-3753

LOAN PERIOD 1	2	3
4	5 ▓▓▓ 1 MONTH	

ALL BOOKS MAY BE RECALLED AFTER 7 DAYS
Renewable by telephone

DUE AS STAMPED BELOW

MAR 11 1999		
OCT 27 1999		
APR 07 '01		
NOV 18 '01		
APR 16 '02		
OCT 07 '04		
DEC 21 2004		

FORM NO. DD5

UNIVERSITY OF CALIFORNIA, BERKELEY
BERKELEY, CA 94720-6000